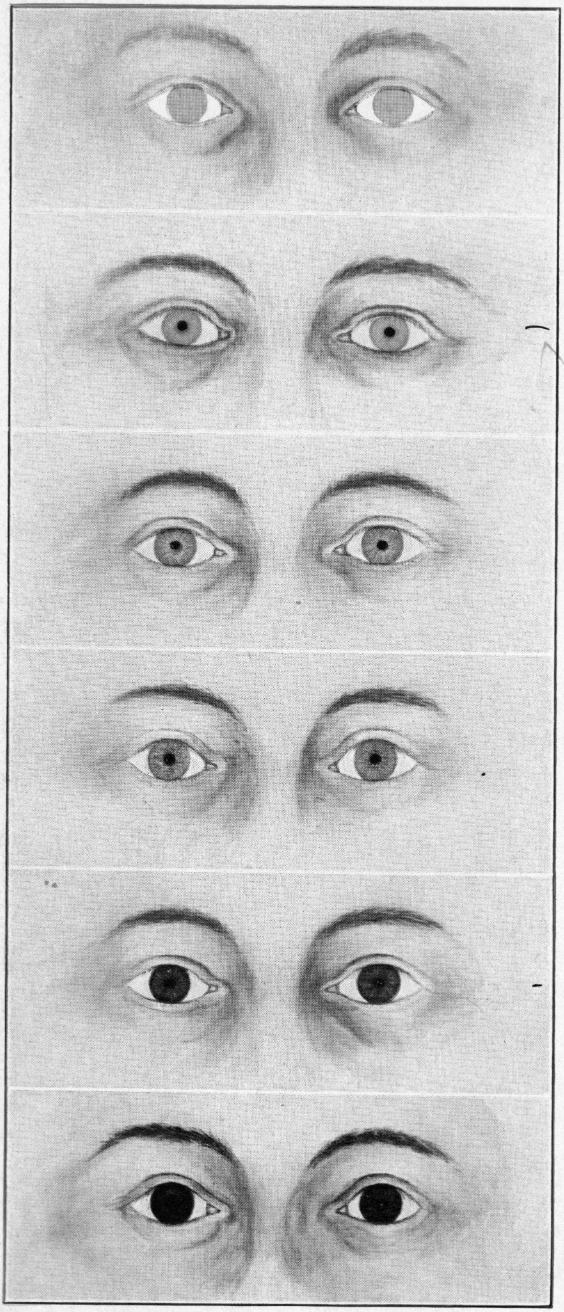

A. Pigment of Choroid Coat and Pigment of Iris Absent. 1. The Albino eye. Red from unobscured blood vessels.

B. Pigment of Choroid Present.

α. Iris without True Pigment. 2. Blue. Due to a purple layer on back of eye.

β. Iris with True Pigments.

a. Lipochrome or yellow pigment. 3. Green or cat eye. Yellow pigment on blue background.

b. Melanic or black pigment. 4. Hazel or gray eye. Dilute brown pigment around pupil only.

5. Brown eye. Melanic pigment; various shades from various dilutions.

6. Black eye. An abundance of melanic pigment.

EYE COLORS IN MAN

12-694

HEREDITY IN RELATION TO EUGENICS

BY

CHARLES BENEDICT DAVENPORT

CARNEGIE INSTITUTION OF WASHINGTON
DIRECTOR, DEPARTMENT OF EXPERIMENTAL EVOLUTION
COLD SPRING HARBOR, LONG ISLAND, N. Y.
SECRETARY OF THE EUGENICS SECTION
AMERICAN BREEDERS' ASSOCIATION

NEW YORK
HENRY HOLT AND COMPANY
1911

PRESS OF T. MOREY & SON
GREENFIELD, MASS., U. S. A.

TO

MRS. E. H. HARRIMAN

IN RECOGNITION OF THE GENEROUS ASSISTANCE
SHE HAS GIVEN TO RESEARCH IN EUGENICS
THIS BOOK IS
GRATEFULLY DEDICATED

PREFACE

Recent great advances in our knowledge of heredity have revolutionized the methods of agriculturalists in improving domesticated plants and animals. It was early recognized that this new knowledge would have a far-reaching influence upon certain problems of human society —the problems of the unsocial classes, of immigration, of population, of effectiveness, of health and vigor. Now, great as are the potentialities of the new science of heredity in its application to man it must be confessed that they are not yet realized. A vast amount of investigation into the laws of the inheritance of human traits will be required before it will be possible to give definite instruction as to fit marriage matings. Our social problems still remain problems. For a long time yet our watchword must be *investigation.* The advance that has been made so far is chiefly in getting a better method of study.

In this book I have sought to explain this new method. An application of this method to some specific problems, especially to the transmission of various human traits and susceptibilities to disease, has been attempted. The suggestions made are by no means final but are made to illustrate the general method and give the most probable conclusions. Only with much more accurate data can the laws of inheritance of family peculiarities be definitely determined.

Some general consequences of the new point of view for the American population have been set forth in Chapters IV to VI. Their essential truth will, I trust, be generally recognized. In any case it will not be amiss to point out the fundamental difference between the modern eugenical and the contrasted or "euthenical" standpoints. As a matter of fact the eugenic teachings that we think of as new are very old. Modern medicine is responsible for the loss of appreciation of the power of heredity. It has had its attention too exclusively focussed on germs and conditions of life. It has neglected the personal element that helps determine the course of every disease. It has begotten a wholly impersonal hygiene whose teachings are false in so far as they are laid down as universally applicable. It has forgotten the fundamental fact that all men are created *bound* by their protoplasmic makeup and *unequal* in their powers and responsibilities.

As indicated, it is the aim of this book to incite to further investigation. Some space is devoted to the eugenics movement—a movement which it is hoped will, in this country, for the present, take mainly the form of investigation. To this movement the Eugenics Record Office (a branch of the work of the American Breeders' Association) is dedicated. The Eugenics Record Office wishes to get in touch with all persons interested in the eugenics movement. It invites every person who is willing to do so to record his heritage and place the record on file at the Record Office. "Drop a postal card" at once to the Eugenics Record Office, Cold Spring Harbor, New York, and ask for the blank schedule they furnish. It is understood that all data deposited in this way will be held as confidential and be used only for scientific purposes. The data received are carefully preserved in a fireproof vault and indexed so as to be available to the student. Specifically, the Record Office seeks pedigrees of families in which one or more of the following traits appear:—short stature, tallness, corpulency, special talents in music, art, literature, mechanics, invention and mathematics, rheumatism, multiple sclerosis, hereditary ataxy, Ménière's disease, chorea of all forms, eye defects of all forms, otosclerosis, peculiarities of hair, skin and nails (especially red hair), albinism, harelip and cleft palate, peculiarities of the teeth, cancer, Thomsen's disease, hemophilia, exophthalmic goiter, diabetes, alkaptonuria, gout, peculiarities of the hands and feet and of other parts of the skeleton. We do not appeal primarily to physicians for this information but to the thousands of intelligent Americans who love the truth and want to see its interests advanced. At the same time, physicians can aid in the work by inducing persons with bodily or mental peculiarities that run through their families to send to the Record Office for blank schedules on which to record the method of inheritance of the trait in question. Thus every one can share in the eugenics movement.

The Eugenics Record Office will be glad to assist in the establishment of local eugenics societies which shall become centers for the study of local blood-lines and for local instruction. The Office seeks to assist state officials in the study of the classes which are supported and protected by the State, and to assist the States to locate the centers in which their defectives and delinquents are being bred. It is believed that a little money spent in studying the sources of reproduction of persons who are destined to become state wards will prove a highly profitable investment, since it may lead to steps that will diminish such reproduction.

In the preparation of the present volume the author has been aided by many hands. Professor James A. Field, of the University of Chicago, has kindly read the proof and made valuable suggestions. The bibliography and the pedigree charts were largely prepared by Miss Amey B. Eaton, of the Eugenics Record Office. Professor E. B. Wilson has generously granted me the use of Figures 1 to 6 from his invaluable book, "The Cell in Development and Inheritance." Hundreds of persons have voluntarily contributed the data upon which the conclusions that have been drawn are based. My friend and colleague, Mr. H. H. Laughlin, Superintendent of the Eugenics Record Office, has assisted in many points and has contributed the frontispiece. My wife has, as usual, revised the manuscript and prepared it for the printer. The Trustees of the Carnegie Institution have granted me exceptional opportunities for the prosecution of the work. Last, but by no means least, this work and the collection of data out of which it has grown have been made possible by the financial assistance and by the personal stimulus and advice given by the lady to whom, in insufficient recognition, this book is, with her permission, dedicated. To all those who have so kindly assisted me I return thanks. I trust the book will be useful to humanity, so as to justify them for the pains they have taken to bring it to pass.

C. B. D.

Carnegie Institution of Washington
Station for Experimental Evolution
Cold Spring Harbor, N. Y.

CONTENTS

CHAPTER I

EUGENICS: ITS NATURE, IMPORTANCE AND AIMS

CHAPTER II

THE METHOD OF EUGENICS

CHAPTER III

THE INHERITANCE OF FAMILY TRAITS

CHAPTER VII

THE STUDY OF AMERICAN FAMILIES

CHAPTER VIII

EUGENICS AND EUTHENICS

CHAPTER IX

THE ORGANIZATION OF APPLIED EUGENICS

PLATES

HEREDITY IN RELATION TO EUGENICS

CHAPTER I

EUGENICS: ITS NATURE, IMPORTANCE AND AIMS

1. What Eugenics Is

Eugenics is the science of the improvement of the human race by better breeding or, as the late Sir Francis Galton expressed it:—"The science which deals with all influences that improve the inborn qualities of a race." The eugenical standpoint is that of the agriculturalist who, while recognizing the value of culture, believes that permanent advance is to be made only by securing the best "blood." Man is an organism—an animal; and the laws of improvement of corn and of race horses hold true for him also. Unless people accept this simple truth and let it influence marriage selection human progress will cease.

Eugenics has reference to offspring. The success of a marriage from the standpoint of eugenics is measured by the number of disease-resistant, cultivable offspring that come from it. Happiness or unhappiness of the parents, the principal theme of many novels and the proceedings of divorce courts, has little eugenic significance; for eugenics has to do with traits that are in the blood, the protoplasm. The superstition of prenatal influence and the real effects of venereal disease, dire as they are, lie outside the pale of eugenics in its strictest sense. But no lover of his race can view with complaisance the ravages of these diseases nor fail to raise his voice in warning against them. The parasite that induces syphilis is not only hard to kill but it frequently works extensive damage to heart, arteries and brain, and may be conveyed from the infected parent to the unborn child. Gonorrhea, like syphilis, is a parasitic disease that is commonly contracted during illicit sexual intercourse. Conveyed by an infected man to his wife it frequently causes her to become sterile. Venereal diseases are disgenic agents of the first magnitude and of growing importance. The danger of acquiring them should be known to all young men. Society might well demand that before a marriage license is issued the man should present a certificate, from a reputable physician, of freedom from them. Fortunately, nature protects most of her best blood from these diseases; for the acts that lead to them are repugnant to strictly normal persons; and the sober-minded young women who have had a fair opportunity to make a selection of a consort are not attracted by the kind of men who are most prone to sex-immorality.

2. The Need of Eugenics

The human babies born each year constitute the world's most valuable crop. Taking the population of the globe to be one and one-half billion, probably about 50 million children are born each year. In the continental United States with over 90 million souls probably 2½ million children are annually born. When we think of the influence of a single man in this country, of a Harriman, of an Edison, of a William James, the potentiality of these 2½ million annually can be dimly conceived as beyond computation. But for better or worse this potentiality is far from being realized. Nearly half a million of these infants die before they attain the age of one year, and half of all are dead before they reach their 23rd year—before they have had much chance to affect the world one way or another. However, were only one and a quarter million of the children born each year in the United States destined to play an important part for the nation and humanity we could look with equanimity on the result. But alas! only a small part of this army will be fully effective in rendering productive our three million square miles of territory, in otherwise utilizing the unparalleled natural resources of the country, and in forming a united, altruistic, God-serving, law-abiding, effective and productive nation, leading the remaining 93 per cent of the globe's population to higher ideals. On the contrary, of the 1200 thousand who reach full maturity each year 40 thousand will be ineffective through temporary sickness, 4 to 5 thousand will be segregated in the care of institutions, unknown thousands will be kept in poverty through mental deficiency, other thousands will be the cause of social disorder and still other thousands will be required to tend and control the weak and unruly. We may estimate at not far from 100 thousand, or 8 per cent, the number of the non-productive or only slightly productive, and probably this proportion would hold for the 600 thousand males considered by themselves. The great mass of the yearly increment, say 550 thousand males, constitute a body of solid, intelligent workers of one sort and another, engaged in occupations that require, in the different cases, various degrees of intelligence but are none the less valuable in the progress of humanity, Of course, in these gainful occupations the men are assisted by a large number of their sisters, but four-fifths of the women are still engaged in the no less useful work of home-making. The ineffectiveness of 6 to 8 per cent of the males and the probable slow tendency of this proportion to increase is deserving of serious attention.

It is a reproach to our intelligence that we as a people, proud in other respects of our control of nature, should have to support about half a million insane, feeble-minded, epileptic, blind and deaf, 80,000 prisoners and 100,000 paupers at a cost of over 100 million dollars per year. A new plague that rendered four per cent of our population, chiefly at the most productive age, not merely incompetent but a burden costing 100 million dollars yearly to support, would instantly attract universal attention. But we have become so used to crime, disease and degeneracy that we take them as necessary evils. That they were so in the world's ignorance is granted; that they must remain so is denied.

3. The General Procedure in Applied Eugenics

The general program of the eugenist is clear—it is to improve the race by inducing young people to make a more reasonable selection of marriage mates; to fall in love intelligently. It also includes the control by the state of the propagation of the mentally incompetent. It does not imply destruction of the unfit either before or after birth. It certainly has only disgust for the free love propaganda that some ill-balanced persons have sought to attach to the name. Rather it trusts to that good sense with which the majority of people are possessed and believes that in the life of such there comes a time when they realize that they are drifting toward marriage and stop to consider if the contemplated union will result in healthful, mentally well-endowed offspring. At present there are few facts so generally known that they will help such persons in their inquiry. It is the province of the new science of eugenics to study the laws of inheritance of human traits and, as these laws are ascertained, to make them known. There is no doubt that when such laws are clearly formulated many certainly unfit matings will be avoided and other fit matings that have been shunned through false scruples will be happily contracted.

CHAPTER II

THE METHOD OF EUGENICS

1. Unit Characters and their Combination

When we look among our acquaintances we are struck by their diversity in physical, mental, and moral traits. Some of them have black hair, others brown, yellow, flaxen, or red. The eyes may be either blue, green, or brown; the hair straight or curly; noses long, short, narrow, broad, straight, aquiline, or pug. They may be liable to colds or resistant; with weak digestion or strong. The hearing may be quick or dull, sight keen or poor, mathematical ability great or small. The disposition may be cheerful or melancholic; they may be selfish or altruistic, conscientious or liable to shirk. It is just the fact of diversity of characteristics of people that gives the basis for the belief in the practicability of improving the qualities of the "human harvest." For these characteristics are inheritable, they are independent of each other, and they may be combined in any desirable mosaic.

The method of inheritance of these characteristics is not always so simple as might be anticipated. Extensive studies of heredity have, of late years, led to a more precise knowledge of the facts. The element of inheritance is not the individual as a whole nor even, in many cases, the traits as they are commonly recognized but, on the contrary, certain unit characters. What are, indeed, units in inheritance and what are complexes it is not always easy to determine and it can be determined only by the results of breeding. To get at the facts it is necessary to study the progeny of human marriages. Now marriage can be and is looked at from many points of view. In novels, as the climax of human courtship; in law, largely as a union of two lines of property-descent; in society, as fixing a certain status; but in eugenics, which considers its biological aspect, marriage is an experiment in breeding; and the children, in their varied combinations of characters, give the result of the experiment. That marriage should still be only an *experiment* in breeding, while the breeding of many animals and plants has been reduced to a science, is ground for reproach. Surely the human product is superior to that of poultry; and as we may now predict with precision the characters of the offspring of a particular pair of pedigreed poultry so may it sometime be with man. As we now know how to make almost any desired combination of the characters of guinea-pigs, chickens, wheats, and cottons so may we hope to do with man.

At present, matings, even among cultured people, seem to be made at haphazard. Nevertheless there is some evidence of a crude selection in peoples of all stations. Even savages have a strong sense of personal beauty and a selection of marriage mates is influenced by this fact, as Darwin has shown. It is, indeed, for the purpose of adding to their personal attractiveness that savage women or men tattoo the skin, bind up various parts of the body including the feet, and insert ornaments into lips, nose and ears. Among civilized peoples personal beauty still plays a part in selective mating. If, as is sometimes alleged, large hips in the female are an attraction, then such a preference has the eugenic result that it tends to make easy the birth of large, well-developed babies, since there is probably a correlation between the spread of the iliac bones of the pelvis and the size of the space between the pelvic bones through which the child must pass. Even a selection on the ground of social position and wealth has a rough eugenic value since success means the presence of certain effective traits in the stock. The general idea of marrying health, wealth, and wisdom is a rough eugenic ideal. A curious antipathy is that of red haired persons of opposite sex for each other. Among thousands of matings that I have considered I have found only two cases where both husband and wife are red headed, and I am assured by red haired persons that the antipathy exists. If, as is sometimes alleged, red hair is frequently associated with a condition of nervous irritability this is an eugenic antipathy.

In so far as young men and women are left free to select their own marriage mates the widest possible acquaintance with different sorts of people, to increase the amplitude of selection, is evidently desirable. This is the great argument for coeducation of the sexes both at school and college, that they may increase the range of their experience with people and gain more discrimination in selection. The custom that prevails in America and England of free selection of mates makes the more necessary the proper instruction of young people in the principles of eugenical matings.

The theory of independent unit characters has an important bearing upon our classifications of human beings and shows how essentially vague and even false in conception these classifications are. A large part of the time and expense of maintaining the courts is due to this antiquated classification with its tacit assumption that each class stands as a type of men. Note the extended discussions in courts as to whether A belongs to the white race or to the black race, or whether B is feeble-minded or not. Usually they avoid, as if by intention, the fundamental question of definition, and if experts be called in to give a definition the situation is rendered only worse. Thus one expert will define a feeble-minded person as one incapable of protecting his life against the ordinary hazards of civilization, but this is very vague and the test is constantly changing. For a person may be quick-witted enough to avoid being run over by a horse and carriage but not quick enough to escape an automobile. A second expert will define a feeble-minded person as one who cannot meet all (save two) of the Binet test for three years below his own; if he fail in one only he is no longer feeble-minded. But this definition seems to me socially insufficient just because there are moral imbeciles who can answer all but the moral question for their proper age. Every attempt to classify persons into a limited number of mental categories ends unsatisfactorily.

The facts seem to be rather that no person possesses all of the thousands of unit traits that are possible and that are known in the species. Some of these traits we are better off without but the lack of others is a serious handicap. If we place in the feeble-minded class every person who lacks any known mental trait we extend it to include practically all persons. If we place there only those who lack some trait desirable in social life, again our class is too inclusive. Perhaps the best definition would be: "deficient in some socially important trait" and then the class would include (as perhaps it should) also the sexually immoral, the criminalistic, those who cannot control their use of narcotics, those who habitually tell lies by preference, and those who run away from school or home. If from the term "feeble-minded" we exclude the sexually immoral, the criminalistic, and the narcotics such a restriction carried out into practice would greatly reduce the population of institutions for that class. Thus one sees that a full and free recognition of the theory of unit characters in its application to man opens up large social, legal and administrative questions and leads us in the interests of truth, to avoid classifying *persons* and to consider rather their *traits*.

2. The Mechanism of the Inheritance of Characteristics

That traits are inherited has been known since man became a sentient being. That children are dissimilar combinations of characteristics has long been recognized. That characteristics have a development in the child is equally obvious; but the mechanism by which they are transmitted in the germ plasm has become known only in recent years.

We know that the development of the child is started by the union of two small portions of the germ plasm—the egg from the mother's side of the house and the sperm from the father's. We know that the fertilized egg does not contain the organs of the adult and yet it is definitely destined to produce them as though they were there in miniature. The different unit characters, though absent, must be represented in some way; not necessarily each organ by a particle but, in general, the resulting characteristics are determined by chemical substances in the fertilized egg. It is because of certain chemical and physical differences in two fertilized eggs that one develops into an ox and the other into a man. The differences may be called *determiners*.

Determiners are located, then, in the germ cells, and recent studies indicate a considerable probability that they are to be more precisely located in the nucleus and even in the chromatic material of the nucleus. To make this clear a series of diagrams will be necessary.

Figure 1 is a diagram of a cell showing the central nucleus in which runs a deeply staining network—the chromatin. In the division of a cell into two similar daughter cells the most striking fact is the exact division of the chromatin (Fig. 2). We know enough to say that the nucleus is the center of the cell's activity and for reasons that we shall see immediately it is probable that the chromatin is the most active portion of the nucleus.

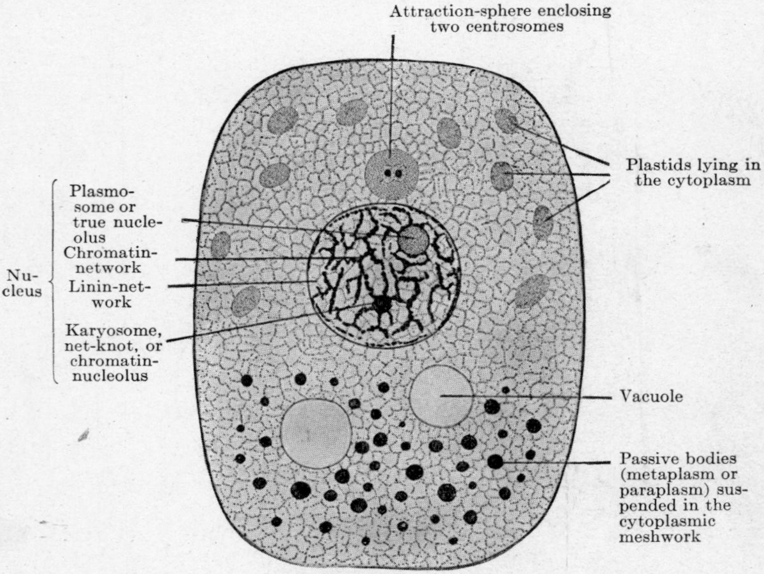

FIG. 1.—Diagram of a cell. Its basis consists of a meshwork containing numerous minute granules (*microsomes*) and traversing a transparent ground substance. From E. B. WILSON: "The Cell in Development and Inheritance."

The fertilization of the egg (Fig. 3) brings together determiners from two germ plasms and we know that, on the whole, the two germ cells play an equal rôle in carrying determiners. Now the germ cells are of very different size in the female (egg) and the male (sperm). Even the nuclei are different; but the amount of chromatic substance is the same. Hence it seems probable that the chromatic substance is the carrier of the equal determiners.

But if determiners from the male are added to those from the female in fertilization it would seem necessary

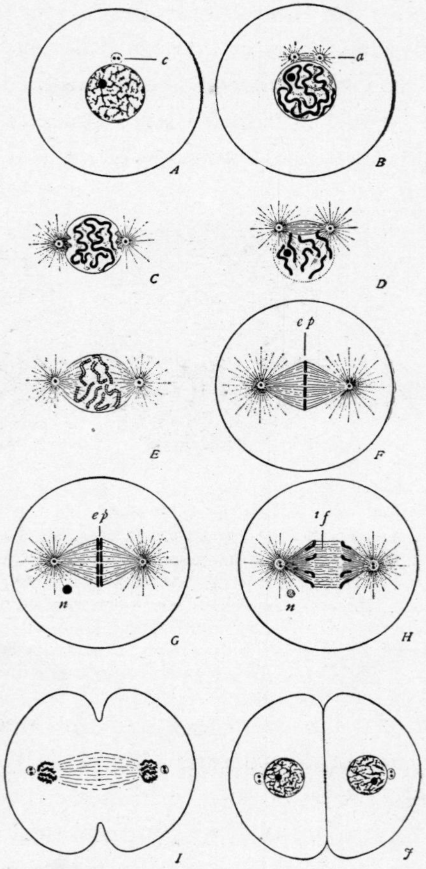

FIG. 2.—Diagrams showing a series of stages in the process of division of the chromosomes during cell division. *A*. Resting cell in which the chromatic material lies (apparently) scattered through the nucleus: at *c* is a pair of recently divided central bodies (*centrosomes*) which come to be the centers of the forces that separate the chromosomes. *B*. The chromatin has fallen into the form of a thick ribbon or sausage-like body, outside of which lies a dark body which is called the "nucleolus." The centrosomes are moving apart. *C*. The centrosomes now lie far apart and the thin membrane around the nucleus is beginning to disappear—a process completed in *D*, where a "spindle" is seen lying between the two centrosomes. The chromosomes are beginning to move under the influence of the new forces centered at the centrosomes. *E*. A later phase in which changes of two sorts are taking place in the chromosomes; first, they are moving to an equatorial position between the two poles, and, secondly, they show their double nature by virtue of which the subsequent

that the number of these determiners should double in every succeeding generation. There must be some special mechanism to prevent this result. An appropriate mechanism is, indeed, ready and had been seen and studied long before its significance was understood; this is the elimina-

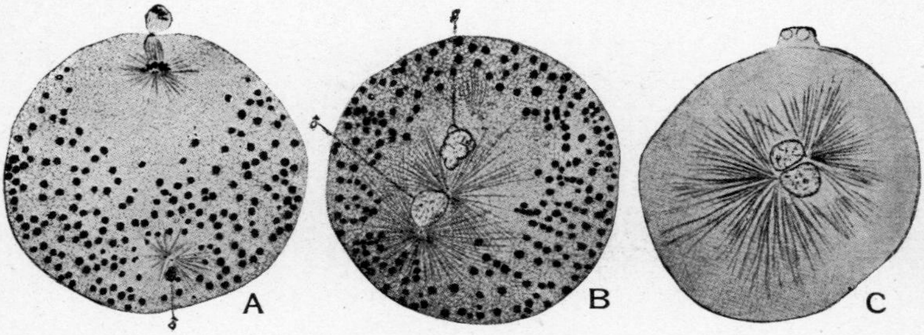

FIG. 3.—Three stages in the fertilization of the egg of a marine ringed worm (*Thalassema*). As seen in thin dyed sections. *A*. At the top of the egg there is occurring a division of the chromosomes that constitutes the ripening or "maturation" of the egg, illustrated in greater detail in Fig. 4. At the bottom a sperm cell (♂) has entered the egg and is penetrating through it toward its center. *B*. The nucleus of the egg is now returning toward the center to meet that of the sperm. *C*. The egg and sperm nuclei are now in contact; henceforth they work in unison; fertilization is completed. After GRIFFIN from E. B. WILSON: "The Cell in Development and Inheritance."

tion from both the immature egg and the immature sperm of half of the chromatic material (Fig. 4). Thus if the immature sex-cell contains four chromatic bodies (chromosomes) each mature sex-cell will contain only two chromosomes. Moreover, each of the chromosomes in the immature sex-cell is double; one half having originated long before in its maternal germ plasm and the other half in its paternal germ plasm. The mechanism for maturation is

process of splitting takes place. *F*. The processes just preceding chromosome division are now completed; the activity of the centers is at its height; the chromosomes now constitute an "equatorial plate," *e. p.* *G*. The chromosomes at the equatorial plate are now beginning to move apart. *H*. The separation of the chromosomes is continuing and in *I* is completed; meanwhile the activity at the centers has declined and division of the body of the cell is beginning. *J*. Division of the cell completed; the nuclei and centrosomes at the condition with which we started at *A*. From E. B. WILSON: "The Cell in Development and Inheritance."

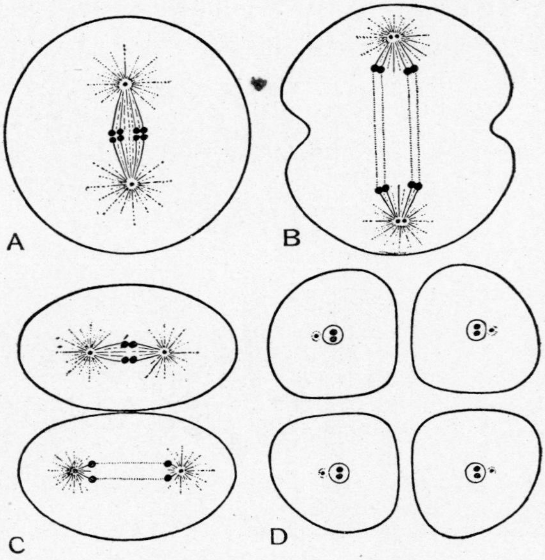

FIG. 4.—Diagrams illustrating the process of *reduction of the chromosomes* by which half of the chromatic material is eliminated from the sex-cell. *A*. The germ cell is beginning its penultimate division—there are four chromosomes but each of them has already begun to divide to go to their respective poles, as seen at *B*. *C*. The last division is taking place, but the four chromosomes do not lie side by side in the equatorial plate as in *A*, but they unite in two pairs and, in the division, the elements of these pairs are sundered again. Thus out of the original cell four ripe sperm-cells (*D*) each with only two chromosomes arise. From E. B. WILSON: "The Cell in Development and Inheritance."

such that either the paternal or maternal component of any chromosome is eliminated in the process, but not both. (Fig. 5). Beyond the condition that one half of each kind of chromosome must go to each daughter cell it seems to be a matter of chance whether the portion that goes to a particular cell be of paternal or of maternal origin. It is even conceivable that one germ cell should have all of its chromosomes of maternal origin while the other cell has all of a paternal origin.

The important point is that the number of chromosomes in the ripe germ cell has become reduced to half and so it is ready to receive an equal half number from the germ cell with which it unites in fertilization.

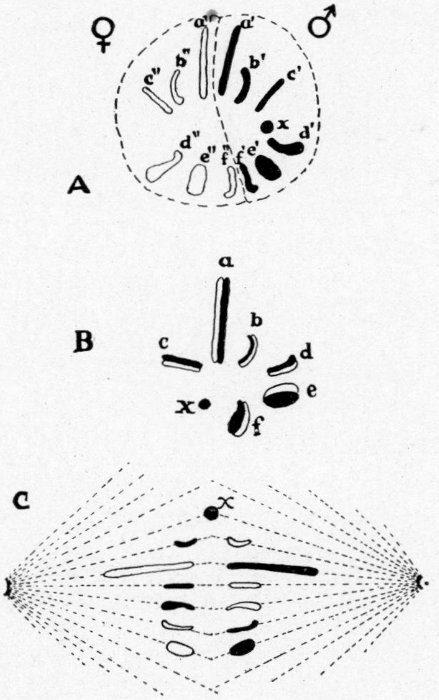

FIG. 5.—Diagram illustrating the mechanism in the chromatic bodies that secures the segregation of determiners. The determiners are assumed to be packed away in the chromosomes. There are equivalent chromosomes (*a′* and *a″*, *b′* and *b″*, etc.) in the nuclei of the male (♂) and female (♀) germ cells that unite in the fertilized egg (Fig. 3) and these two sets of chromosomes pass into all the embryonic cells—whether of the soma or germ gland—that develop in the young individual. In the division of ordinary body-cells, as illustrated in Fig. 2, each rod *a′*, *a″*, *b′*, *b″*, etc., splits lengthwise and half of each goes to each daughter cell. But in a division just before the germ cells become ripe, as in Fig. 4*C*, the like chromosomes unite in pairs as at *B*. Thus *a′* unites with *a″* to form *a*; *b′* unites with *b″* to form *b;* etc. Consequently, the number of chromosomes is reduced to half the typical number. When cell-division thereupon occurs (*C*) and the chromosomes split, either the chromosomal element that was derived from the father (black) or that derived from the mother (white) goes, indifferently, to either daughter cell. Consequently, each germ cell contains some chromosomes of maternal and some of paternal origin but not two chromosomes of the same kind. Since, by hypothesis, each chromosome contains particular kinds of determiners it follows that the same germ cell does not contain the (sometimes contrasting) characters of both parents, but some have the paternal character and others the *corresponding* maternal character.

3. The Laws of Heredity

We are now in a position to understand the modern laws of heredity. First of all it will be recognized that nothing is inherited except the determiners in the germ cells; the characters themselves, on the contrary, are not directly inherited. A clear grasp of this fact gives the answer to many questions. Thus the possibility of the transmission of somatic mutilations is seen to depend upon the capacity of such mutilations to modify the determiners in the germ plasm, and such capacity has never been proved. On the other hand, the germ cells receive nutritive and other particles from the blood and they may receive also poisons from it. Hence arises the possibility of depauperization of the germ plasm and of "race poisons;" but these are exceptional and little known phenomena.

To understand the way heredity acts, let us take the case where both germ cells that unite to produce the fertilized egg carry the determiner for a unit character, A. Then in the child that develops out of that fertilized egg there is a *double* stimulus to the development of the unit character A. We say the character is of *duplex* origin. If, on the other hand, only one germ cell, say the egg, has the determiner of a character while the other, the sperm, lacks it, then in the fertilized egg the determiner is *simplex* and the resulting character is of simplex origin. Such a character is often less perfectly developed than the corresponding character of duplex origin (Fig. 6). Finally, if neither germ cell carries the determiner of the character A, it will be absent in the embryo and the developed child. A person who shows a character in his body (soma) may or may not have the determiner for that character in all of the ripe germ cells he carries, but a person who lacks a given unit character ordinarily lacks the corresponding determiner

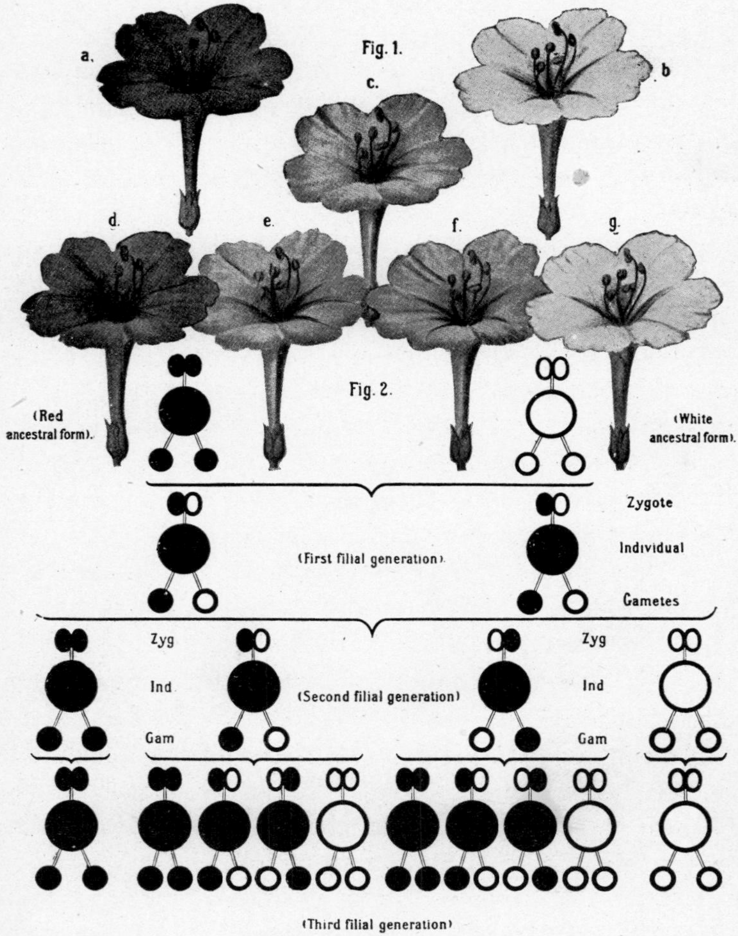

FIG. 6.—Illustration of laws of inheritance drawn from the crossing of red (*a*) and white (*b*) flowered four-o'clocks (*Mirabilis jalappa*). The offspring of this cross, having the determiner for red from one side only, produced pink flowers only (*c*). But when these pink-flowered plants were bred together they produced plants of which one in four had red flowers (duplex, *d*), two in four had pink flowers (simplex, *e. f.*), while one in four had no red pigment (nulliplex, *g*). In the lower part of the chart is a diagram showing for each generation the sort of germ cells involved in the union (zygote), the color of the adult, and the nature of the germ-cells he produces; all carried out to the third generation of descendants. From V. HAECKER: "Wandtafeln zur allgemeinen Biologie" (Nageli: Leipzig).

in all of his germ cells; for, were the determiner present anywhere in his organization (including his germ cells) the corresponding character would ordinarily show in his soma.

In connection with the so-called Mendelian analysis of heredity a nomenclature has grown up which is somewhat different from that here employed. Thus the absent character is often called *recessive*, the present character *dominant* and the condition in the offspring resulting from a crossing of the two is called *heterozygous*, which is the equivalent of simplex. It is to be kept in mind that in this work "absence" does not always imply absolute but only relative absence. Thus the pigmentation of light brown hair is "absent" to "black," and "tow" is absent to light brown; but pigment is present in all these grades of hair. To avoid the confusion between relative and absolute absence the terms recessive and dominant are often used to advantage, wherever a series of grades of a character is under consideration.

These general principles may be rendered clearer by means of a Table of the different sorts of matings of germ cells. And, to focus attention, let us have in mind a concrete example; that of pigment of the iris of the human eye. In the following table P stands for the determiner of brown pigment and p for its absence. Six sorts of unions are possible. See also Plate I, frontispiece.

TABLE I

LAWS OF INHERITANCE OF CHARACTERS BASED ON CONDITIONS OF THE DETERMINERS IN THE PARENTAL GERM PLASMS

	DETERMINERS			
Case	*One parent*	*Other parent*	*Offspring*	*Characteristics of offspring*
1	PP	PP	PP, PP	All with pigmented iris (brown-eyed)
2	PP	Pp	PP, Pp	All pigmented, but half simplex

DETERMINERS—*continued*

Case	*One parent*	*Other parent*	*Offspring*	*Characteristics of offspring*
3	PP	pp	Pp, Pp	All pigmented and all simplex
4	Pp	Pp	PP, Pp, pP, pp	¼ duplex pigmented; ½ simplex; ¼ unpigmented (blue-eyed)
5	Pp	pp	Pp, pp	½ simplex; ½ unpigmented (blue-eyed)
6	pp	pp	pp, pp	All unpigmented (blue-eyed)

In the case of an individual who has received the determiner for one of his unit characters from one side of the house only (say from mother), not only is the character simplex, but when the germ cells mature in that person they are of two types, namely, with the determiner and without the determiner; and these two types are equally numerous (Fig. 5). This is the phenomenon known as segregation of presence and absence in the germ cells. If both parents are simplex in a character, so that they produce an equal number of germ cells with and without the character then in a large number of offspring, 1 in 4 will have the character duplex; 2 in 4 simplex, and 1 in 4 will not have the character at all (nulliplex). This gives in the offspring of such a pair the famous 3 to 1 ratio, sometimes called the Mendelian ratio.

TABLE II

LAW OF CONDITION OF EYE-CHARACTERS IN CHILDREN BASED ON THE CHARACTERS OF THEIR PARENTS

One parent	*Other parent*	*Cases*	*Offspring*
brown	brown	1, 2, 4	Either all of the children have brown eyes, or one fourth have blue eyes
brown	blue	3, 5	Either all children brown-eyed (though simplex) or half blue-eyed
blue	blue	6	All blue-eyed

Now the foregoing rules, which we have illustrated by the case of eye-color, hold generally for any positive determiner or its unit character.

4. Inheritance of Multiple Characters

In the foregoing section we considered the simplest case, namely that in which a single character is taken at a time—*i. e.*, one parent has some character that the other lacks. We have now to consider the cases which are still commoner in nature where the parents differ in respect to two independent characters. Let, for example, the two characters be eye-pigment and hair curliness. Then each one of the six matings given in Table I for eye-color may occur combined with any one of the six matings for hair form; so that there would be a total of 6 times 6 or 36 possible combinations of matings. Similarly Table II would be replaced by one of 9 entries as follows.

Table III

LAW OF COMBINED INHERITANCE OF EYE-COLOR AND HAIR FORM

One parent	*Other parent*	*Offspring*
Brown eye, curly hair	Brown eye, curly hair	Either all brown-eyed and curly-haired; or one-fourth blue-eyed and also one-fourth of all straight-haired (with or without blue eyes)
Brown eye, curly hair	Brown eye, straight hair	All (or all but one-fourth) brown-eyed, and either all or one-half straight-haired
Brown eye, straight hair	Brown eye, straight hair	All (or all but one-fourth) brown-eyed; all straight-haired
Brown eye, curly hair	Blue eye, curly hair	All (or one-half) brown-eyed; all (or three-fourths) curly-haired
Brown eye, curly hair	Blue eye, straight hair	All (or one-half) brown-eyed; all (or one-half) curly-haired
Brown eye, straight hair	Blue eye, straight hair	All (or one-half) brown-eyed; all straight-haired
Blue eye, curly hair	Blue eye, curly hair	All blue-eyed; all (or three-fourths) curly-haired
Blue eye, curly hair	Blue eye, straight hair	All blue-eyed; all (or one-half) curly-haired
Blue eye, straight hair	Blue eye, straight hair	All blue-eyed; all straight-haired

The lessons that this enforces are: first, that characters are often and, indeed, usually, inherited independently and, secondly, that the outcome of a particular mating may be predicted with some precision; indeed, in many matings with certainty.

This study might be extended to cases of three or more independent characters but the tables in such cases become more complex and little would be gained by making them as the principle has been learned by the cases already given. In view of the great diversity of parents in respect to their visible characters the variability of children is readily accounted for.

5. Heredity of Sex and of "Sex-limited" Characters

In most species, as in man, there are two sexes, and they are equally numerous. For a long time this equality has been a mystery; but of late years, through the studies of McClung, Wilson, Stevens and Morgan, the mystery has been cleared up. For there has been discovered in the germ plasm a mechanism adequate for bringing about the observed results. We now know that sex is probably determined strictly by the laws of chance, like the turn of a penny. The cytological theory of the facts is as follows. One sex, usually (and herein taken as) the female, has all cells, even those of the young ovary, with a pair of each kind of chromosome, of which one pair is usually smaller than the others and more centrally placed. The chromosomes of this pair are called the X chromosomes. In the male, on the other hand, the forerunners of the sperm cells have one less chromosome, making the number odd. This odd chromosome [exceptionally paired] is usually of small size and is also known as an X chromosome. In the cell-division that leads to the formation of the mature spermatozoon, this odd chromosome goes *in toto* to one of the two daughter cells (Fig. 5). The X chromosomes are commonly regarded as the "sex-chromosomes." With them are associated various characters that are either secondary sex characters or "sex-limited" characters. Consequently in respect to each and every such character the primordial egg cells are duplex and all the ripe eggs have one sex determiner and its associated characters. The primordial male cells are simplex and consequently, after segregation has occurred, the spermatozoa are of two equally numerous kinds—with and without the sex-determiner. The fertilization of a number of eggs by a number of sperm will result in two equally common conditions—namely a fertilized egg, called *zygote*, that contains *two* sex determiners—such develops into a female; and a zygote that contains only one sex determiner—such develops into a male. The nature of the germ cells in the germ gland of the future child and of the associated secondary sex-characters thus depend on which of the two sorts of sperm cells go into the make-up of the zygote.

Whenever the male parent is characterized by the absence of some character of which the determiner is typically lodged in the sex chromosome a remarkable sort of inheritance is to be expected. This is called sex-limited inheritance. The striking feature of this sort of heredity is that the trait appears only in males of the family, is not transmitted by them, but is transmitted through normal females of the family. Striking examples of this sort of heredity are considered later in the cases of multiple sclerosis (Fig. 64); atrophy of optic nerve (Fig. 77); color blindness (Fig. 88); myopia (Figs. 90, 91); ichthyosis (Figs. 106, 108); muscular atrophy (Fig. 125); and haemophilia (Fig. 134).

The explanation is the same in all cases. The abnormal condition is due to the absence of a determiner from the male X chromosome. Its inheritance can be followed from Figure 7, adapted from Wilson, 1911.

If the trait be a positive sex-limited one, originating either on the father's or the mother's side, its inheritance

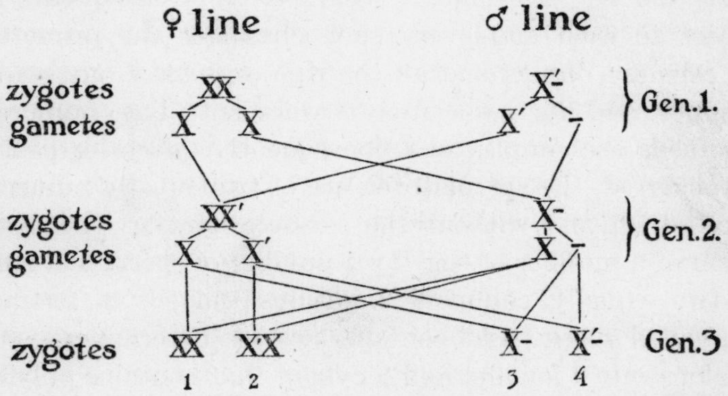

FIG. 7.—Diagram illustrating the method of inheritance in sex limited heredity. *X*, the sex chromosome, double in the female individual, single in the male. When ripe germ cells are formed in the female, each contains the sex determiner, but in the male half of the germ cells have and half lack the determiner (represented by the dash—). Let *X′* represent the sex chromosome of the original male that showed the defect (absence of some unit character). Let such a male be mated with a female of an unaffected strain. Then all children will have the determiner for the positive condition (Gen. 2, zygotes, *i. e.*, fertilized eggs and the individuals that develop from them). In the third generation four kinds of zygotes will appear: 1, the normal female who is not capable of transmitting the defect; 2, the normal female who is capable of transmitting the defect; 3, the normal male who is incapable of transmitting the defect; 4, the defective male. Based on E. B. WILSON, 1911.

will be more irregular; but it can be worked out by the aid of Figure 7.

6. THE APPLICATION OF THE LAWS OF HEREDITY TO EUGENICS

If one is provided with a knowledge of the methods of inheritance of unit characters it might seem to be an easy matter to state how each human trait is inherited and to show how any undesirable condition might be eliminated from the offspring and any wished for character introduced.

Unfortunately, such a consummation cannot for some time be achieved. The reason for the delay is twofold. First, we do not yet know all of the unit characters in man; second, we can hardly know in advance which of them are due to positive determiners and which to the absence of such.

Unit characters can rarely be recognized by inspection. For example the white coat color of a horse is apparently a simple character, but experimental breeding shows that it is really due to several independently inheritable factors. The popular classification of traits is often crude, lagging far behind scientific knowledge. Thus insanity is frequently referred to a single trait. It is clear, however, that insanity is a *result* merely and not a specific trait. Some cases of insanity indicate an innate weakness of the nervous system such as leads it to break down under the incidence of heavy stress; other cases of insanity are due to a destruction of a part of the brain by a wound as, for instance, of a bullet. In some cases, through infection a wide-spread deterioration of the brain occurs; in other cases a clot in a cerebral blood vessel may occlude it, cut off nutrition from a single locality of the brain and interfere with movements that have their centres at the affected point. Now these four results cannot be said to be due to the same unit defect; and they can hardly be compared in the study of heredity.

On the other hand, the original expectation that progress must wait on a complete analysis of unit characters proves not to be correct. There are a number of forms of insanity that are sharply separable symptomatically and structurally which have a common basis in that they are due to a nervous weakness; and "nervous weakness" may behave in heredity with relation to "nervous strength" like a lower grade, or the absence, of a highly developed character. Even without a complete analysis of a trait into its units we may still make practically important studies by using the principle that when both parents have low grades of a trait-complex the children will have low grades of that complex.

The matter of dependence of a character on a determiner or its absence is of great importance and is not easy to anticipate. For instance, long hair as in angora cats, sheep or guinea pigs is apparently not due to a factor added to short hair but rather to the absence of the determiner that stops growth in short-haired animals. One can only conclude whether a character is due to a determiner or to its absence by noting the effect of breeding likes in respect to the given trait. If all offspring are like the parents in respect to a trait, the trait (if simple) is probably a negative one. But if the offspring are very diverse, the trait (if simple) is probably due to a positive determiner and the germ cells of the parents are of two kinds; some with and some without the determiner.

The determination of unit characters is complicated by the fact that a character due to a simplex determiner often differs from one due to a duplex determiner. In the former case the character is slow in developing and frequently fails of reaching a stage of development found in the latter case. The offspring of red and black-eyed birds may have at first a light iris which gradually darkens. This fact is spoken of as the imperfection of dominance in the simplex condition.

Despite the difficulties in analysis of units of heredity and despite the complications in characters it is possible to see clearly the method of inheritance of a great number of human traits and to predict that many more will become analyzed in the near future.

CHAPTER III

THE INHERITANCE OF FAMILY TRAITS

Before any advice can be given to young persons about the marriage that would secure to them the healthiest, strongest children it will be necessary to know not only the peculiarities of their germ plasms but also the way in which various characters are inherited. The work of the student of eugenics is, consequently, to discover the methods of inheritance of each characteristic or trait. After we get precise knowledge of the methods of inheritance of the commoner important traits we shall be in a position to advise, at least in respect to these traits. It would seem a self evident proposition, but it is one too little regarded, that knowledge should precede teaching. In this chapter an attempt will be made to consider many of the traits that are known to run in families and to set forth, so far as known, the laws of their inheritance. We shall begin with some of the general characteristics of man that have been best studied and then pass to a consideration of some human diseases.

In the study of many of these traits I have made use of data that have been furnished by numerous collaborators, chiefly on questionaires know as "Family Records." These are frequently referred to in the following pages, but always anonymously. The Family Records or "Records of Family Traits," as they are also called, are largely derived from professional circles, but not a few from farmers and business men. In respect of several of the special abilities the collaborators have voluteered a numerical grading as follows: 1, poor; 2, medium; 3, exceptionally good. These grades are frequently referred to below.

1. Eye Color

This depends upon the condition of pigmentation of the iris—the colored ring around the pupil. According to Mr. Charles Roberts (1878, p. 134)[1] the iris has on its inner surface "a layer of dark purple called the *uvea* . . . and in brown eyes there is an additional layer of yellow (and, perhaps, brown-red) pigment on its outer surface also, and in some instances there is a deposit of pigment amongst the fibrous structures. In the albino, where the pigment is entirely absent from both surfaces of the iris, the bright red blood is seen through the semi-transparent fibrous tissue of a pink color; and in blue eyes, where the outer layer of pigment is wanting, the various shades are due to the dark inner layer of pigment—the uvea—showing through fibrous structures of different densities or degrees of opacity.

"The eyes of new born infants are dark blue, in consequence of the greater delicacy and transparency of the fibrous portion of the iris; and as these tissues become thickened by use and by advancing age the lighter shades of blue and, finally, gray are produced, the gray, indeed, being chiefly due to the color of the fibrous tissues themselves." Yellow pigment is laid down upon the blue, forming yellow-blue or green eyes. "In the hazel and brown eyes the *uvea* and the fibrous tissues are hidden by increasing deposits of yellow and brown pigment on the anterior surface of the iris, and when this is very dense, black eyes are the result."

While in most races of the globe brown pigment is heavily

[1] For titles of works referred to in text, see Bibliography, at end of book.

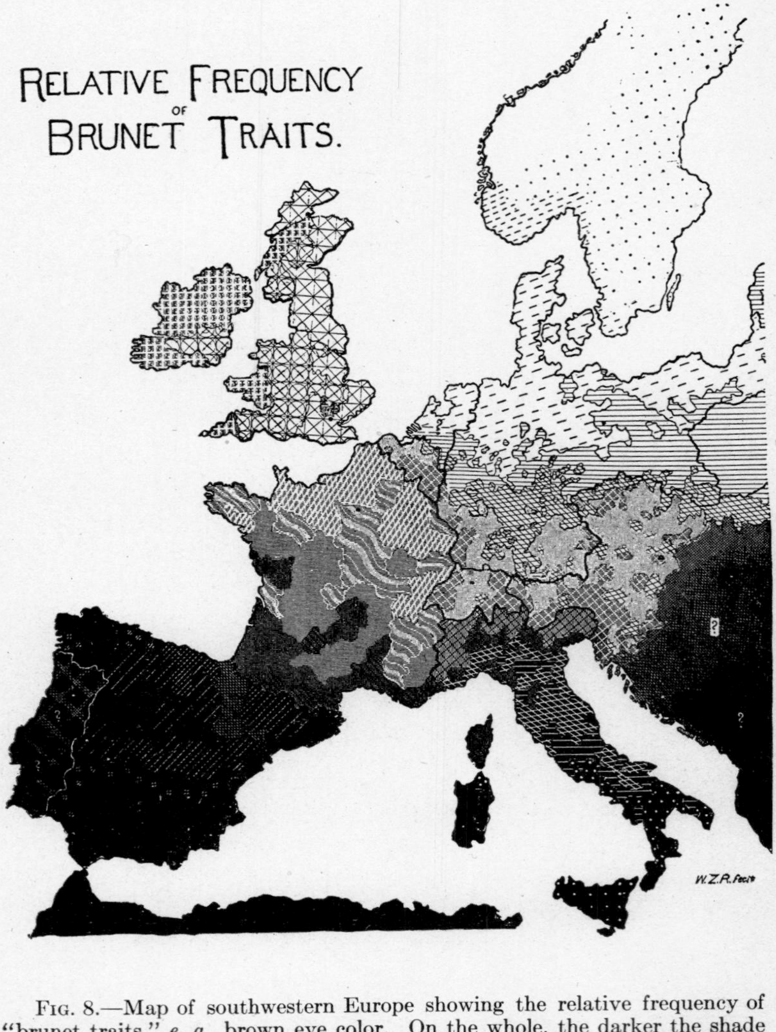

FIG. 8.—Map of southwestern Europe showing the relative frequency of "brunet traits," *e. g.*, brown eye color. On the whole, the darker the shade the greater the proportion of brunet persons in the given area. The lightest areas represent about 20 to 25 per cent brunetness; the darkest European areas over 90 per cent brunetness. At the northern limit of the map "about one third of the people are pure blonds, characterized by light hair and blue eyes;" on the other hand, in the south of Italy the pure blonds have almost entirely disappeared. From W. Z. RIPLEY: "The Races of Europe."

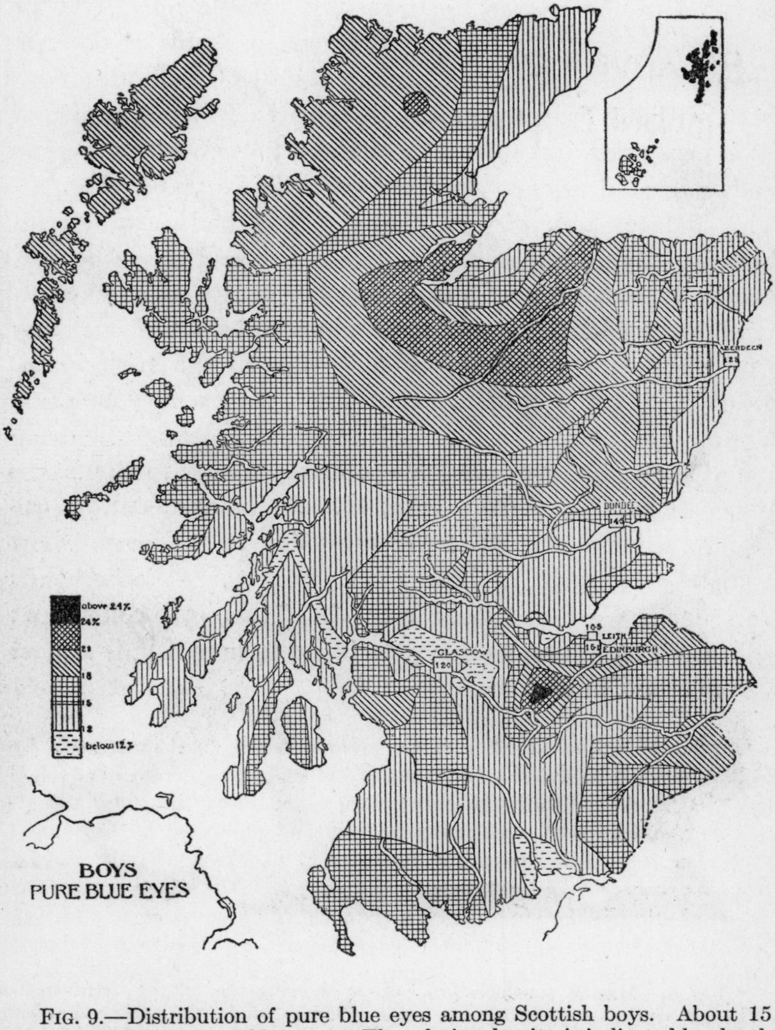

FIG. 9.—Distribution of pure blue eyes among Scottish boys. About 15 per cent of all boys have blue eyes. The relative density is indicated by depth of shading as indicated in the key at the left. A very high density (21 to 24 per cent) occurs in the lower Spey Valley in the northwest. This is the region of the Norse invasion which brought in much protoplasm that was defective in pigmentation. The highest density (over 24 per cent) exists in the coal and iron districts of East Lanarkshire and "this is probably due to the Irish immigrants." J. GRAY, 1907.

secreted in the iris, in northwestern Europe blue, gray or yellow-blue eyes are found. It seems probable that, once upon a time, or perhaps at many times, an individual was born without brown pigment in the iris. The offspring of such prospered and spread throughout northwestern Europe and migrated thence to America and Australia (Fig. 8). This defect, lack of eye pigment, has had a wonderful history. By noting its distribution the migrations of peoples can be traced. Thus Gray (1907) has shown that, in Scotland, pure blue eyes are most abundant in the coal and iron districts. "This is probably due to the Irish immigrants, it being well known that blue eyes are very common among the Irish." In the Spey valley of Scotland the density of pure blue eyes is high—probably owing to the Norse invasion at that point. (Fig. 9). So in our country the pigmentation survey that will some day be made will show a high percentage of blue eyes where the Scandinavians and north Germans have settled. Thus eye color, just because it shows no tendency to blend in heredity, is a most valuable aid in history.

Our knowledge of heredity of eye color depends on studies made by Galton, 1899, who noted its alternative nature but otherwise overlooked the true method of its inheritance; more recently, by three studies carried on simultaneously and independently and published by G. C. and C. B. Davenport, in November, 1907; by C. C. Hurst in 1908; and by Holmes and Loomis in December, 1909. Since 1907 the present author has collected additional data. Hurst's data have the advantage of having been collected from personal observation, hence the chance of error due to a diversity of collaborators was eliminated. In the other studies the data were supplied by unprejudiced, if not always critical, recorders.

Applying the test of the 6 (strictly 5) kinds of unions we get the results shown in Table IV.

TABLE IV

		Hurst		Daven-port		Holmes & Loomis		Total		P'ortion	
One Parent	*Other Parent*	*Blue*	*Pig't*	*Blue*	*Pig't*	*Blue*	*Pig't*	*Blue*	*Pig't*	*Blue*	*Pig't*
pure blue	pure blue	101	0	77	0[1]	51	1	229	1	99.5	0.5
pigmented (Pp)	blue	137	121	428	506	89	85	654	712	48.0	52.0
pigmented (PP)	blue	0	66	0	70			0	136	0	100
pigmented (Pp)	pigmented (Pp)	18	45	98[2]	169	5	34	121	248	33	67
pigmented (PP)	pigmented (Pp)	0	195	0	99			0	294	0	100

Table IV supports the following conclusions:

1. When both parents have pure blue eyes all of the children will have pure blue eyes (the discordant case is probably due to an error).

2. When one parent has pigmented iris while the other has blue, either the fraternity of children will show no blue eyes or else half of them will be blue-eyed. The sum of the latter class, the second case, gives 654:712 or 48 per cent to 52 per cent.

3. When both parents have brown iris either all the children will have brown iris (last case in Table IV) or else about a quarter will lack brown pigment and so will be blue-eyed.

The eugenic value of the inheritance of eye color lies in the consideration, advanced by Major Woodruff, that pigmentation of the eye, skin, etc., better fits a child for life in the tropics or in a country, like the United States, of bright sunlight. Brown-eyed children can be secured from blue-eyed stock by mating with pure brown-eyed stock. We have heard of two blue-eyed parents regretting that they had no brown-eyed children. They wished for the impossible.

[1] Eight hundred and sixty-six additional cases collected subsequently are not included because unchecked.

[2] A number of these blues are doubtless destined to become pigmented in later life.

2. Hair Color

This character is due to the presence of brown granules in the hair and sometimes also to the presence of a diffuse reddish pigment. The study of heredity of hair color is complicated—more than that of eye color—by the fact that the hair grows darker with age, at least until maturity is achieved. If you compare the light browns and the blacks in children under 16 and over 16 you will find twice as many light browns in the younger lot as in the older; but only half as many blacks. In other words, half of the persons who will eventually have black hair still have light to medium brown at 16 years of age.[1] While this tends to obscure the result yet the general fact of segregation in hair color cannot be gainsaid. Let us examine the results of various matings. (Table V).

Table V

The hair-color of the offspring of parents with different classes of hair pigment.

One parent	*Other parent*	*Offspring*
Little brown pigment	Little brown pigment	All with tow, yellow, golden or red hair.
Brown pigment	Little or no brown pigment	Half with light hair, half with brown; in other families all children may eventually gain brown hair
Brown pigment	Brown pigment	Most children have brown hair; some (about one-quarter) have light hair. In some families all children eventually gain brown hair.

The most striking result is that dark-haired children probably never come from flaxen-haired parents. Indeed, a good practical rule is that the children will not acquire hair darker than that of the darker parent.

The inheritance of red-hair color has a certain eugenic importance. There can be little doubt that a young person

[1] Holmes and Loomis, 1909, p. 55.

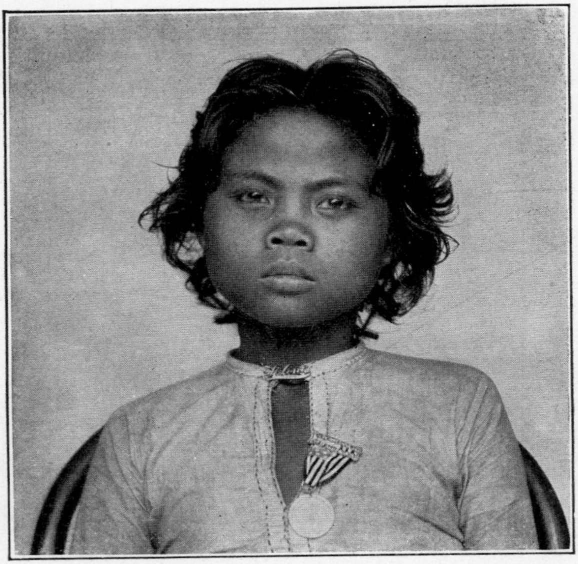

FIG. 10.—Wavy hair; a Segumbar, female, Philippine Islands. (Lent by the American Museum of Natural History.)

who has red hair has a strong antipathy to a red-haired person of the opposite sex. This testimony comes to me from the father of a red-haired daughter. It is confirmed by the fact that, despite prolonged inquiry among thousands of families I have succeeded in obtaining only two cases where both parents had red hair. Though the red was not a clear red in all parents all of the 8 children had red hair. If one parent only forms "red-hair" germ cells exclusively while the other forms exclusively germ cells containing the determiner for black pigment the offspring will show no red; still less will red-haired offspring appear if neither parent forms "red-hair" germ cells. Red-haired offspring may come from two brown or better from glossy black-haired parents provided both form red-hair germ cells. In that case both dark-haired parents will probably

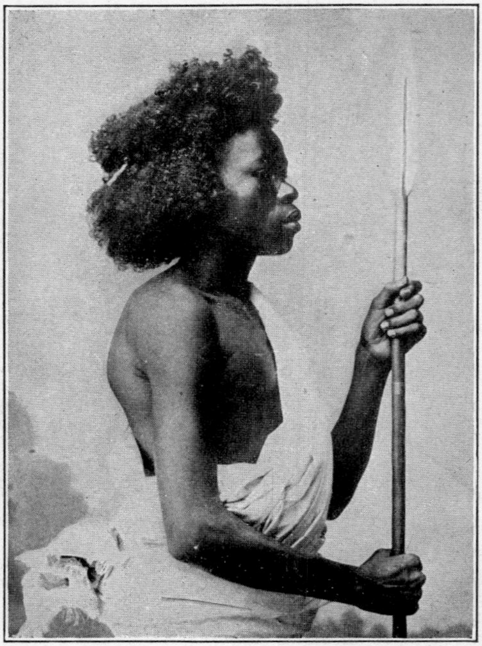

FIG. 11.—Frizzy or kinky hair; a Soudanese male. (Lent by the American Museum of Natural History from a photograph in the Philadelphia Museum.)

have ancestors or other close relatives with red hair. Glossy black hair in the parents is especially apt to produce red hair in the children because the glossiness is usually due to red hidden by black pigment.

3. Hair Form

The form of the hair varies from straight through wavy and curly (Fig. 10) to kinky (Fig. 11) and woolly (Fig. 12), depending largely upon the closeness of the spiral. These different types of hair have a different form on cross-section; *i. e.*, the cut end of a straight hair is nearly circular while

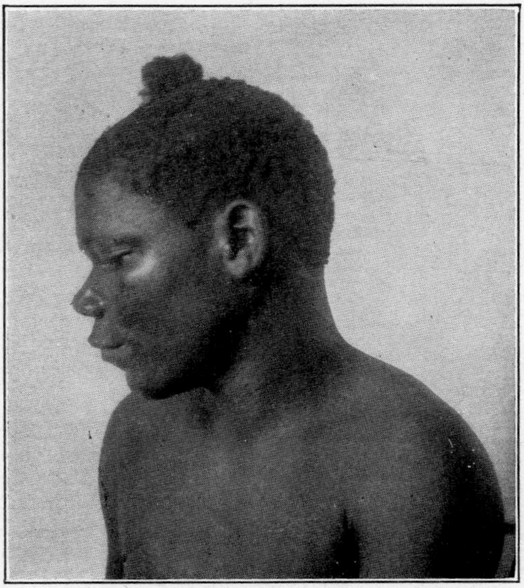

FIG. 12.—Woolly hair; a Congo negro. (Lent by American Museum Natural History.)

that of woolly hair is much flattened, being only half as thick as it is broad. Both the flattening and the curving of hair are due to a modification of the cup or "hair follicle" in which the hair develops. Thus, while straight hair develops in a plain, cylindrical follicle that of the flattened types is curved and inclined in relation to the surface of the skin. Straight hair is the simple condition; curving is due to a special modification. What, now, is the method of inheritance of this special modification?

First, if both parents have hair that from childhood up has been straight, without natural tendency toward curving, then all of the children will have straight hair. There are exceptional cases reported of wavy haired children from straight haired parents, but the exceptions constitute less than 2 per cent.

If one parent has wavy hair while the other has straight hair then, since in wavy haired persons half the germ cells are without the determiner for curved hair, half of the offspring will have straight and half curved hair. If both parents have wavy (simplex) hair about 75 per cent of the children will have curved hair and the others straight hair. But two curly haired parents, both of curly haired stock on both sides, will probably have all curly or wavy haired children. In a word, when either of the germ cells that unite to form the fertilized egg contains the curly determiner the offspring will have curved hair.

4. Skin Color

The pigment of the skin is due to brown granules lying in the deep stratum of the skin. Such granules occur in most people, are common in brunets and still more abundant in negroes. Besides the brown granules a yellow-red pigment is present, but this has been little studied.

Now when both parents are clearly blonds most, if not all, of their offspring are blonds. In 513 offspring reported as derived from this sort of mating 91.4 per cent are recorded as blonds and 6.8 per cent as intermediate, while only 1.8 per cent are stated to be brunet—quite within the limit of error due to inaccuracy of the collaborators. If one person is blond and the other darker, about half of the children will, on the average, be blond and half pigmented but rarely darker than the darker parent. If both parents be dark the percentage of brunets ranges from about 25 to zero. In general, whatever the mating, the children will not be darker than their darker parent.

When one parent is white and the other as dark as a full-blooded negro the offspring are, as is well known, of an intermediate shade (mulatto, mezzotint). If two such mulattoes marry their offspring vary in color. In one fraternity derived from two such mulattoes having 45 per cent and 13 per cent respectively of black in the skin, the proportion of black in the 7 offspring whose color was measured ranged from 46 to 6 (Fig. 13). The lighter limit was as light as most Caucasian skins. In another fraternity whose parents had 29 per cent and 13 per cent of black respectively, the children ranged from 28 per cent to 8.5 per cent of black in the skin color.[1] Here, again, the light-

W. Family

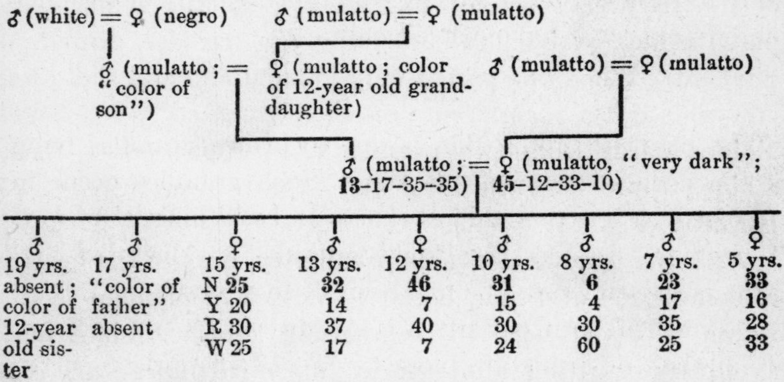

Fig. 13.—Pedigree chart of "W" family of mulattoes, showing the percentages of the four colors; black (*N*), yellow (*Y*), red (*R*) and white (*W*) that combined (as in the color wheel) will give the skin color. ♂, male; ♀, female. For fuller details see Davenport, G. C., and C. B., 1910.

est child has practically a white skin. In the case of the two other families, in which the parents were dark mulattoes (30 to 40 per cent black) none of the children were lighter than 27 per cent black. The germ cells of the parents probably lack the lower grades of pigmentation. On the other hand two very light "colored" parents will have (probably) only light children, some of whom "pass for whites" away from home. So far as skin color goes they are as truly white as their greatgrandparent and it is quite

[1] All colors were determined by means of the Bradley color top.

conceivable that they might have mental and moral qualities as good and typically Caucasian as he had. Just as perfect white skin color can be extracted from the hybrid, so may other Caucasian physical and mental qualities be extracted and a typical Caucasian arise out of the mixture. However, this result will occur only in the third, or later, hybrid generation and the event will not be very common.

Albinism. This is an extreme case of blondness—all pigment being lost from skin, hair and eyes. The method of inheritance resembles that of eye color. When both parents lack pigment all offspring are likewise devoid of pigment. When one parent only is an albino and the other is unrelated the children are all pigmented. Whenever albinos occur from two normals the proportion of these albinos approaches the ideal and expected condition of 25 per cent (Fig. 14).

Albinism is not a desirable peculiarity, despite the beauty of complexion and hair, because the lack of pigment in the retina makes it hard to bear strong light. Albinos may avoid transmitting albinism by marrying *unrelated*, pigmented persons. Pigmented persons belonging to albinic strains must avoid marrying cousins, even pigmented ones, because both parents might, in that case, have albinic germ cells and produce one child in four albinic. Albino communities, of which there are several in the United States are inbred communities; but not all inbred communities contain albinos.[1]

5. Stature

The inheritance of stature has long been a subject of study. It has great interest both because it is easily determined and because it has a great racial range, namely,

[1] This matter is discussed more fully in the "American Naturalist," December, 1910.

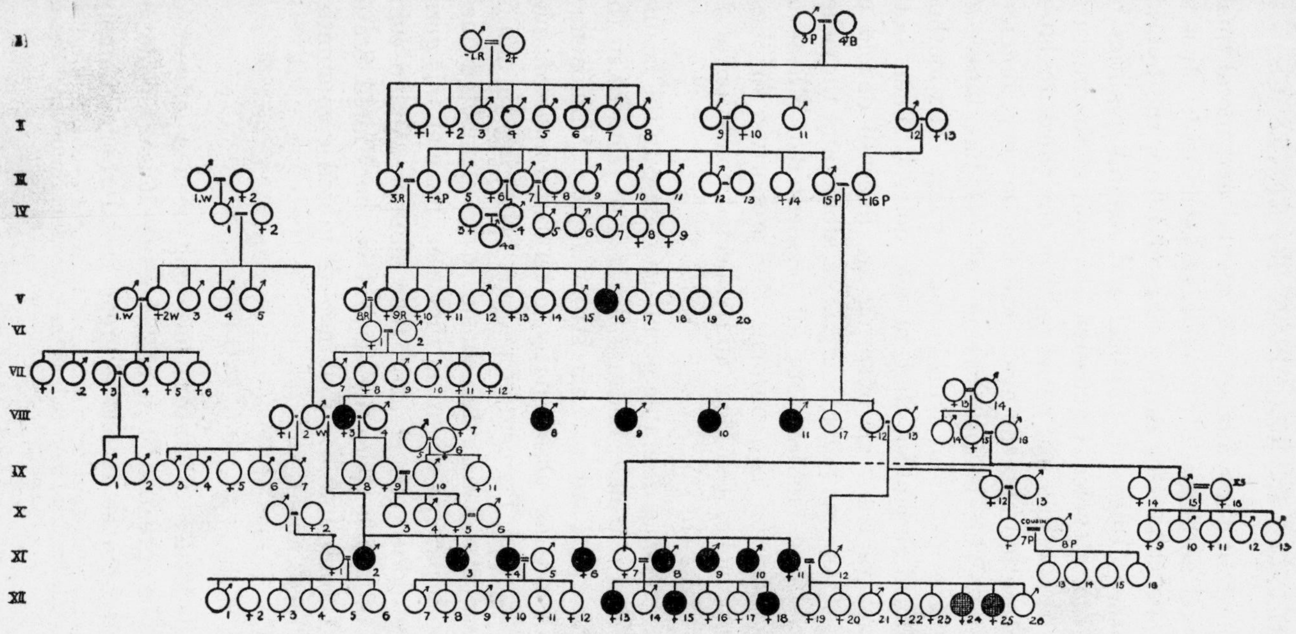

23*a* Family

FIG. 14.—Pedigree chart of an albino family. The letters *B*, *P*, *R*, *W*, represent the four common surnames in this highly inbred community. All black circles represent abinos, ♀ female, ♂, male, O, unknown sex.

from 138 centimeters (or 54 inches) in the negrilloes of Africa to 180 centimeters (or 71 inches) in the Scotch. Among European males, stature ranges from 150 centimeters (60 inches) to 190 centimeters (75 inches), while that of women rarely exceeds 180 centimeters (71 inches).[1]

The importance of stature as a definite character is seen in its distribution in Europe. Apart from the variations ascribed to environment there are clear racial (*i. e.*, inherit-

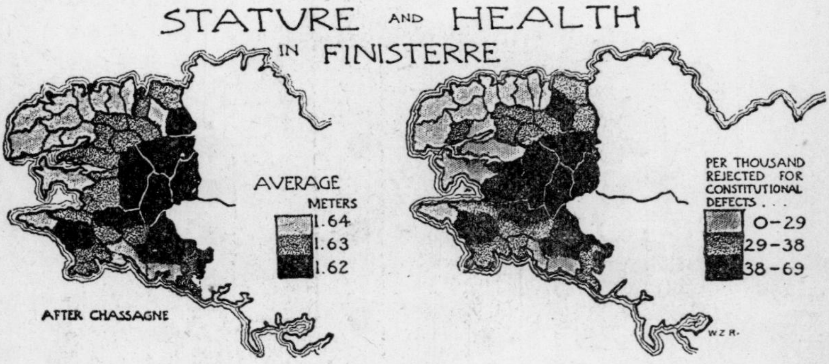

FIG. 15.—Two maps of Brittany, France. On the left is shown the distribution of the various mean statures ranging from 1.62 meters to 1.64 meters. On the right is shown the distribution of rejection of recruits for constitutional defects. RIPLEY: "The Races of Europe."

able) differences. The rugged hills of Scotland harbor a race that are, relatively, giants; the mild and productive shores of the Gulf of Tarent, Southern Italy, hardly more populous, are inhabited by a people that are, relatively, dwarfs. Conditions of life cannot account for the difference; there is a difference of blood. It is easy to go astray in assigning environmental causes for stature. Thus Ripley (1900, p. 85) referring to a map of Brittany says: "In the interior cantons, shorter on the average by an inch than the population along the sea coast, there is a corresponding

[1] Deniker, "Races of Man," p. 584.

increase of defective or degenerate constitutional types. The character of the environment is largely responsible for this." (Fig. 15). Two maps are given of this territory showing the practical coincidence of the areas of shortest stature and greatest number of rejections of recruits for physical defects. Fifteen pages later, however, practically the same map is used (Fig. 16), the greater height of the

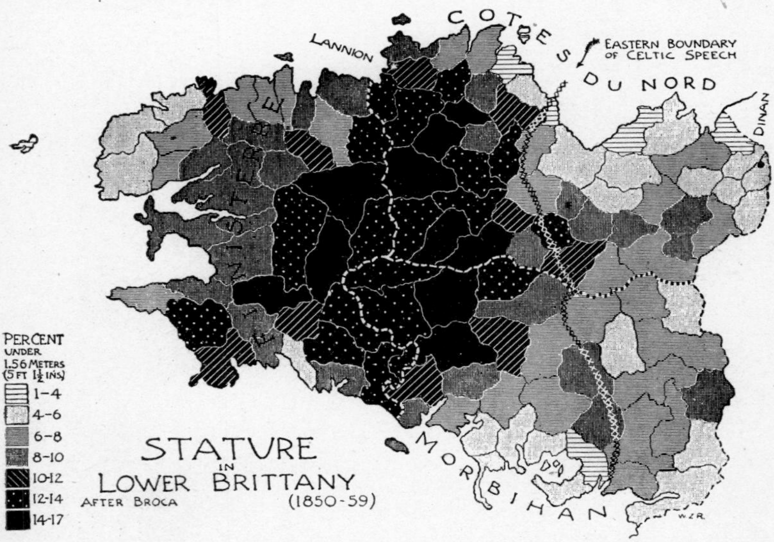

FIG. 16.—Map of stature in Brittany showing smaller proportion of men whose stature is under 1.56 meters in the region subject to Teutonic invasions. RIPLEY: "The Races of Europe."

coastal people referred to, and explained by Teutonic invasions. "The result has been to infuse a new racial element into all the border populations in Brittany, while the original physical traits remain in undisturbed possession of the interior." It appears, then, probable that the greater rejection of recruits in the central country is due less to its unfavorable environment than to its inadequate blood.

Recognizing the inheritable nature of stature it remains

to inquire how it is inherited. First of all it must be conceded that stature is hardly a single unit. It is composed of three elements that would seem to be unrelated, namely, the height of the cranium, the length of the neck and trunk, and the length of the legs. Sitting height is a more significant measure from the standpoint of heredity; but, unfortunately, few persons know their sitting height. A second complication is dependence of stature on age. It increases up to 20 years in the male and about 19 years in the female. Beyond these ages the increase may be neglected. A third complication is that stature is, to a certain degree, dependent on sex. To transmute female measurements to corresponding male measurements Galton (1889) used the method of multiplying them by 1.08 since the mean of male stature is that much greater than the mean of female stature. We can avoid this complication by using, in place of the absolute or transmuted measures, the deviation in each sex from its own mean. The mean stature for the adult males of the white population of the United States may be taken at 69 inches (175 cm); that of females at 64 inches (163 cm). Despite all these complications, which tend to obscure the result, we can still seek an answer to the question: What general laws are there of inheritance of stature?

The first general law is that, in case the four grandparents are very unlike, the adult children will vary greatly in stature, whereas when the grandparental statures are closely alike those of the children will be also. This is shown in the following Table:

	Inches					
Difference between the shortest and the tallest child:	3	4	5	6	7	8
Difference between the shortest and the tallest grandparent:	4.6	5.0	6.0	6.5	6.9	7.2

This law seems to indicate that the reason why in some

families the children vary greatly in stature while in others they vary little is because more diverse elements have entered into the make-up of the children in the first case than in the second. In the first case long and short blood are commingled in the ancestry while in the second case exclusively long or exclusively short ancestry as the case may be.

The second general law is that when both parents are tall all of the children tend to be tall; but, on the contrary, if both parents are short some of the children will be short and some tall in ratios varying from 1:1 up to 2:1. If all of the grandparents are short then there tend to be twice as many short children as tall; but if one grandparent on each side be tall there will tend to be an equality of short and tall offspring.

The evidence for the foregoing is found in the study of 104 families which furnished quantitative data as to stature for children, parents and grandparents.

To illustrate the inheritance of extreme short stature in a family I may quote from C. F. Swift (1888). He says (p. 473) "I am unable to give a particular account of the Little Hatches of Falmouth. [Mass.] They were children of Barnabas, who married in 1776 his relative Abigail Hatch and had two sons and seven daughters. Six daughters were less than 4 feet in height. None married. The seventh daughter Rebecca was of common size and married Robert Hammond. The two sons, Barnabas, born in 1788, and Robinson, b. 1790, were both of low stature, one, scarce 4 feet in height, was a portly gentleman almost as broad as long." It may be predicted that the tall daughter who married had only tall children.

6. Total Body Weight

Adult weight (assuming density to be constant) depends upon stature and circumference. It is, therefore, still more complicated than stature and still further removed from any semblance of a unit character. Moreover, it is much more dependent upon conditions of life, for, as is well known, a sedentary life with overfeeding and drinking tends, *in persons so disposed*, to increase weight, even as strenuous activity and dieting favor the reduction, within certain limits, of weight.

Despite this dependence of weight on environment we may attempt to learn if it shows any trace of heredity. First, it is necessary to avoid the use of absolute weights on account of sex differences. So we find the mean weight of American fathers and mothers and calculate our weights as deviations from these means. The mean weight of fathers in our data is 162 pounds; of mothers 131 pounds. The range in weight of fathers is from 110 to 250 pounds. The range in weight of mothers is from 90 pounds to 360 pounds.[1] In our study we are, however, concerned less with absolute deviations in weight from the average than in the deviations in corpulency and so we make our starting point the weight for a given stature and calculate in each case the deviation from the weight that is normal for the given stature. The table of normal weight that we employ is Table VI.

TABLE VI

NORMAL WEIGHT, IN POUNDS, FOR EACH INCH OF STATURE AND EACH SEX

Inches of stature		59	60	61	62	63	64	65	66	67
Normal weight in pounds for	male		131	132	134	137	140	143	147	152
	female	107	112	117	122	126	131	136	139	141

Inches of stature		68	69	70	71	72	73	74	75
Normal weight in pounds for	male	157	162	167	172	177	182	190	198
	female	144	150	155	160	165	170		

The first result is that when both parents are slender in build or of relatively light weight the children will tend all to be slender.

[1] This maximum occurred in a single case of our records; the next lower weight is 225 pounds.

The evidence for this has never been fully set forth. It rests on five fraternities in which the ten parents diverged (in pounds) from the normal as follows: 1, 1, -2, -7, -7, -9, -11, -12, -33, -47. Every grandparent was below normal in weight except one who was just normal. Of 23 children only 3 are above normal. Their total excess weight amounts to 25 pounds, while the total deficiency of the 20 remaining children is 374 pounds—an average deficiency for the 23 children of 15 pounds. Truly, a slender population.

If both parents are heavy and of heavy ancestry their children tend, on the whole, to be heavy (Fig. 17).

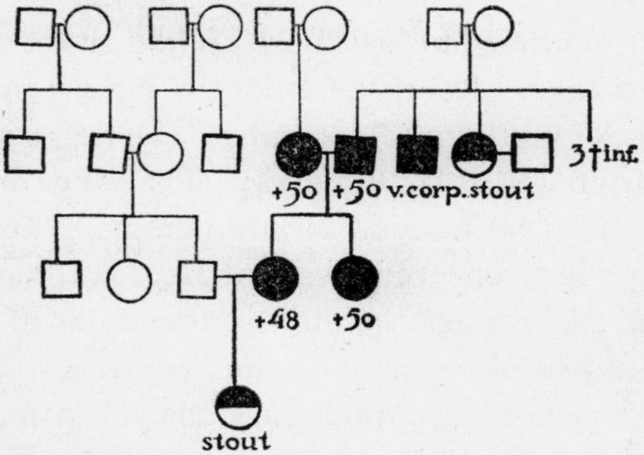

FIG. 17.—Pedigree of family with corpulency. Great-grandparents, grandparents and one of the parents are much above normal weight for their stature and the same tendency is found throughout the fraternities to which they belong. The father is slender. His daughter is, at an early age, inclined to stoutness. F. R.; Hal. 3.

I have data on four families that meet these conditions and give in Table VII all the data concerning their deviations in weight from the normal.

TABLE VII

THE DEVIATIONS FROM NORMAL STOUTNESS (WEIGHT ÷ STATURE) OF THE ANCESTORS AND CHILDREN WHEN BOTH PARENTS ARE HEAVY

Reference letters	FF	FM	MF	MM	F	M	C^1	C^2	C^3	C^4	C^5	C^6
Ave.—2	23	25	24	28	27	35	—10	—6	23			
Gan.—1	1	23	3	9	18	21	— 6	8	8	9	13	18
Eld.—1	8	11	21	33	33	5	—12	32	38	53		
Elt.—1	3	11	3	44	8	18	—22	—2				

C, child; F, father or father's; M, mother or mother's.

It is to be kept in mind that the children are mostly young, 18 to 25, and consequently do not show their potentialities in weight. Nevertheless, while there are 6 children below the normal in weight, giving a deficiency of 58 pounds, there are 9 above the normal with an excess of 202 pounds.

When both parents are heavy (disregarding grandparents) the numbers of light and heavy children are practically equal (39 light to 34 heavy or 465 pounds total deficiency to 490 pounds total excess).

When one of the parents is heavy and the other slender both heavy and slight offspring occur and, in youth at least, the slight are more numerous than the heavy. Table VIII gives the data on this mating.

TABLE VIII

THE DEVIATIONS FROM NORMAL STOUTNESS (WEIGHT ÷ STATURE) OF THE ANCESTORS AND CHILDREN IN SIX FAMILIES WITH ONE SLENDER AND ONE HEAVY PARENT

Reference letters	FF	FM	MF	MM	F	M	C^1	C^2	C^3	C^4	C^5	C^6
Bab.	21	44	—32	29	10	—7	—10	—6	23			
Bra.—3	—2	—6	8	44	—17	9	—8	—16	—16	—33	7	7
Cro.—2	3	33	—43	3	58	—26	3	—7	—17	—25	8	—28
Elk.—1	8	48	—20	2	33	—14	—13	—26	—10	—13		
How.—1	—32	—17	63	78	—45	78	—27	—26	—10	—12	19	
Ran.—1	17	—11			—40	44	13	—17	—4			

In Table VIII are included 27 children, 7 above the normal stoutness and 20 below, or a total of 30 pounds excess to 324 pounds deficiency.

A pedigree of a family with hereditary obesity is described by Rose (1907). A girl of 15 with a stature of 145 centimeters (57 inches) weighed 75 kilograms (165 pounds). The father and his parents were not obese.[1] The mother, on the other hand weighed 88 kilograms and her father 99 kilograms, while the mother's mother is slender. Of the four children

[1] There is no evidence that they did not carry the factor that favors obesity or that they were wholly unrelated to the maternal side.

two (including the girl of 15) are very obese, one normal and one under weight. This result accords with the hypothesis that obesity is due to a defect. It is noted that the mother's mother had a goitre; and it is probable that in this family there is an hereditary deficiency in growth control.

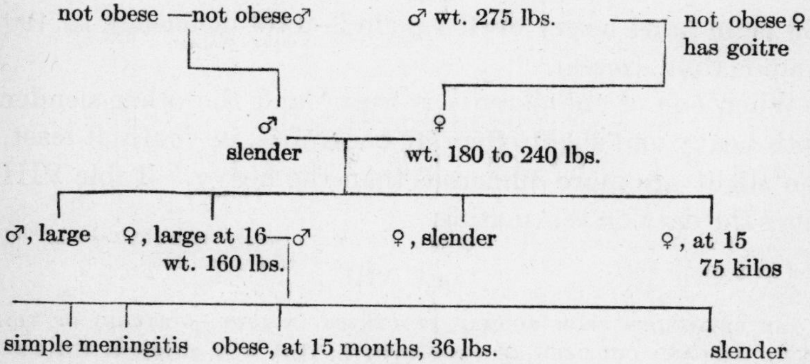

Longevity. When Dr. O. W. Holmes was asked for specifications for a long life he advised, in effect, first to select long-lived grandparents. This advice accords with a widespread opinion that longevity is inheritable. But length of life is not a unit character. It is a resultant of many factors; especially

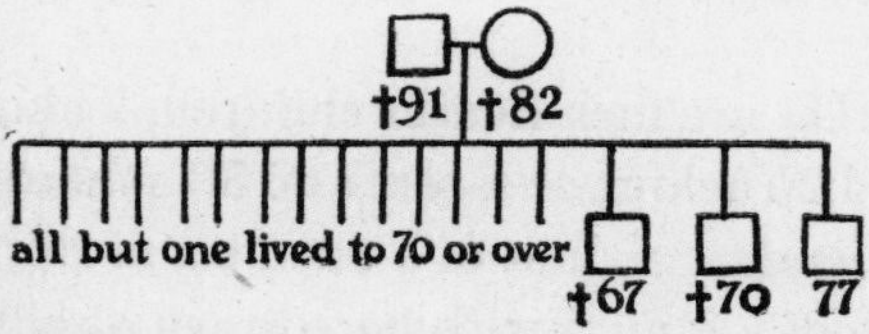

FIG. 18.—A short pedigree (early 19th century in United States) illustrating "inheritance" of longevity. F. R.; Att. 1.

of those factors that resist causes of death. Such factors are absence of defects of bodily structure, resistance to the commoner virulent germs of disease, and environmental conditions that maintain at its highest point internal resistance. The first two factors are "inheritable" and the last remains tolerably uniform for the people of a certain social class such as the members of one and the same family belong to; so it is not strange that some families with perfect structure and high resistance should be long lived (Fig. 18) and others, with organic defects and low resistance, should be short lived

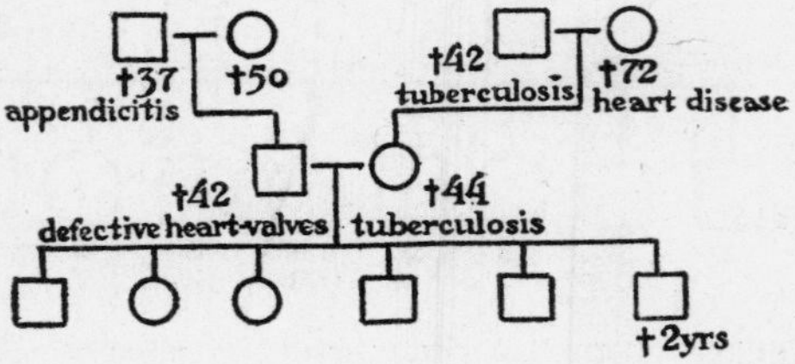

Fig. 19.—Fragment of pedigree of a high class family with slight longevity due in part to heart defects and non-resistance to tuberculosis. The latest generation comprises only young children. F. R.; Pyn. 1.

(Fig. 19). Thus, while longevity is not a biological unit of inheritance a person belonging to a long lived family is a better "risk" for a life insurance company than a person belonging to a short lived family.

7. Musical Ability

Bull!!!

This quality is one that develops so early in the most marked cases that its innateness cannot be questioned. A Bach, matured at 22; a Beethoven, publishing his compositions at 13 and a Mendelssohn at 15; a Mozart, composing at 5 years, are the product of a peculiar protoplasm of whose tenacious qualities we get some notion when we learn that the Bach family comprised 20 *eminent* musicians and two score others less eminent. The exact method of inheritance of musical ability has not been sufficiently analyzed. Hurst (1908) suggests that it behaves as a recessive, as though it depended on the absence of something. The "Family Records" afford some data on this subject. A statement of the grade of musical ability of each person, whether poor,

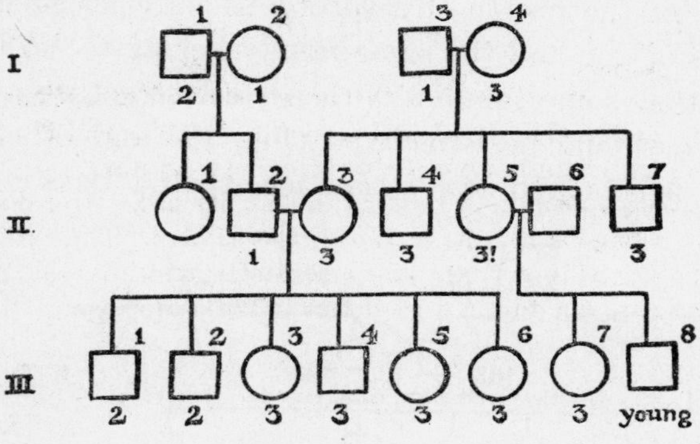

FIG. 20.—Pedigree of an American family of singers. Numbers below symbols designate grades; thus: 1, little or no musical ability; 2, medium ability; 3, exceptionally high ability. Numbers above the individual symbols are for reference.

I, 1. Extremely fond of music, had organ and piano in his home; a very cultivated man of artistic tastes. Married I, 2, non-musical, belonging to an utterly non-musical family. Their son, II, 2, is not musical.

I, 3. Fond of music, could "carry a tune" easily. A mathematician and astronomer. His wife, I, 4, was sufficiently musical to sing in such a simple church choir as was to be found in the State of Maine in the middle of the nineteenth century and her mother and mother's sisters were singers. All of their four children were musical. One son, II, 7, who died unmarried had a fine voice and was a good singer. The other son, II, 4, had a musical ear and a fine voice; he sang much without having taken lessons. His wife is non-musical and their 14-year old daughter is as non-musical as her mother. One of the daughters, II, 5, had a fine voice and still keeps up her music; she married an utterly non-musical man and they have one son who cannot even "carry a tune" and one daughter who is *a famous opera singer*. The other daughter, II, 3, is a fine singer, and plays the piano, organ and guitar. She married the above-mentioned non-musical man, II, 2. They had six children all of whom have fine voices; III, 1, has a fair baritone voice; III, 2, has an unusually deep bass voice; III, 3, died at 27 years. Her voice was said by good judges, such as the De Reszkes, Anton Seidl, etc., to be more beautiful even than that of III, 8. III, 4, is organist and choir master in a large church in New York City. III, 5, is very musical; III, 6, died young but had already developed much musical talent and could read music with wonderful ease. F. R.; H.

medium or exceptionally good was asked for. Altogether data were obtained for 1008 children, their parents and most of their grandparents. The following rules are deduced from these data.

When both parents are exceptionally good in music

(whether vocal or instrumental) all the children are medium to exceptionally good.

There were 48 cases where both parents showed exceptional musical ability. Of the 202 children 81 had exceptional ability and 120 fair musical ability. Only one is returned as being poor in music; and this case may be cast aside as quite within the probability of an error due to carelessness in making the returns or to bad classification. These results come out so smoothly as to indicate that high attainment in vocal and instrumental music are due to the same defect in the protoplasm.

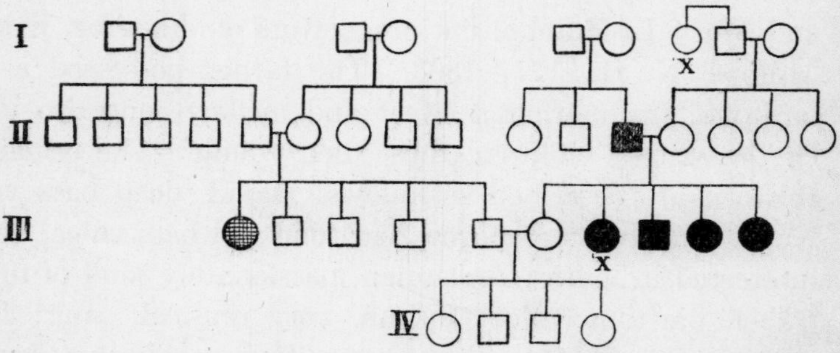

FIG. 21.—Pedigree of singing ability and peculiar form of toes. I, 7. (X) has bones of both fifth toes cartilaginous and toe crossed over upon fourth toe; and her granddaughter III, 7, has exactly the same peculiarity; II, 12, has an exceptionally good bass voice; his daughter III, 6, cannot sing; but III, 7, has a beautiful soprano voice; III, 8, has an exceptionally good baritone voice; III, 9, has a 'beautiful contralto voice' and III, 10, has great musical ability. On the other side of the house, III, 1, has good musical ability. But in the fourth generation there is no musical ability. F. R.; Ait. 1.

To illustrate inheritance of musical ability by a concrete example the pedigree of a noted New England singer is appended (Fig. 20). This particular example alone could not be used to demonstrate either the hypothesis that musical ability is due to a new unit or that it is due to a defect.

When both parents are poor in musical ability and come of ancestry that lacks on one or both sides such ability the children will all be non-musical.

Four families of this sort are given in the *Records*. All 29 children are poor in music. Compare Fig. 21.

When one parent has high musical ability and the other has little the children will vary much in this respect.

Thus of 257 offspring of such matings 45 are without musical ability, 84 are exceptionally good at music while 128 are intermediate. The result indicates a partial blend in the musical ability of the offspring of mixed origin.

As an example that illustrates the law approximately may be cited the Hutchinson family (Hutchinson, 1876). According to the statement of Wm. Lloyd Garrison, Jesse and Mary L. Hutchinson, progenitors of the tribe, lived in Milford, N. H., 1777–1863. The father possessed a rare baritone, the mother a sweet and mellow contralto voice. Of the sixteen children, three died young. The remaining thirteen are described as follows: David, deep bass voice; Noah, tenor voice; Andrew, baritone and bass voice, deeply interested in music; Zephaniah, passionately fond of music; Cabel, baritone voice; Joshua, very musical, sang; Jesse, editorial work; Benjamin, not gifted musically; Judson, musical genius; Rhoda, high contralto; John, most commanding vocal talents of all; Asa, inherited a large share of musical gift; Abbe, contralto voice, one of quartette. Details are lacking concerning the voice of Jesse, and the description of Benjamin is all too vague, considering the importance of this case, and so too much emphasis cannot be laid on these two cases; but aside from them the uniformity of testimony as to vocal talent of the family is striking.

8. Ability in Artistic Composition

Like musical ability, artistic talent shows itself so early as to demonstrate its innateness. Thus extraordinary talent was recognized in Francesco Mazzuoli (though ill taught) at 16, in Paul Potter at 15, in Jacob Ruysdael at 14, in Titian Vecelli at 13. Galton gives the following pedigree of the Vecellis. All the persons named were painters. "The connecting links indicated by crosses are, singularly enough, every one of them lawyers" (Fig. 22).

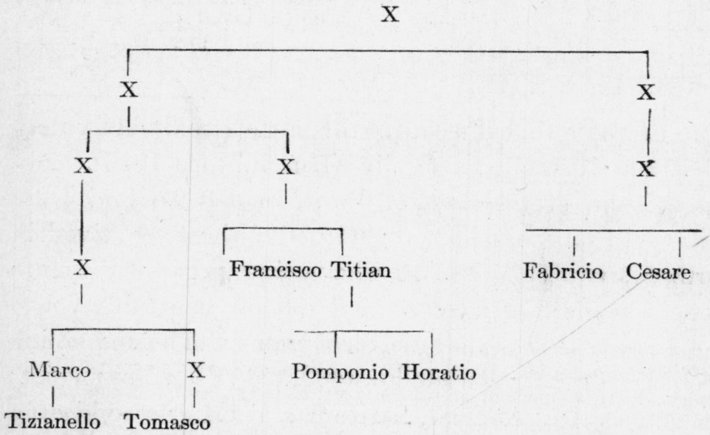

FIG. 22.—Pedigree of the painter family Vecelli. ×, father (always a lawyer).—GALTON, 1869.

The data furnished by the Family Records seem to justify the following conclusions.

When both parents have exceptional artistic ability their children will, in most cases, all have high artistic ability (Fig. 23).

The data for this generalization are sparse. Four matings of this sort furnished 13 children of whom 10 had a high grade, 1 is recorded as medium and two as poor; but both of the latter occur in one record that gives internal evidence that the question was not clearly understood.

When both parents are devoid of artistic talent and come from an unartistic ancestry none of the children show exceptional ability in art.

From 103 such matings (grade 1) there were derived 391 children of whom 185 are given as of grade 1 and 206 as of grade 2, while to none was ascribed grade 3.

When one parent is artistic and the other neither himself artistic nor of artistic ancestry then probably none of the

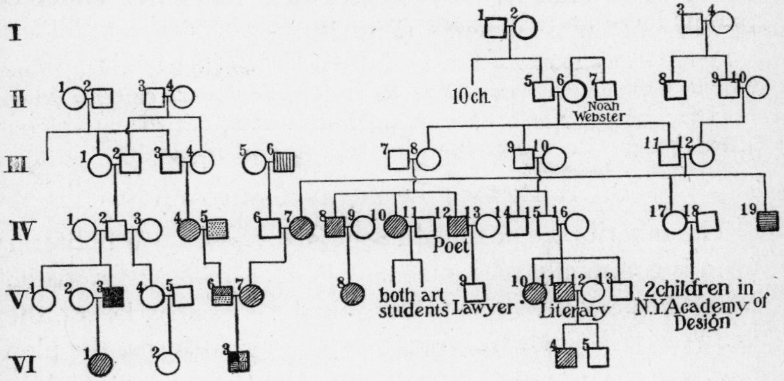

FIG. 23.—Pedigree of artistic ability (solid black for high talent, oblique shading for talent of a less degree). The family shows also the traits of taste for history (dots), of mechanical talent (vertical lines), and of wood carving (horizontal lines). II, 3, Nathan P, had son Wm. F. (III, 2) who was grandfather of an artist, V, 3; and a daughter Mary (III, 4) who was the great grandmother of artist J. W. F. (VI, 3). This brother and sister (III, 2, and III, 4) married a brother and sister, (III, 1 and III, 3) and it is in this stock that we first find the inheritance of artistic ability. IV, 4, married John E. F. (IV, 5) a man who through life had a love of historic research. This love of history appeared again in George E. F. (V, 6) who became a journalist and subsequently author of several valuable works on Indian history. In his son (VI, 3) in turn this love of history cropped out, as shown both in his Art History researches and as a painter of Indian history scenes. On his father's side, the lineage of VI, 3, has been traced back to 1630. No artistic genius was found in the male line except in V, 6 and VI, 3. His grandmother (IV, 4) displayed artistic tendencies, painting notable pictures throughout life.

We turn now to the mother of VI, 3, and her family. Her great-grandfather, Joel L., II, 5, married Jerusha, sister of Noah Webster, II, 7. Their son Chester's second son, Edward, IV, 15, a distinguished clergyman married Mary J. S., IV, 16, an educated lady and great lover of art. Their son, V, 11, was editor of the N. Y. "Sun," educator, Regent of the State of New York and fond of drawing and painting in an amateurish way. Artistic gift exists in his sister Anna and his older son, Kenneth.

III, 8, married Rev. S. P., graduate Andover Theological Seminary, first Presbyterian missionary to Oregon. Their first son, IV, 8, entered the ministry and was afterward a physician, also having marked artistic genius. His daughter Florence, V, 8, had marked artistic ability. His sister, IV, 10, was also a natural artist and this talent developed in her children and grandchildren to some extent. A brother, IV, 12, was clergyman, author-poet and professor in art. His son, V, 9, was a lawyer. Of children of III, 11–12, IV, 19, was gifted as a wood-carver, a trait which appeared in his great-nephew, VI, 3. IV, 17, married, and two children were proficient in the N. Y. Academy of Design. IV, 7, had an artistic turn of mind and her daugh-

children will have high artistic talent. But if the unartistic parent have artistic ancestry there will be artistic children.

From 15 such matings there were derived 37 children of whom 15 were poor in artistic ability and 22 medium. Among the 120 children derived from the mating: non-artistic parent having some artistic ancestors × artistic parent, there were 43 with exceptional artistic ability.

9. Ability in Literary Composition

The inheritance of the ability to express oneself in literary form is commonly recognized. "Poets are born; not made." Many literary men show their talent very early, before they had received much training in expression. Burns, the plowboy, was celebrated as a poet at 16, Calderon at 14, Goldoni produced comedy at 8, Charlotte Brontë published "Jane Eyre" at 22, Fénélon was known at 15, Sir Philip Sidney was famous at 21. As illustrations of heredity we have two of Charlotte Brontë's sisters writing a famous book, besides a brother Patrick said to be the greatest genius of them all. The father and the father's father of T. B. Macaulay, two uncles, a cousin and a nephew were all writers of note. Four generations of Taylors in England were authors of an "evangelist disposition."

The precise method of inheritance of literary ability has not hitherto been made clear; but a study of the Family Records seems to justify the following conclusions.

When both parents have high to good literary ability all (or nearly all) of the children will have likewise good literary ability.

There are 643 offspring of such matings in the Family Records and of them 93 per cent have medium to high literary capacity. No doubt these terms are used somewhat loosely and this may account for the exceptional cases.

---

ter, Mary L. B., had a decided artistic talent which she inherited from her father's family as well as her mother's.

It may be of interest to state further that VI, 3, possessed a mechanical genius, as did his great-grandfather, Joseph B., III, 6, a skilled jeweler, many of whose descendants to the fourth generation were also skillful jewelers.

When both parents have poor literary ability and come from a strain devoid of it the children will, typically, have poor literary capacity. This generalization is based on the 19 children, all non-literary, of four matings of this sort. But when literary ability appears in remoter ancestry it will occur in some of the children. Thus in 23 matings of this sort only 25 per cent of the children are without literary capacity.

10. Mechanical Skill

There can be little doubt of the inheritance of some of the elements of mechanical ability. The case of John Roebling and his sons, builders of the first great suspension bridge over the East River, New York City, and of Charles Martin, long chief engineer of that bridge, and his son, Kingsley Martin, for some years chief engineer of the bridges of New York City, are examples familiar to modern Americans. Not less striking is the family of boat designers whose pedigree is shown in Fig. 24. Five of the seven sons of the illustrious head of the family were inventors and boat designers, and high technical ability has appeared also in the third generation.

The Pomeroys are another American family that illustrates the inheritance of mechanical skill. The first of the family in America was Eltweed Pomeroy at Dorchester in 1630 and later at Windsor, Connecticut. He was by trade a blacksmith, which in those days comprehended practically all mechanical trades. His sons and grandsons, with few exceptions, followed this trade. "In the settlement of new towns in Massachusetts and Connecticut the Pomeroys were welcome artisans. Large grants of land were awarded to them to induce them to settle and carry on their business." "The peculiar faculty of the Pomeroys is not the result of training and hardly of perceptible volun-

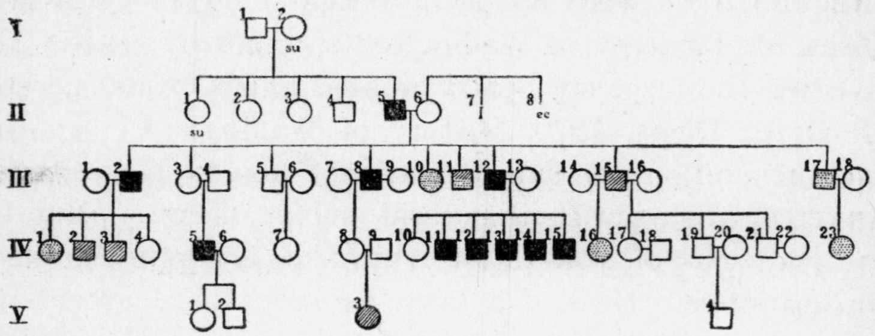

FIG. 24.—Pedigree of family with mechanical and inventive ability, particularly in respect to boat-building. I, 2, a suicide: II, 1, a suicide. His brother, II, 5, a builder of swift boats and yachts, II, 7, insane; II, 8, eccentric. The union of these two strains with evidence of nervous instability resulted in a family of 9 children and 18 grandchildren. Four of the sons show a high degree of inventive ability and 2 of these III, 8–12, developed the genius of their father in designing and building swift and beautiful boats. Three are musicians, III, 10, 11, 17, and one of them, III, 11, shows also mechanical ability. In the next generation these traits reappear in the various fraternities. IV, 1, is a musician; 2 has much mechanical skill and 3 is inventive; 5, is a builder of fine boats; IV, 11–15 represent 5 boys, none over 22, but already designing boats; two other daughters of this generation show artistic and musicial talent and, finally, in the next generation we have a girl of 14, V, 3, designing boats. F. R.; H.

tary effort in the individual. Their powers are due to an inherited capacity from ancestry more or less remote, developed for generations under some unconscious cerebration." There was Seth Pomeroy (1706–1777) an ingenious and skillful mechanic who followed the trade of gunsmith. At the capture of Louisburg in 1745 he was a major and had charge of more than twenty smiths who were engaged in drilling captured cannon. Other members of the family manufactured guns which in the French and Indian wars were in great demand and in the Revolution, also, the Pomeroy guns were indispensable. "Long before the United States had a national armory, the private armories of the Pomeroys were famous. There was Lemuel Pomeroy, the pioneer manufacturer of Pittsburg, stubborn but clear headed, of whom a friend said: There would at times be no living with him if he were not always right." There was also Elisha M. Pomeroy of Wallingford a tinner by trade. He invented the razor strop and profited much by its success. [C. H. S. Davis, 1870, History of Wallingford.] In the sixth generation we find Benjamin Pomeroy a successful lawyer entrusted with important public offices. "But he was conscious of powers for which his law practice gave him no scope. He had a taste for mechanical execution, and as a pastime between his professional duties undertook the construction of difficult public works—the more difficult the better he liked them. The chief of the United States Topographical Engineers was a friend of Mr. Pomeroy and repeatedly consulted him in emergencies wherein his extraordinary capacity was made useful to the government. By him were constructed on the Atlantic coast beacons and various structures in circumstances that had baffled previous attempts." The value to this country of the mechanical trait in this one germ plasm can hardly be estimated. Especially is it to be noted that, despite constant out-marriages, it goes its course unreduced and unmodified through the generations.

The Fairbanks family of St. Johnsbury, Vermont, illustrates the inheritance of inventiveness combined with executive ability, specialized in the iron trade. The inventor of the "platform scales" belonged to a family not merely of iron workers but to one with imagination such as made other members literary men (Fig. 25).

The Family Records give rather definite information as to the method of inheritance of mechanical skill.

When both parents have good or exceptional mechanical skill all of their children will have it also.

Out of 413 children of such matings (including both sexes) all but 7 show some mechanical ability, and 118 of them ability of an exceptional order. Indeed, most persons of exceptional skill come from this mating.

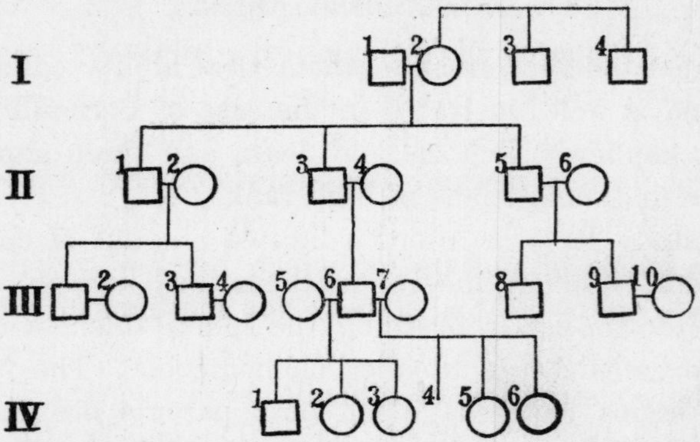

FIG. 25.—Pedigree illustrating inheritance of special ability in the Fairbanks family of Vermont. I, James Fairbanks; I, 2, Phoebe Paddock. Her two brothers, I, 3 and 4, were *iron workers*, II, 1, Erastus Fairbanks moved at 19 years to St. Johnsbury, Vermont and began to manufacture stoves, plows, etc.; II, 2, Lois Crossman; II, 3, Thaddeus, a natural mechanic, invented the platform scales; II, 4, Lucy Barker; II, 5, the third brother, Joseph P. Fairbanks was a lawyer, with literary tastes.

Erastus and Lois had two sons of whom the elder, III, 1, went into the scale business, showed much inventive ability and a strong taste for natural history. His brother Horace, III, 3, was an excellent administrator and became Governor of Vermont. Dr. Henry Fairbanks, III, 6, son of Thaddeus went into the ministry, but his love of invention drew him into the iron business. He combined mechanical and literary gifts. III, 8, was a minister and III, 9, a sagacious and exact man, was secretary and treasurer of the Fairbanks Company.

If both parents lack mechanical skill and come from an ancestry that lacks it no offspring will have mechanical ability. Even if mechanical skill is found in the ancestry of one side, but not of the other, still there will be no marked mechanical ability in the children.

If one parent has mechanical ability and the other belongs to a strain that lacks it then exceptional mechanical ability will be absent or uncommon. But if the parent that lacks mechanical ability comes from an ancestry that possessed it a large proportion of the children will have such ability. Also when both parents that have slight mechanical ability are descended, on one side, from persons with skill, such skill will reappear in approximately one child in four.

11. Calculating Ability

The inheritance of great mathematical ability cannot be denied and is well illustrated in the case of Bernoulli: Jacques, his nephews Nicholas and Jean, and three nephew's sons were mathematicians of high rank.

Our Family Records afford a limited amount of data on the subject of inheritance of mathematical ability. They do give information concerning the inheritableness of the ability to calculate—a broader phenomenon. The following rule seems justified: When both parents are good at calculating all (or nearly all) of their children will be so likewise.

Of 728 offspring of this class of matings all but 48 (or 8 per cent) were good at calculating. In no case were both parents returned as poor at calculating; but in 47 matings both parents were only medium and 13 per cent of their children were poor at calculating.

12. Memory

There is no doubt that people vary in their ability to remember and there is no question that a good memory is an innate quality. Phenomenal memories are often associated with mental defect in which case it is clear they are independent of training. In other cases they are associated with high scholarship. Thus Galton cites the case of Richard Porson, an eminent Greek scholar, whose memory became stupendous. His mother had a remarkable memory and so did his sister.

The Family Records throw some light on the inheritance of a good memory; although the term is a relative one and lacks in precision. Nevertheless for a preliminary study the data are not to be despised although there are not a few exceptions to any generalizations one may hazard.

When both parents have an exceptionally good memory

most, if not all, of the children have a memory that is medium to exceptional.[1]

When both parents have a poor memory and come from ancestry so characterized few if any of the children have an excellent memory.

Two "poor" parents (with "poor" grandparents) have 10 children all with poor memory.

When one parent has a memory that is either excellent or fair and the other has one that is "poor" all children have a medium memory; and, conversely, parents with medium memory may have 20 to 25 per cent of children with excellent and as many with poor memory.

13. Combined Talents and Summary of Special Abilities

While the separate talents may, for purposes of analysis, be considered separately they usually, as our illustrations suggest, occur in combination in a single family. And such talents are frequently enough associated with insanity or mental defect in some of its members as apparently to justify the poet's conclusion: "Great wits are sure to madness near allied" (Fig. 26).

In many cases artistic, literary and musical talent are found in the same family—two or all three of them are occasionally found in the same person (Fig. 27, Fig. 28). The conclusion seems justified that artistic, literary and musical skill are unit characters that may occur in any combinations—the common inherited factor may be only a highly developed imagination.

In the foregoing cases the method of inheritance of many of the elements of the mental makeup have been considered

[1] The Family Records give 4 per cent of children of such matings as having a poor memory.

and the remarkable result has been deduced that the higher grades of all these qualities act, in inheritance, as though they were due to the absence of something that is present

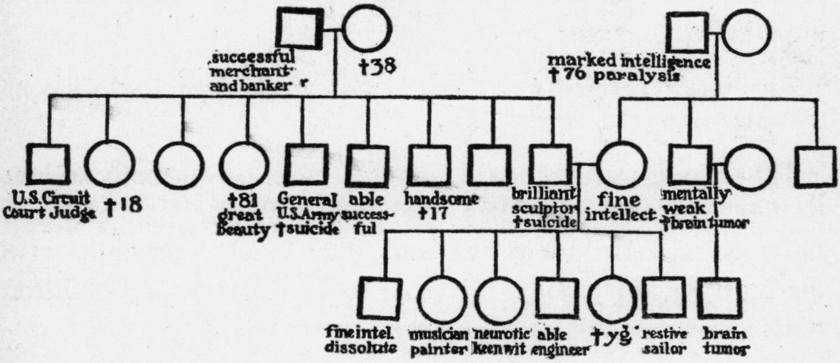

FIG. 26.—Pedigree of brilliancy combined with defect and melancholia. F. R.

in persons of poorer ability. It is as if the difference between a person of high ability and one of low ability in respect to any mental trait is that the person of high ability has

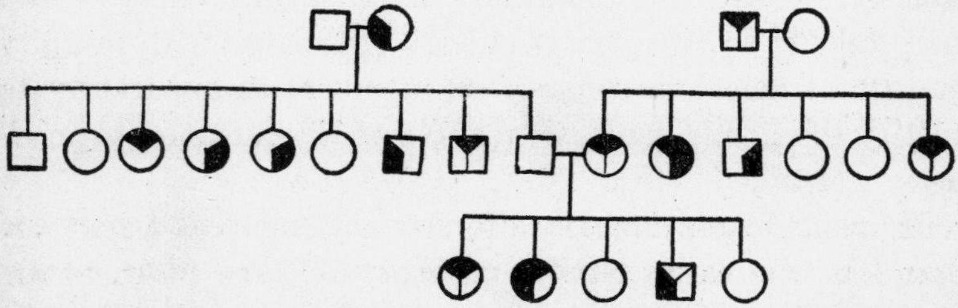

FIG. 27.—Pedigree of family with artistic (dark upper section), literary (right section) and musical (left section) ability.

got rid of a something possessed by the person of lower ability that prevents the latter from fully exercising his faculties;—he has sloughed off one or more inhibitors.

14. TEMPERAMENT

Two contrasted temperaments are usually recognized. One phlegmatic, slow, rarely depressed; the opposite ner-

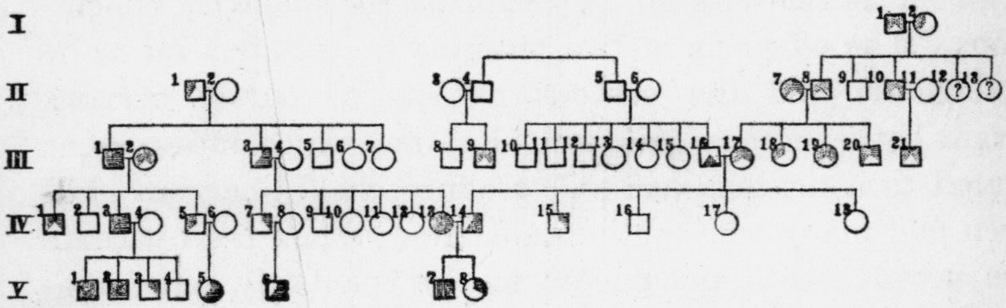

FIG. 28.—Pedigree of a pedigree-complex (Abbott-Buck-Wolff) showing inheritance of musical (dots), literary (horizontal lines) and inventive (vertical lines) ability. Variations in the area covered by each symbol indicate roughly a variation in degree of ability of the given kind. I, 1, a musician of the eighteenth century and I, 2, his wife, the daughter of a professor of music. One of his sons adopted a seafaring life and died in Mozambique. Two sons, II, 8, 11, were instructors in the Geneva Conservatory of Music. The son, III, 21, of one of these was a professor of music and a composer. The other married a woman, II, 7, with literary and musical ability and had four children of whom III, 19, was a literary composer; III, 18, had good musical ability; III, 20, was brilliant piano player with a fine baritone voice and literary; and III, 17, both literary and musical, married a man with inventive ability whose first cousin, III, 9, was an organist and musical composer of high rank. Two of their children, IV, 14, 15, show literary ability and IV, 14, inventive ability also. He married into a family famous in American literature and with much musical ability and the product was two children both literary and one, V, 7, an inventor of high rank. III, 1 and 3, derived from a musical father, have literary ability of a high order. One who has also some musical ability married a very musical wife and of the 4 sons at least 3 have musical ability. One of these, IV, 3, combined with the musical also literary ability, married a woman with some literary ability and had 4 sons of whom 3 at least are litterateurs and two have much musical ability. V, 5, is a well-known authoress.

vous, quick, often elated or alternately elated and depressed. Between the extremes lie, as is usually the case, many intermediates. While it is clear that there are no sharp lines to be drawn between these conditions, some insight into their hereditary behavior may be gained by an examination of the opinions furnished by collaborators in the Family Records.

When phlegmatic is assumed to be a condition recessive to the "intermediate" and nervous conditions we find that in three families with 13 offspring, 10 or 77 per cent, are likewise phlegmatic. On the other hand, when nervous is assumed to be recessive to intermediate and phlegmatic in 130 offspring of nervous parents 64 or 49 per cent were nervous.

So far as the data go they support the following conclusions. The offspring of two phlegmatic parents tend to be phlegmatic and the nervous parents of purely nervous origin have nervous children. But one phlegmatic parent mated to a nervous one will produce chiefly nervous children and many who are intermediate. When both parents are nervous with phlegmatic ancestry a fairly large proportion (up to about a quarter?) will be phlegmatic.

15. Handwriting

Inheritance of peculiarities of handwriting is often alleged (Darwin, 1894, p. 449), but it is difficult to get satisfactory evidence about it. A correspondent (Hal-2) writes:—"We belong to a family of penmen. My four brothers and myself inherited our handwriting (the English legal copyist's handwriting) from my father. Two of our uncles and two cousins also wrote the family hand. I believe it was asserted that our paternal grandfather wrote the same. We could distinguish the writing of each, but the general family resemblance was there, especially when we were all young men and my father was not old. . . . We descended from a family that included officemen, lawyers, recorders to whom expert penmanship was necessary."

16. General Bodily Energy

Of the inheritance of this quality there can be no doubt. If we take the class of commanders as one characterized above all by bodily energy we see the intensity of its heredity. It is exemplified in the family of Alexander the Great from Philip of Macedon down, the family of Charlemagne including Pepin le Gros and Charles Martel, of Gustavus Adolphus, and of Scipio Africanus.

Can we discover how bodily energy, which reaches its highest degree in such commanders, is inherited? Here again I appeal to the Family Records in which energy is recorded in the three grades: below average, medium, decidedly above average. The following principles seem established.

When both parents have bodily energy that is regarded as "decidedly above average" all of their children will have either exceptional or at least medium energy.

The mating of two energetic parents in 192 families produced 413 offspring (or 2.2 children to the family). Of these 301 (73 per cent) are placed in the highest grade; 100 (24 per cent) in the middle grade and only 12 (3 per cent) in the low grade. Considering the probability of errors this lowest grade is negligible.

When both parents have medium to low energy and come from ancestry of this sort all offspring have medium to low energy.

There are 54 matings of this sort, with 219 children (or 4.1 children to the fraternity). All but 4 are in the medium class.

When one parent has great bodily energy while the other has no great energy in himself or his ancestry all of the children (86) have medium (82) or low energy (4). But if there be energy in the grandparents on the low side about half of the children will have energy that is decidedly above the average.

There are 105 matings of the latter sort, producing 456 children (or 4.3 children to the fraternity) of whom 226 were classed as of great energy, 208 of medium and only 22 as low.

On the whole the facts support the hypothesis that excessive bodily energy is due to a loss of something—perhaps an inhibitor that prevents persons from achieving the best that is in them. However, the whole subject deserves a more thorough investigation.

17. General Bodily Strength

Like other bodily traits general strength is clearly inherited. This appears repeatedly in our records. An example is given in Fig. 29.

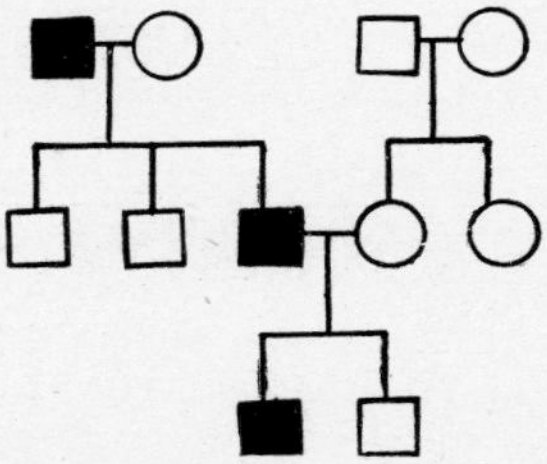

Fig. 29.—Inheritance of muscular strength. I, 1, of great physical strength. His son II, 3, was likewise possessed of unusual strength. His elder son in turn was athletic but became dissipated. F. R.; St. 1.

18. General Mental Ability

The general mental ability of a person is a vague concept which is, however, in common use. We speak of a man as weak minded, as of mediocre ability, as exceptionally able without attempting a closer analysis of the subject.

General mental ability, like stature and weight, undergoes a progressive development so that in studying its heredity we must compare it in adult persons or else measure it by the deviation the person shows from the normal of his age. Thus we may call "weak mindedness" such a defect as would keep a child of 10 in a school grade where the other children are 6 or 7; a child of "mediocre" ability is not more than two years behind the average grade for his age; "exceptionally able" would imply, say, two years in advance of children of his age. A series of tests (the Binet-Simon tests) have been devised to gauge mental ability by gauging a variety of capacities such as general information, ability to count and to repeat phrases, to recognize names and describe common things and to make fine sense discriminations. Such tests show that there are all grades of mental ability. At one extreme is the idiot, without language and incapable of attending to his bodily needs. He may retain to maturity the mentality of a child of a few months. In a higher grade mentality of a child of 3 to 5 years is retained throughout life; such are the imbeciles; then come the merely backward children who make dull adults of all

Fig. 30.—Family group from a long-settled valley where much consanguineous marriage has taken place.

grades to the normal condition (Fig. 30). Finally, there are the exceptionally bright, quick children some of whom at least, become superior adults. It is hard to recognize a unit character in such a series any more than in human hair color. Nevertheless there are laws of inheritance of general mental ability that can be sharply expressed. Low mentality is due to the *absence* of some factor, and if this factor that determines normal development is lacking in both parents it will be lacking in all of their offspring.

Two mentally defective parents will produce only mentally defective offspring. This is the first law of inheritance of mental ability. It has now been demonstrated by the study of scores of families at the Vineland (N. J.) Training School for defectives by Dr. H. H. Goddard. Some pedigrees illustrating this law, and those that follow, are given in Figs. 31-35.

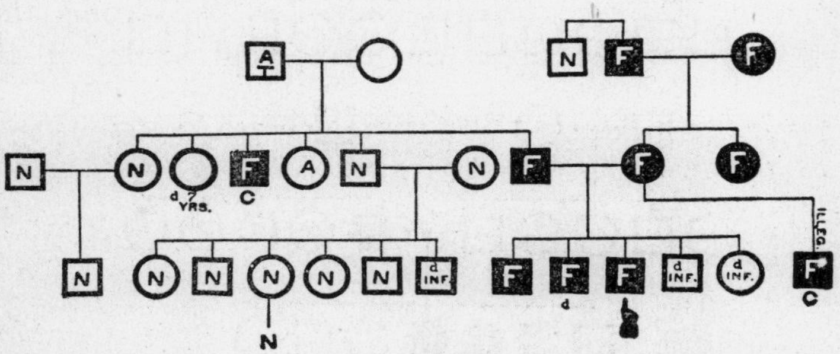

FIG. 31.—Pedigree chart illustrating the law that two defective parents have only defective children. *A*, Alcoholic; *C*, criminalistic; *D*, inf., died in infancy; *F*, feeble-minded; *N*, normal, *T*, tubercular. GODDARD, 1910.

The second law of heredity of mentality is that, aside from "mongolians," probably no imbecile is born except of parents who, if not mentally defective themselves, both carry mental defect in their germ plasm. Fig. 36 (left side of chart). Many a person of strong mentality may carry defective germ cells and, whenever two such persons marry, expectation is that one-fourth of their offspring will be defective. If a person that belongs to a strain in which defect is present (and who, consequently, may be carrying the defect in his germ plasm) marry a cousin or other near relative (in whom the chance is large that the same defective germ plasm is carried) the opportunity for *two* defective germ cells to unite is enhanced. Such consanguineous marriages are fraught with grave danger.

In view of the certainty that all of the children of two feeble-minded parents will be defective how great is the folly, yes, the crime, of letting two such persons marry. It

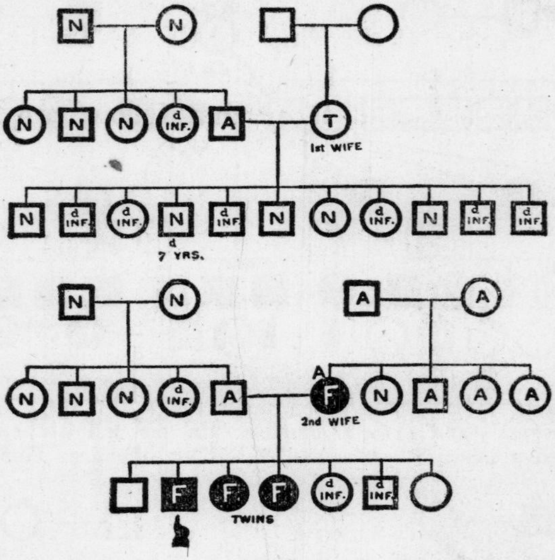

FIG. 32.—Pedigree chart illustrating the inheritance of feeble-mindedness. In chart *A*, the central mating is of an alcoholic man with a normal woman who died of tuberculosis. Of their 11 children, 5 are known to be normal, the others died early. Then (B) this man married a feeble-minded woman and of 7 children 3 are certainly feeble-minded, and 2 were, as young children, killed at play, in a fashion indicating a lack of ability to avoid ordinary dangers. GODDARD, 1910.

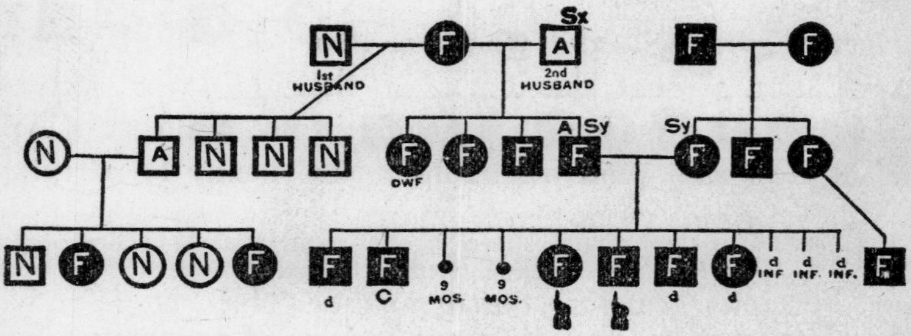

FIG. 33.—Here a feeble-minded woman (of the first generation) has married a normal man and has 4 normal children (except that 1 is alcoholic); then she marries an alcoholic sex-offender (who is probably also feeble-minded) and has 4 feeble-minded children. Here the mental strength of the first husband brought the required strength into the combination, so as to give good children. GODDARD, 1910.

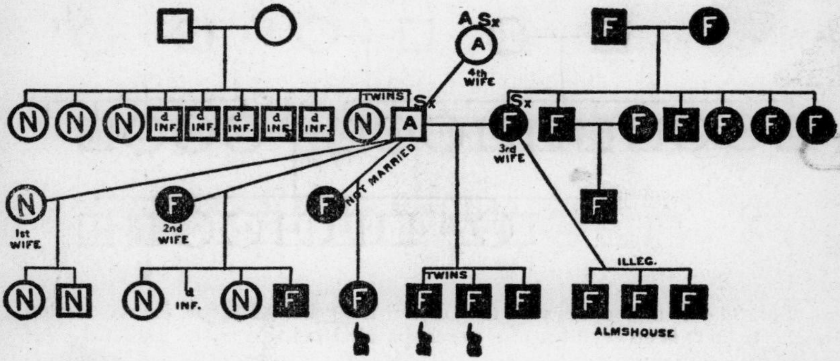

FIG. 34.—An alcoholic man of good family but probably simplex in mentality has by a normal woman 2 normal children and by a feeble-minded woman 2 normals and 1 feeble-minded. He has had 4 other children by feeble-minded women, all feeble-minded. *Sx*, sex-offender. GODDARD, 1910.

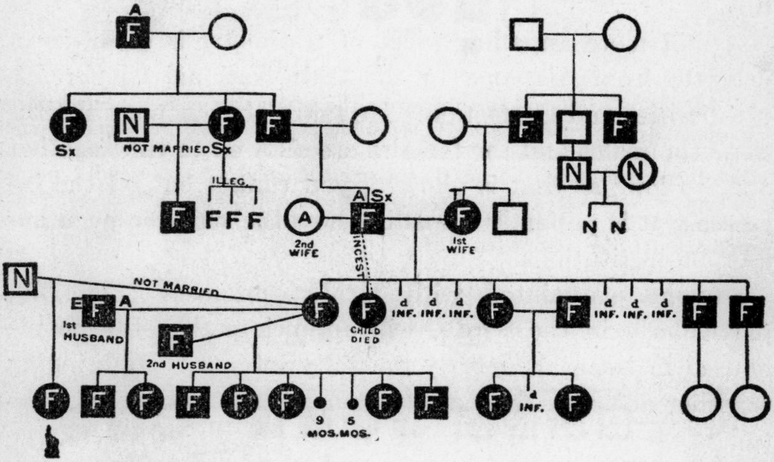

FIG. 35.—This chart shows several cases of entirely feeble-minded progeny from two defective parents. GODDARD, 1910.

has happened many times that keepers of poorhouses have let feeble-minded women in their charge go to marry a half-witted farmer in order to relieve the town of the burden of maintaining her. Some years later both she and her husband come to the poorhouse as permanent inhabitants and

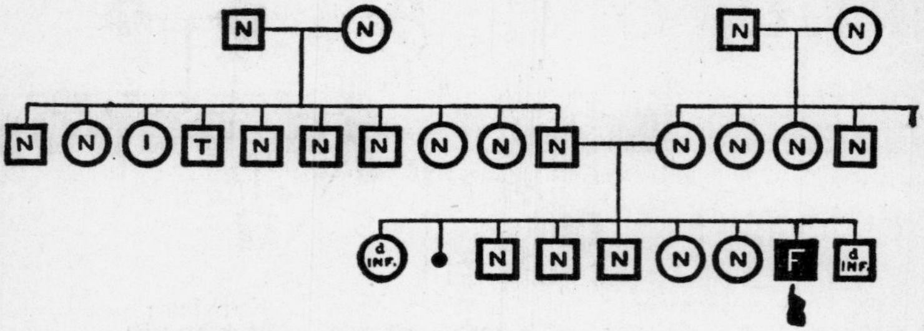

FIG. 36.—Pedigree of a "mongolian" imbecile. Except for an insane uncle (1) there is no evidence of a psychopathic condition in the parental germ plasms. GODDARD, 1910.

bring half a dozen imbecile children to be a permanent charge on the community. Surely there is no economy in this.

A still more appalling piece of testimony is given by a delegate from Alabama to the 26th National Conference of Charities and Correction. He said: "In our poor institutions the males and the females are allowed to run together and, so long as that is allowed, you cannot cut off the increase. It is perfectly appalling how the children accumulate in institutions."

Anyone acquainted with rural poorhouses (Fig. 37), particularly in the South, will appreciate that the people housed in them are mostly mentally inferior. By bringing together defective men and women, without proper segregation of the sexes, and by protecting and nursing the defective offspring of defective parents and then turning them out upon the community, the improperly conducted county poorhouses constitute one of the country's worst dangers. What is the state of your county poorhouse, reader?

An apparent paradox may well have occurred to the reader, and that is that mental defect and the elements of exceptional ability are inherited in the same way. This certainly looks like a self-contradiction. Are not the feeble-

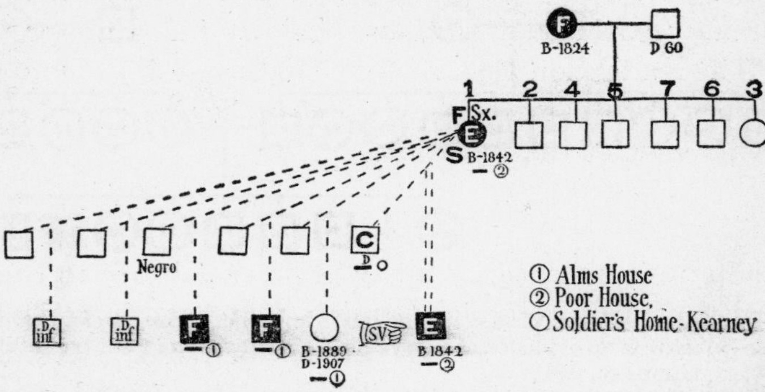

FIG. 37.—The "*poorhouse*" type of reproduction of the feeble-minded and epileptic. A lewd, feeble-minded and epileptic woman whose mother was certainly feeble-minded (but of whose father, brothers and sisters nothing is known) was the inmate of a county poorhouse. While there she had 6 children, of whom 2 died in infancy, 1 died at 18 in the almshouse, 2 were feeble-minded and are now living in the almshouse (1 the son of a negro) and 1 was epileptic, the son of a man with a criminal record. *C*, criminalistic; *D*, dead; *E*, epileptic; *F*, feeble-minded; *S*, syphilitic; *Sx*, sexually immoral.

minded and the talented at opposite extremes of the mental series? Why, then, this resemblance in the inheritance of their traits? Improbable as the result may appear it is precisely that to which students of hereditary genius have come. Says Havelock Ellis: "We may regard it (genius) as a highly sensitive and complexly developed adjustment of the nervous system along special lines, with concomitant tendency to defect along other lines. Its elaborate organization along special lines is often built up on a basis even less highly organized than that of the ordinary average man. It is no paradox to say that the real affinity of genius is with congenital imbecility rather than insanity." Ellis notes that eminent men are more apt to be eldest or youngest sons. Now this fact is in agreement with the observation that feeble-minded persons of certain types ("mongolians,") are more apt to be eldest or youngest children than intermediates. This type seems to be caused solely by the defects in development due to imperfect nutrition of the child born of parents (particularly mothers) that are immature or too old. The contention that geniuses and some defectives are born chiefly at the extremes of the reproductive period supports the view of their relationship.

19. Epilepsy

This term is believed by many professional men to cover a number of distinct brain disorders that have in common the symptoms known as convulsions or "fits." All too little is known about the physiology of the forced movements of convulsions, accompanied as they typically are by temporary loss of consciousness. It is known that convulsions may sometimes be induced in guinea pigs by a heavy blow on the brain case, and similar injuries are stated to have produced epilepsy in man. In other cases the "cause" is stated to be disturbance in the cerebral circulation due to a local stoppage in the blood vessels. However, it may well be questioned whether such causes are sufficient and not merely *inciting*, whether an inherent weakness did not first exist, which was only disclosed by the blow or disturbance in the circulation. A fall on the ice may result in a child's first epileptic fit but thousands fall on the ice without more than temporary discomfort; it was not the fall merely but the fall plus the too delicate nervous organization.

The hereditary basis of epilepsy has been studied and, rather remarkably, it follows the same laws as feeble-mindedness. Two epileptic parents probably produce only defective offspring, and the defect sometimes takes the form of epilepsy, sometimes that of feeble-mindedness. It does not seem necessary to repeat the laws of heredity for epilepsy since in them the words epilepsy and feeble-mindedness are almost interchangeable (Figs. 38–43).

The warning against the evils of poorhouses as breeding

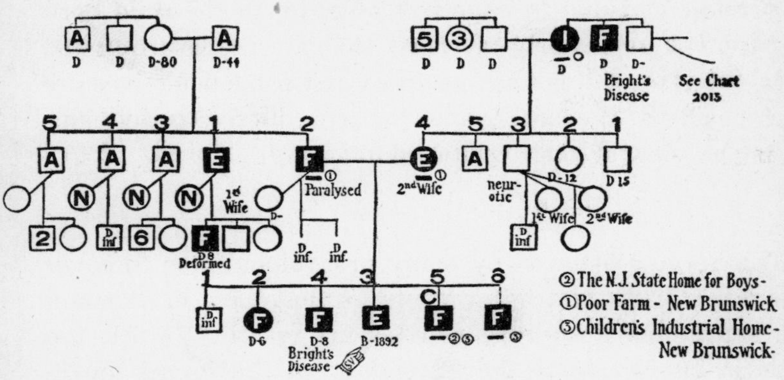

FIG. 38.—The product of a feeble-minded man (who has an epileptic brother) and his epileptic wife (whose father was insane and uncle feeble-minded); the first child died in infancy, the next two were feeble-minded and died young, the next is an epileptic at the New Jersey State Village; the next is feeble-minded, has a criminal record and is in the State Home for Boys; the last is feeble-minded and is in the Children's Industrial Home. Six in this family have been or are wards of the State. *A*, alcoholic; *C*, criminalistic; *D*, deaf; *E*, epileptic; *F*, feeble-minded; *I*, insane; *N*, normal. *SV* in the ☞ means an inmate of a State Village for Epileptics.

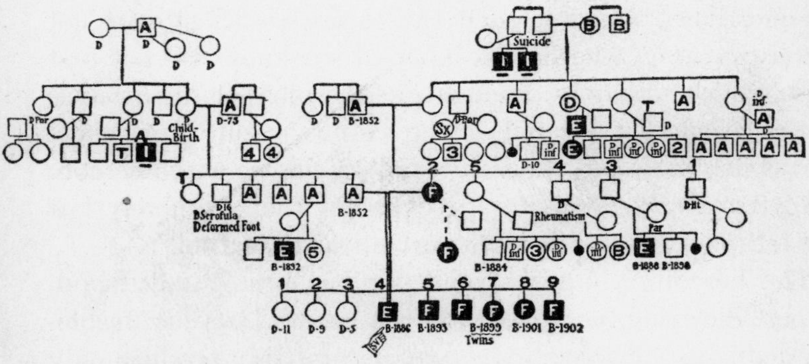

FIG. 39.—The central mating is that of a feeble-minded woman of an intensely neuropathic strain and an alcoholic man, who has 3 alcoholic brothers, father and grandfather alcoholic, an insane cousin and an epileptic nephew. The husband, though recorded as alcoholic, is probably also feeble-minded, at least all (6) of his children who survived were feeble-minded or epileptic. This chart shows 4 wards of the State and many others who should have been segregated. *A*, alcoholic; *B*, blind; *B*, (below), born; *D*, deaf; *D*, (below), died; *E*, epileptic; *F*, feeble-minded; *Ht*, heart-disease; *I*, insane; *Par*, paralysis, *Sx*, sex-offense; *T*, tubercular.

places of feeble-mindedness needs to be repeated for epilepsy and the dangers of consanguineous marriage are equally great (Fig. 43). If these two sources of epileptics—namely the poorhouse and the hovel (Fig. 44)—were cut off the supply of epileptics would be markedly reduced. And it is

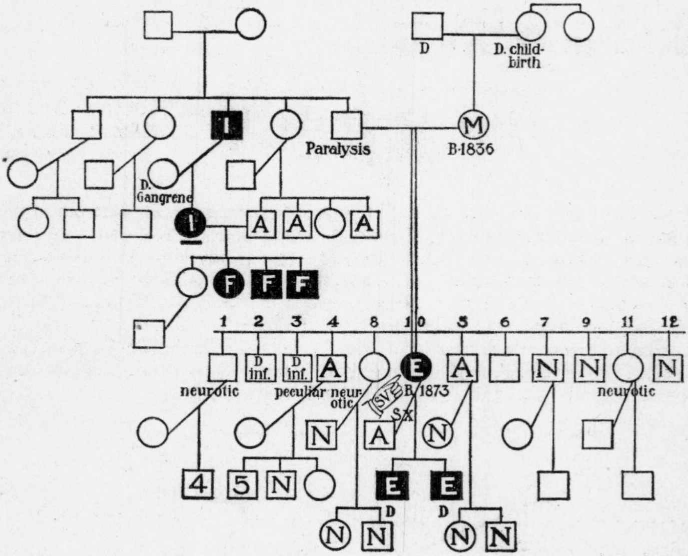

FIG. 40.—This mating illustrates the principle that migraine (*M*) and paralysis frequently indicate the presence of defective germ cells, as well as normal. In the central mating the paralytic father has an insane brother, an insane niece and 3 feeble-minded grandnephews, besides a grandniece, who died in convulsions. By his migrainous wife he had 12 children about 9 of whom something is known. One is epileptic, 3 "neurotic" or very nervous, 1 "peculiar" and alcoholic, while 3 are normal. The epileptic child has by an alcoholic husband 2 epileptic sons. Abbreviations as in Figs. 38, 39.

to be observed that these two sources of supply are quite within the control of society. A little larger appropriation to provide for the complete segregation of the sexes and a better superintendence will shut off the poorhouse supply and the inmates of the hovels should be brought under surveillance,—if necessary under public care.

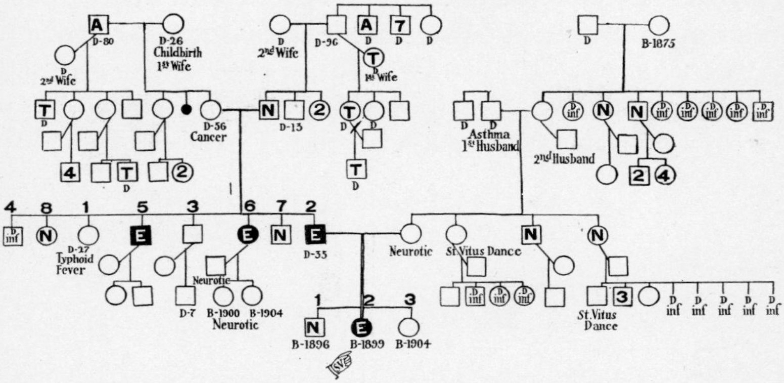

FIG. 41.—The central mating in this chart is that of an epileptic man, of a highly neuropathic strain, and a neurotic woman, whose sister and nephew have had chorea or St. Vitus' dance. The product is 1 normal child, 1 epileptic, and 1 as yet only 7 years old. Abbreviations as in Figs. 38, 39.

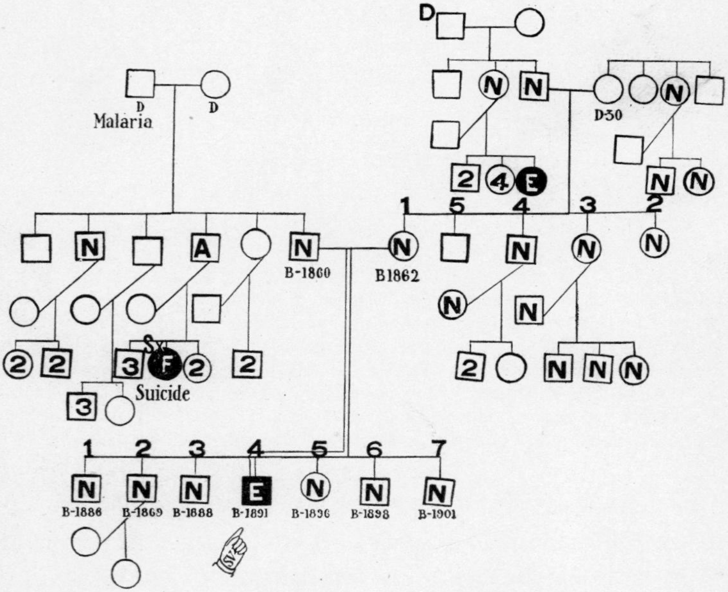

FIG. 42.—The central mating is that of 2 normal parents, both of whom belong to stock that shows evidence of being neuropathic. Doubtless some of the germ cells of both parents are defective in mental strength. Along with 6 normal children appears 1 epileptic. Abbreviations as in Figs. 38, 39. Figs. 37–43, are contributed by Dr. DAVID F. WEEKS.

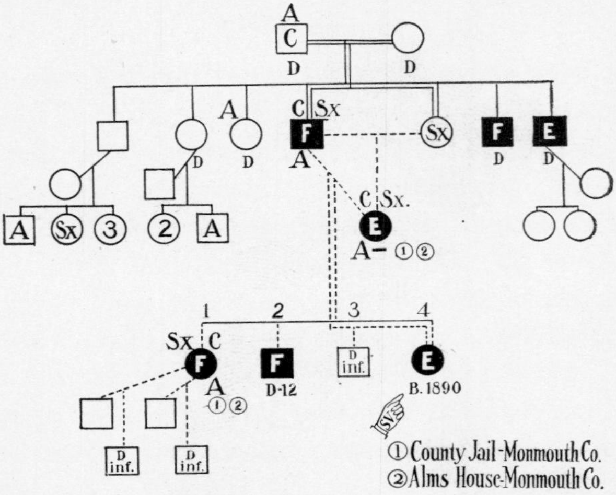

FIG. 43.—The "*Hovel*" type of reproductions of defectives. In a hut in the woods there was brought up a family of defectives. One of the boys, who is a drunken, feeble-minded fellow with criminalistic tendencies, had by his own sister a daughter who is a drunken epileptic, who has been the inmate both of the county jail and the county poorhouse. By her father she had 4 children of whom 1 is epileptic, 2 are feeble-minded (the girl has a very bad record of drunkenness, crime and immorality) and the other one was an idiot monster who died directly after being born. Close inbreeding of such a strain results only in this imperfect fruit. Abbreviations as above.

FIG. 44.—A hovel in a rural district, removed from social influences and liable to become the scene of anti-social acts. F. W.; 5, 1911.

20. Insanity

If the word epilepsy is a wardrobe then the word insanity is a veritable lumber room, including a great variety of mental diseases which have this in common that they render their victim incompetent and irresponsible before the law. Two great classes of insanity are distinguished: the "organic" and the "functional." The first group includes cases of mental deterioration associated with venereal diseases, alcoholism, degeneration of the blood vessels and trauma; the second includes cases of distinct neuropathic taint which shows itself in the slighter forms as melancholia or manic depressive insanity and in the profounder forms as dementia precox. Concerning heredity in the functional forms there is no doubt. Berze (1910) gives a case of dementia precox in a father and three sons; another of two children, their mother and her father; and numerous other cases with two or three to the family—all with a more or less typical form of dementia precox. But the mental defect that is "inherited" is not always of the same type. Thus in the same family may be found cases of manic depressive insanity, of senile dementia, of alcoholism and of feeble-mindedness. It would seem to be the neuropathic taint that is inherited.

This is the conclusion to which Cannon and Rosanoff (1911) have come in their study based on house to house investigations of the families of patients at a State Hospital. They omit from consideration the "organic" class of cases as "probably purely exogenous in origin." Aside from these they find that when both parents have any form of insanity all of their children will "go insane." If one parent is insane and the other normal but of insane stock half of the children tend to become insane; when both parents, though normal, belong to an insane stock about one-fourth of the

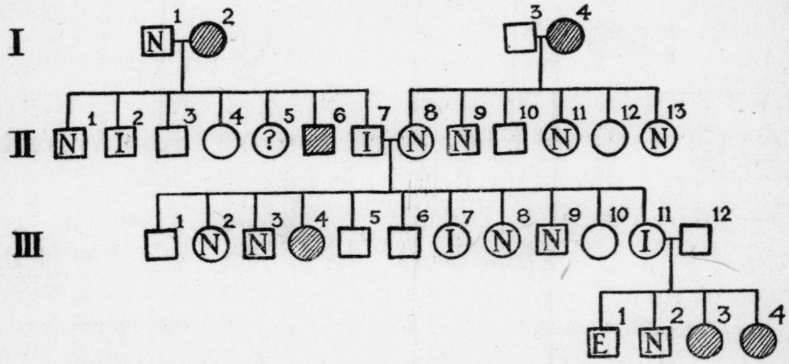

FIG. 45.—The central mating, II, 7, II, 8, is that of a man, II, 7, who is subject to melancholia and has an insane brother and another who is neuropathic. His wife is normal but her mother was neuropathic. The product of this union is 11 children of whom 3 are neuropathic. One of these insane children marries a normal person (probably of neuropathic ancestry), and has 2 neuropathic children besides 1 that is epileptic, IV, 1. *E*, epileptic; *I*, insane; *N*, normal; shaded symbols imply some neuropathic condition other than insanity. CANNON and ROSANOFF, 1911.

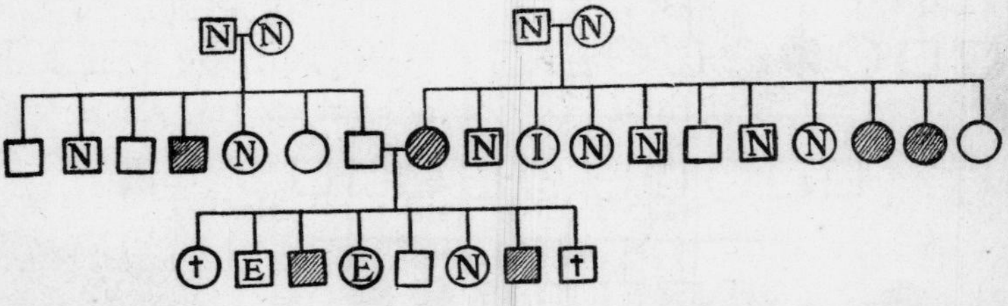

FIG. 46.—The central mating is that of a normal man of neuropathic stock with a neuropathic woman who has an insane sister. Since by hypothesis all of her germ cells and half of his are "neuropathic" it is to be expected that half of their offspring will be neuropathic in some degree. Actually, of 6 surviving children 2 are epileptic, 2 highly nervous and 2 normal so far as known. There is a slight, but not unreasonable deficiency of normals, namely, 1. The shaded symbols represent nervous subjects. CANNON and ROSANOFF, 1911.

children become insane. The typical laws of heredity are followed here (Figs. 45–47).

But is it so certain that alcoholic, traumatic, even syphilitic dementia have no hereditary basis? On the contrary

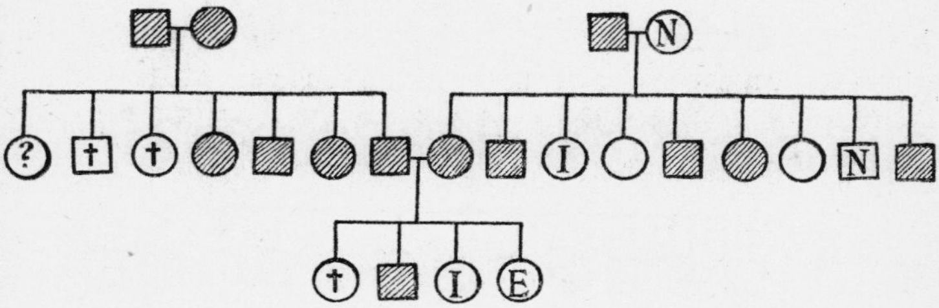

FIG. 47.—The central mating is that of a pair who, though not insane, have pronounced neuropathic manifestations. The mother has an insane sister and the father comes of neuropathic stock. Of the 3 surviving children 1 is neurotic, 1 insane and 1 epileptic. A similar mating of 2 neuropathic persons is seen in the parents of the father—all of their offspring are neuropathic. The shaded symbols represent neuropathic individuals. CANNON and ROSANOFF, 1911.

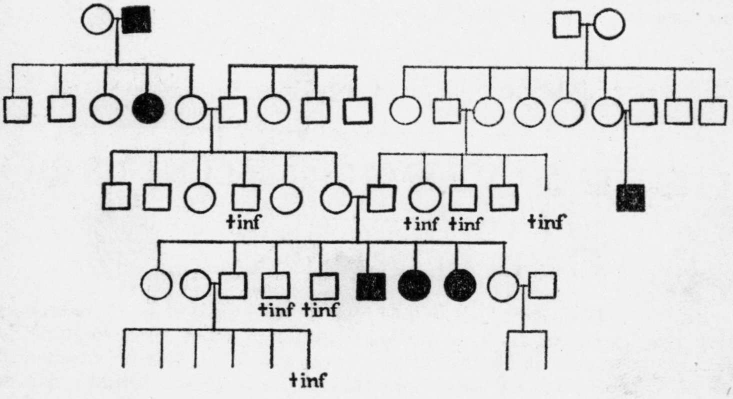

FIG. 47a.—Inheritance of "insanity." From the central mating of 2 normal persons there are derived 8 children, 3 insane. But there is the hereditary tendency in the germ plasm of *both* parents. MOTT, 1905.

it is fairly open to debate whether alcoholics are not usually mentally defective and the delirium tremens that develops is a symptom of their mental weakness. Similarly a blow is often just the stress that reveals the mental weakness;

the syphilitic poison in some, if not most cases, likewise acts most disastrously on the neuropathic constitution. Thus, probably an hereditary predisposition lies at the basis of most cases of insanity; and this predisposition behaves in heredity like a defect.

21. Pauperism

Pauperism is a result of a complex of causes. On one side it is mainly environmental in origin as, for instance, in the case when a sudden accident, like death of the father, leaves a widow and family of children without means of livelihood, or a prolonged disease of the wage earner exhausts savings. But it is easy to see that in these cases heredity also plays a part; for the effective worker will be able to save enough money to care for his family in case of accident; and the man of strong stock will not suffer from prolonged disease. Barring a few highly exceptional conditions poverty means relative inefficiency and this in turn usually means mental inferiority. This is the conclusion that social workers in many places have reached. Thus from Harrisburg, Pa., come these cases: (a) Mr. and Mrs. R., applicants for relief and living in a slum district, are parents of 14 children of whom 10 are living. These parents are both epileptic and feeble-minded. (b) Mother and father are both feeble-minded. There are 6 children, all of marriageable age, all unfit to earn in any case more than $1.50 per week, and all recipients of public alms. Such cases might be multiplied indefinitely.

In the larger pedigrees of the Jukes and Zero families more definite data as to inheritance of some of the elements of poverty can be gained. Let us take "shiftlessness" as an important element in poverty. Then classifying all persons in these two families as very shiftless, somewhat shiftless, and industrious the following conclusions are reached. When

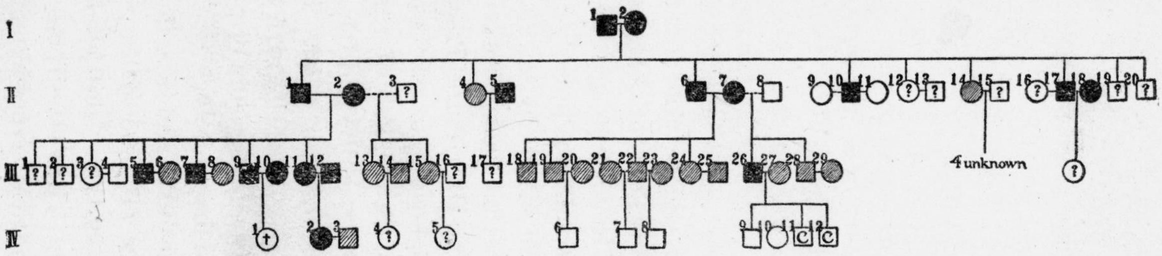

FIG. 48.—A fragment of the Jukes pedigree, being descendants of the elder daughter of "Ada Jukes." Showing occurrence of *shiftlessness* (black symbols) and partial shiftlessness (striated symbols).

I, 1, a lazy mulatto; I, 2, a non-industrious harlot, but temperate; II, 1, a frequent recipient of out door relief, in jail for assault; II, 2, lazy and a harlot; II, 4, twice recipient of out relief; II, 5, laziness, assault, vagrancy; II, 6, vagrant, out relief, jail; II, 7, vagrancy; II, 10, lazy, in poorhouse; II, 14, a harlot recipient of a little out relief; II, 17, lazy, licentious; II, 18, a harlot; II, 19, died young; II, 20, unknown; III, 1, 2, 3, little known; III, 5, 6, received out relief; III, 7, vagrant in jail; III, 8, received a little out relief; III, 9, soldier, pauper; III, 10, harlot, poorhouse inmate; III, 11, harlot, jail, out relief, III, 12, out relief; III, 18, bad boy; III, 19, licentious, pauper; III, 20, harlot; III, 22, licentious; III, 24, harlot, pauper; III, 26, pauper and drunkard; III, 28, basket-maker and pauper who later acquired some property; IV, 2, harlot; IV, 11, 12; criminalistic. DUGDALE, 1902, Chart II.

both parents are *very* shiftless practically all children are "very shiftless" or "somewhat shiftless." Out of 62 offspring, 3 are given as "industrious" or about 5 per cent (Fig. 48). When both parents are shiftless in some degree about 15 per cent of the known offspring are recorded as industrious. When one parent is more or less shiftless while the other is industrious only about 10 per cent of the children are "very shiftless." It is probable that both shiftlessness and lack of physical energy are due to the absence of something which can be got back into the offspring only by mating with industry.

22. Narcotism

The love of alcoholic drink, opium, etc., is commonly regarded as due solely to its use. It has even been asserted that the "taste" is usually an acquired one; and we are assured that drunkenness results from bad associates and imitation of bad habits. Cases are cited of persons who, after an exemplary youth, have suddenly through drink been started on the downward road. On the other hand there are those who maintain that the desire for narcotics is a symptom of a neurasthenic tendency. "So long as there is a call for these narcotics must our race be stamped as degenerate" (Gaupp quoted by Mason, 1910). Says Lydston (1904, p. 200) "Practically, then, inebriety means degeneracy, the subject being usually primarily defective in nervous structure and will-power. It is a noteworthy fact that the family histories of dipsomaniacs are largely tinctured with nerve disorders. Hysteria, epilepsy, migraine and even insanity are found all along the line. In such cases inebriety is but one of the varying manifestations of bad heredity." Each of these contrasted views is partial. Whether a person who has taken a first glass of alcoholic liquor shall take another is determined largely by the effect upon him of the first. If the alcohol is very distasteful he will probably not continue to drink; if it wakens a strong desire for more he will probably become (or is) a dipsomaniac.[1] The result in these extreme cases is determined by innate tastes which are doubtless hereditary. But in most cases the person who takes a first glass finds it indifferent. His subsequent relation to alcohol depends largely upon his associates; but his selection of associates again depends on innate tastes. Some like the steady, quiet, serious youth for their companions; others select the reckless, jolly fellows, careless of the proprieties and—"birds of a feather flock together." The influence of precept is not to be overlooked; this is, however, most important in determining the first drink. No doubt a strong susceptibility to social sentiment restrains many of the border line cases.

A strong hereditary bias toward alcohol runs through not a few families of the United States. A pedigree of one such is given in Fig. 49. The neighbors say: "It is a family of drunkards," yet some of the individuals never touch liquor. The bad environment has its result first and chiefly on those individuals with an hereditary predisposition toward narcotics and this hereditary bias is stronger in some families than others, depending on the nature of the family trait, and it occurs in a larger proportion of the cases in some families than others, depending on the nature of the matings that have occurred in that family.

23. Criminality

In connection with the subject of nervous defect and disease the topic of an hereditary tendency to crime must be

[1] Dr. L. D. Mason, head of the Inebriates' Home for Kings County (N. Y.) tells this story from his experience. He knew of a young man of such ancestry that a dipsomaniac was predicted. For years the youth refrained from drink, and led an exemplary life. Finally, he was operated on for appendicitis and, to hasten recovery, the surgeon gave him some brandy. An uncontrollable appetite was awakened and the man soon died from alcoholism.

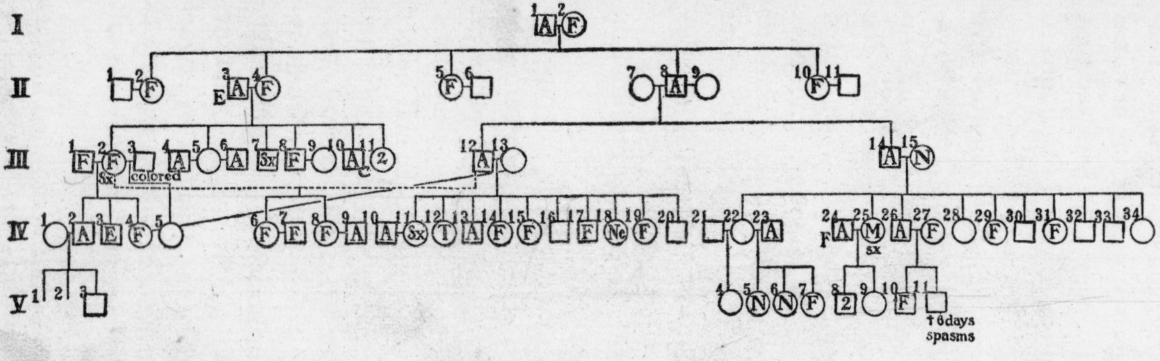

Fig. 49.—Pedigree of a Massachusetts family comprising much feeble-mindedness or imbecility, F; associated with alcoholism, *A*; criminality, *C*; sex immorality, *Sx*; epilepsy, *E*; *M*, migrainous; *Ne*, neurotic; *T*, tubercular. Note the association of alcoholism with imbecility.

I, 1, a basket-maker, alcoholic, married a feeble-minded woman. Of their 5 children (II, 2–10) 4 were feeble-minded and the other, II, 8, shiftless and an alcoholic. II, 4, married an epileptic alcoholic and they had 7 children. The oldest Amanda, III, 2, feeble-minded and sexually immoral, married, first, a feeble-minded man, III, 1, by whom she had 3 children, 1 alcoholic and immoral, 1 epileptic and a cripple, 1 feeble-minded; secondly, by a colored man, III, 3, she had 1 illegitimate colored child, IV, 5; thirdly, by an alcoholic, she had 2 other feeble-minded illegitimate offspring, both of whom married, the first a feeble-minded man, the second an alcoholic consumptive. The second daughter, III, 5, married twice, both alcoholics, but had no offspring; III, 7, was sexually immoral as was also the imbecile son, III, 8. III, 10, was alcoholic and criminal and two daughters, III, 11, were normal. II, 8, a shiftless alcoholic known as "Woodchuck Pete" married twice. By his first wife, a normal woman, he had two sons, both alcoholic. The oldest, III, 12, we have met above as the illegitimate husband of III, 2. He married later her daughter, IV, 4, they had 11 children. The oldest daughter, sexually immoral, IV, 11, married an alcoholic but had no children. IV, 12, was a consumptive; IV, 13, an alcoholic, and of the others, 4 are imbeciles and 1 neurotic, 4 being state wards. III, 14 married a normal woman and they had 10 children. IV, 22, married first a normal but shiftless man whom she left for non-support; her second husband was an alcoholic wanderer, by whom she had 2 normal and 1 feeble-minded child. IV, 25, migraine and immoral, married an alcoholic imbecile by whom she had 3 normal but scrofulous children. IV, 26, an alcoholic, married a feeble-minded woman and had 2 children, 1 feeble-minded, 1 died at 6 days of spasms. Of remaining 7 children, 2 are feeble-minded. F. W., 1.

alluded to. Despite the conservatism of the courts, despite the fact that scientifically ascertained general principles usually weigh less than precedent, the treatment of the criminal has made progress during the past century. It is stated that "Mackintosh speaking in the English House of Commons so late as March 2, 1819 said 'I hold in my hand a list of those offenses which at this moment are capital, in number two hundred and twenty three'" (Johnston, 1887, p. 106). Physical severity, frequent floggings, chaining to the floor, unsanitary surroundings, insufficient and improper food were the elements of a treatment by a society that was exasperated into severity by the realization of its impotent ignorance. Only slowly has the idea of hospitals for insane criminals spread; but though several states maintain great institutions of this sort they still receive a quite insufficient proportion of those convicted of crime.

A few pictures of the youth with hereditary criminal instincts may properly be quoted here.

1. O. L., female, father and mother both intemperate and degenerate, and always on the verge of pauperism. The patient is cruel to animals and children; thus, she put a cat on a red hot stove, threw knives and stones at playmates, wished to have a small baby to strike and kick; and helped drown a comrade in a bath tub. She is very untruthful and a chronic thief; has fits of temper when she screams, tears clothing, and pulls out her hair; is in a state of chronic rebellion against the constituted authorities, a trouble maker and inciter of mischief. She talks fluently, is sly and cunning, vain as to her personal appearance and boastful to attract attention. Age 16. This person has committed the crimes of wanton cruelty to animals, petty larceny, truancy, assault and murder. She is a moral imbecile.

2. O. K., male, entered a school for feeble-minded at 9, at the time of the description is 11. He has a bright, knowing,

intelligent manner, has a fund of general information and is very talkative. He is very cruel to younger children, has an ungovernable temper, is an inciter of discontent and rebellion among the other patients, lies maliciously, ingeniously and convincingly, and steals inveterately and without motive.

This child, removed into an excellent school with the best of surroundings, at the tender age of nine reveals striking criminalistic traits which no care can correct. In this case the hereditary history is unknown. In those that follow it has been precisely ascertained.

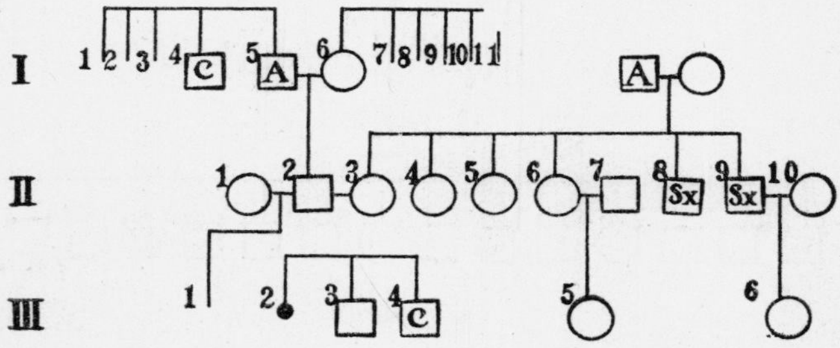

FIG. 50

3. Figure 50, III, 4 is an eleven year old boy who began to steal at 3 years; at 4 set fire to a pantry resulting in an explosion that caused his mother's death; and at 8 set fire to a mattress. He is physically sound, able and well informed, polite, gentlemanly and very smooth, but he is an inveterate thief and has a court record. His older brother, 14, has been full of deviltry, has stolen and set fires but is now settled down and is earning a living. Their father is an unusually fine, thoughtful intelligent man, a grocer, for a time sang on the vaudeville stage; his mother, who died at 32, is said to have been a normal woman of excellent character. There is however a *taint* on both sides. The father's father was wild and drank when young and had a brother who was an inveterate thief. The mother's father was alcoholic and when

drunk mean and vicious. Some of the mother's brothers stole or were sexually immoral.

4. A healthy man (Fig. 51, II,1) employed on a railroad as a fireman and using neither alcohol nor tobacco married a woman who was born in the mountains of West Virginia near the Kentucky line and who shows many symptoms of defectiveness. She has epileptic convulsions as often as 2 or 3 times a week, has an ungovernable temper, smokes, chews and drinks, is illiterate and sexually immoral. There

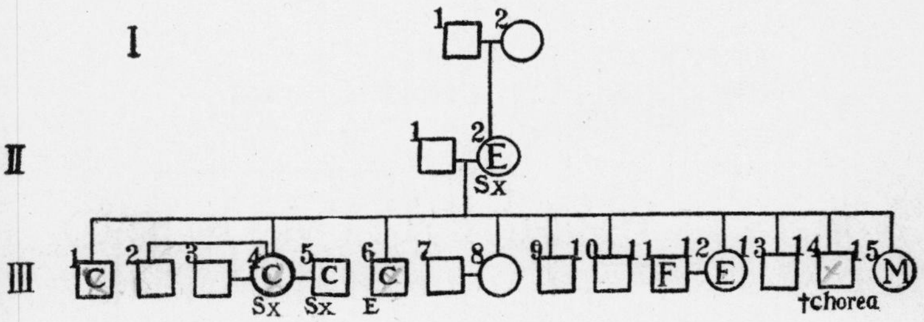

Fig. 51

are 10 children, of whom something is known about 7. One died early of chorea, one of the others (III, 8) seems normal; III, 1 has killed two men including a policeman; III, 4 had her husband killed and lives with his slayer; III, 6, an epileptic and cigarette fiend, convicted of assault; III, 12 has hysterical convulsions and is afraid in sleep; III, 15 has migraine. The combination in the fraternity of migraine, chorea, hysteria, epilepsy and sexual immorality and tendency to assault is striking and appalling.

5. A 10 year old boy (Fig 52, IV, 4) who was precocious as a raconteur at 22 months, does well at school except for inattention; is fond of reading and athletics, cheerful, and polite. But he prefers the companionship of older, wild boys and cannot be weaned from them. He lies, runs up accounts in his parents' name, is acquiring bad sexual habits, and runs

away from home. He has two fine, studious brothers. His father is a strong character and a successful lawyer, his mother an excellent woman, intelligent and firm. She has a brother who left home at 14 to seek a life of adventure. He finally settled down to a steady life. Their father's father was erratic. He loved Indian outdoor life, always used an Indian blanket and at over 70 years swam the Mississippi River. He traced back his ancestry to Pocahontas. He has another grandson, III, 2, who is an unruly character with a

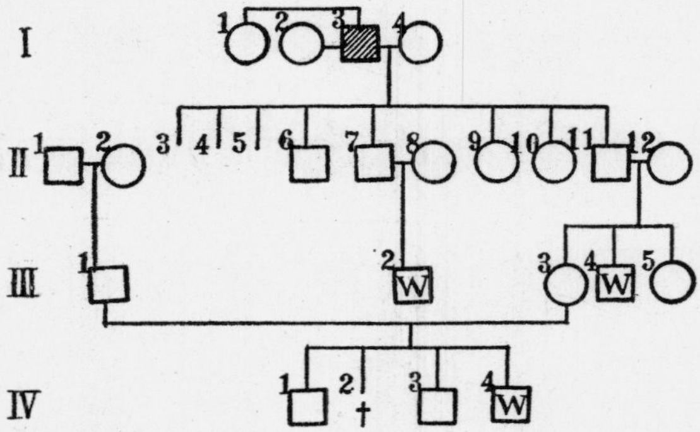

Fig. 52

roving disposition; he joined the navy and his whereabouts are unknown; his father was a lawyer and a fine character.

6. Another case of truancy (Fig. 53, III, 2) is a 7 year old boy whose home conditions are not favorable. His selfish father consorts with lewd women so that his mother has left her husband and now conducts an employment agency. She has hysterical attacks with blank periods during which she may wander. The boy is bright and able but is subject to hysterical attacks; he runs away from school and home and says he does not know why; goes for a long period without food or sleep. His father's father was erratic, a soldier, very superstitious, used to walk in a graveyard and perform incantations at Christmas time. The mother's father was also

erratic and disappeared from home about the time his mother was born. Two of his sons have hysterical fuges and one of them served a term in prison; he is now quite lost to the family. This is a remarkable history of hysteria with a slight criminalistic tendency.

7. An intelligent and esteemed physician (Fig. 54, II, 2) with training abroad as well as in this country and of a good family (his brother, II, 1, is a college professor and his father a methodist preacher) married a lady (II, 3) of good family,

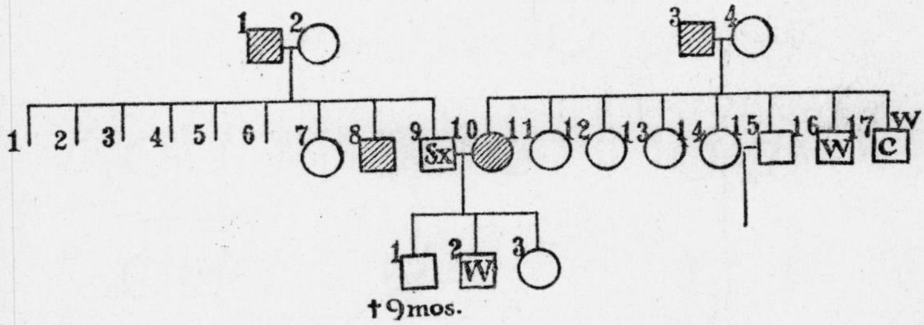

FIG. 53

with much musical talent, but subject to migraine and formerly to chorea. They have two sons born in the best of environments. The younger (III, 3) is still in the kindergarten, seems wholly normal, truth-telling and lovable; the other, (III, 2) now 13, developed normally, has had no convulsions, and has never been seriously sick and ordinarily sleeps well. He has regular, refined features and a normal alert attitude and is very industrious. He attends sunday school regularly, has excellent talent for music. At 3 years of age he walked to a near by railroad, boarded a train and was carried 12 miles before the conductor discovered him; since then he has run away very many times. From an institution for difficult boys, where he was placed, he ran away 13 times. He escapes from his home after dark and sleeps in neighboring doorways. His mother used to make Saturday a treat day. She would take a violin lesson with him and spend the afternoon in the Public Library which he much enjoyed but he would slip away from her on the way home and be gone till midnight. He is an unconscionable liar. He contracts debts, steals when he has no use for the articles stolen and has been convicted for burglary. Much money and effort have been spent on him in vain. His mother's father, (I, 3) (of whom he has never heard) was a western desperado, drank hard and was involved in a murder, but finally married a very good

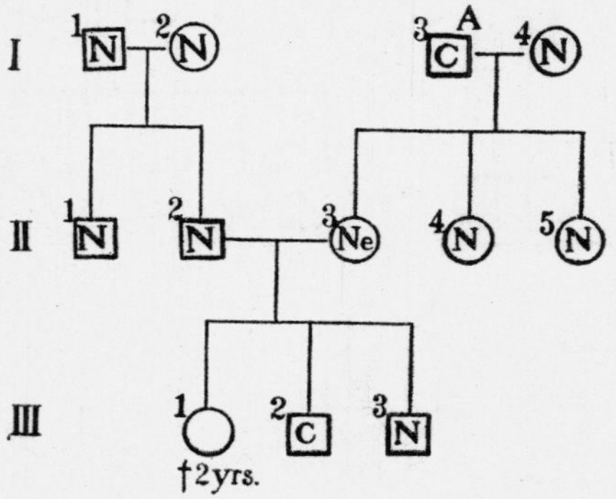

FIG. 54

woman (I, 4) and has 2 normal daughters in addition to this boy's mother.

The typical skipping of a generation, seen in these pedigrees of the wandering instinct, suggests that it is a recessive, like most neuroses—and strengthens the probability that it is due to a real mental defect.

The following case suggests the inheritance of an extremely erotic instinct also as a defect (Fig. 55).

A large, healthy man (II, 4) engaged in an engineering profession, has much ability in music and is an inventor. He drinks very little alcohol, has always been a good worker and is highly esteemed by those who employ him. But he is "crazy about women." He left his first wife and married another, was convicted of bigamy and served a term in prison; later he married a third wife without undergoing the formality of a divorce from the others and was again imprisoned for bigamy. He has had also other, even looser, relations with women. His second wife (II, 5) was a healthy young girl who comes from a long lived family. Since her husband deserted her she has had to work very hard to support their children and is much broken down in consequence. She is

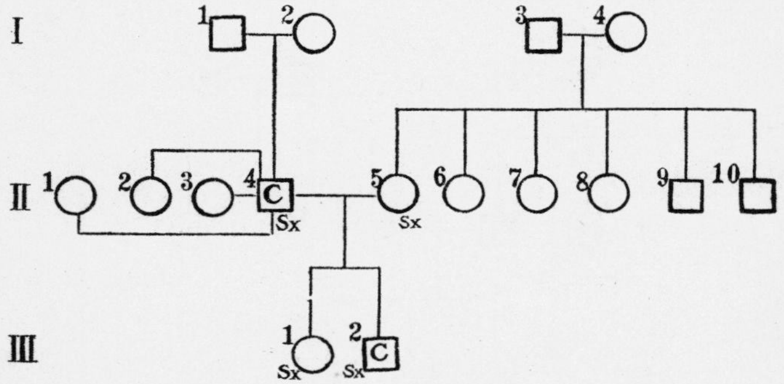

FIG. 55

not a strong character, she keeps boarders and is currently believed to be sexually immoral. Nothing is known about her parents nor those of her husband. The daughter of this pair (III, 1), is thirteen years old. She is wilful, refuses to study, runs on the streets, has stayed out all night on two occasions and has been in court as a delinquent. The son, (III, 2), eight and a half years old, has a fair physical development, but his face is unsymmetrical and his mouth open despite removal of adenoids when he was 5. His speech is thick and rough. He seems dull at times but can brighten up. He has had convulsions. Like his sister he is wilful, won't learn, and runs on the streets where he sells papers and where he has stolen many articles. He throws stones and garbage and despite his tender years he indulges in vile language, exposes his person to little girls, masturbates and is sexually misused by men. All attempts at reformation have failed,—orphan asylum, home for boys, life on a farm; from all these he runs away and returns to the life he loves.

The foregoing cases are samples of scores that have been collected and serve as fair representations of the kind of blood that goes to the making of thousands of criminals in this country. It is just as sensible to imprison a person for feeble-mindedness or insanity as it is to imprison criminals belonging to such strains. The question whether a given person is a case for the penitentiary or the hospital is not primarily a legal question but one for a physician with the aid of a student of heredity and family histories.

24. Other Nervous Diseases

a. The General Problem.—The marvellous complex of neurones (nerve cells and fibres), sustentative tissue, and blood vessels that constitute the central nervous system forms, perhaps, the most wonderful mechanism in nature. Little wonder that it should vary greatly in different individuals, or that it should become easily deranged. Such variations in structure and such derangement though ordinarily hidden from view can be inferred from the behavior of the person. For the general principle holds that every psychosis (or peculiar mental manifestation) has its neurosis (or aberrent nervous basis). Peculiar or abnormal behavior, then, is an index of peculiar or abnormal brain condition.

That heredity plays a part in nervous disease is indicated by the familiar fact of high incidence of some or other psychic disturbance in the members of a single family. We have already seen how incomplete mental development is a consequence of the absence of a definite inheritable defect in the germ plasm, such that when the factor that stimulates to complete mental development is absent from the germ plasm of both parents it will be absent from all their offspring. Varied as are the mental conditions of the persons in a family containing feeble mindedness the children do not ordinarily surpass in mental development the better developed parent.

In considering heredity of mental disease we must not forget that what is inherited is not, as in imbecility, a tendency to incomplete mental development, but rather a tendency such that a completely developed and apparently normal mentality is liable under ordinary, or still more under extraordinary, conditions to show disturbance of a temporary or permanent nature. The more intimate nature of this inherited tendency is probably varied. In some cases there is doubtless an idiosyncrasy in the neurones, in other cases there is a lack of resistance to infection or specific poisons, again the trouble may be outside the neurones in the supporting tissue or even in the blood vessels whose walls may be peculiarly liable to weaken and burst; to waste away; to thicken, occluding the lumen and shutting off nutrition to a part of the brain.

Before considering the inheritance of specific nervous diseases it may be pointed out that what is inherited is often a general nervous weakness—a neuropathic taint—showing itself now in one form of psychosis and now in another. Especially the lower types of mental defect may be carried in the higher, *i. e.*, departing least from the normal.

b. The Neuropathic Makeup.—We have seen (page 77) that imbecility, epilepsy and many forms of insanity are due merely to the absence of some factor. It remains to be considered how they behave amongst each other in heredity. A pedigree worked out by Barr (1907) gives the desired information (Fig. 56).

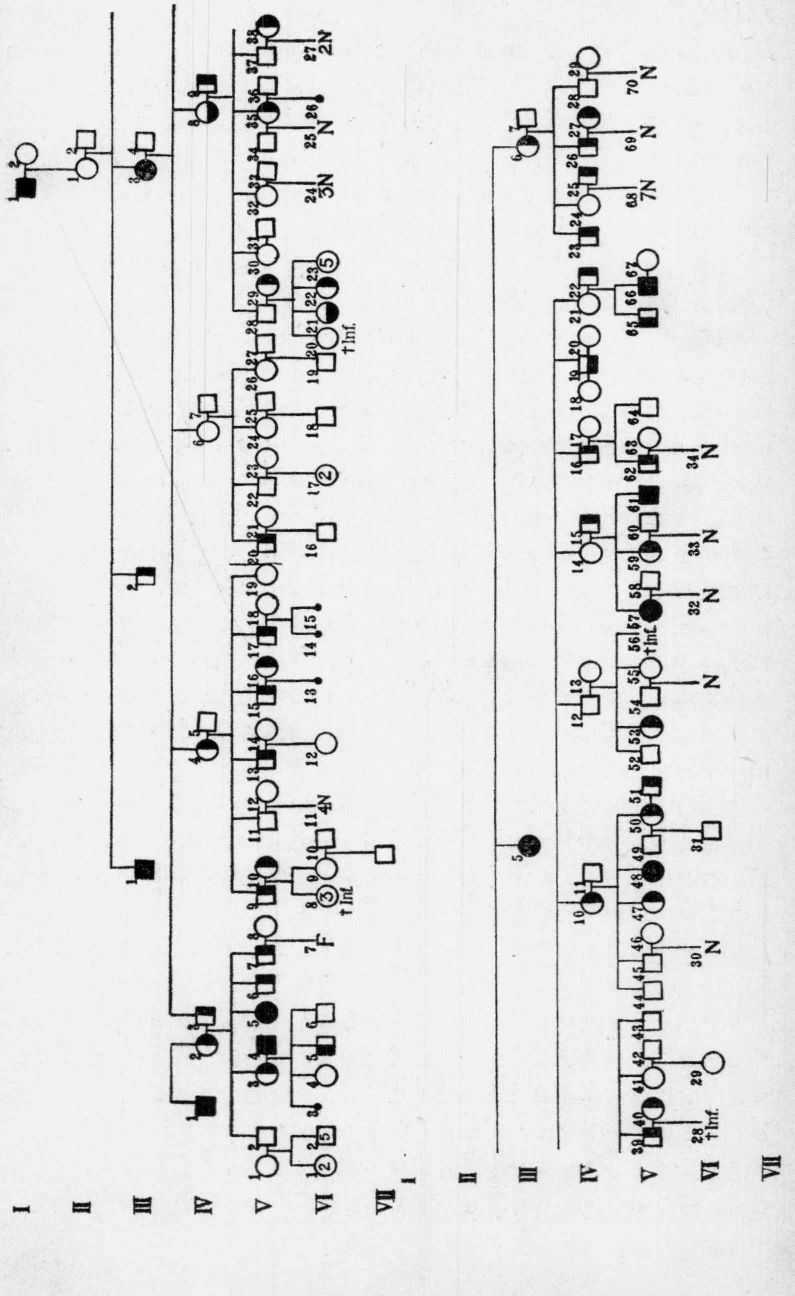

FIG. 56.—Pedigree of a family of neuropathic makeup.—I, 1, insane; I, 2, normal; II, 1, 2, normal but evidently simplex; III, 1, insane; III, 2, neurotic; III, 3, insane; III, 4, normal; III, 5, insane; III, 6, neurotic.

Gen. IV–VI. Full black symbols indicate insanity; symbols blacked on the right half represent neurotic persons; symbols blacked on the lower half indicate epileptics; symbols blacked at the left indicate feeble-minded.

III, 3, herself insane, married into good stock, had 10 children, 4 normal, 4 neurotic, and 2 epileptic. Oldest son George, IV, 3, neurotic and unprincipled, married a neurotic woman whose brother is insane; of 5 children, one, V, 5, is insane; 3 others neurotic and 1 normal. One of these neurotic daughters married a man who died insane whose father was semi-insane and whose brother was an imbecile. One child, of 3, is an imbecile and has a feeble-minded cousin. IV, 4, Rebecca, herself neurotic, married a man of good stock, had 4 neurotic and 2 normal children. One of these neurotic sons, V, 9, married a woman of loose character, a harlot, sprung from a neurotic family, and they had 3 children who died young and 1 normal. Another neurotic son, V, 15, married a harlot, also neurotic, and had one still-born child only. Other two neurotic sons married women of good stock.

Mary, IV, 6, herself normal, exceptionally beautiful and accomplished, married into a good stock. Cf her four children, only 1 was neurotic but all married into good stock, and their children were all normal. Her sister, Olivia, IV, 8, an epileptic, married neurotic stock and 2 out of 8 children only were neurotic. The oldest son, V, 28, himself normal, but peculiar, married a neurotic woman of loose character. Of 8 children, 1 was epileptic (seduced by a negro), 1 neurotic, 1 died in infancy and 5 were normal. IV, 10, neurotic, married a man of good stock, had puerperal insanity at birth of first child. Of 5 children, 2 were normal, 2 neurotic and 1 insane. IV, 12, normal, married a woman of good stock and had 9 children, 4 boys normal, 2 girls neurotic, 1 child died in infancy. IV, 14, Agnes, herself normal, married a man of neurotic stock who had himself had mania several times. Of 3 children, 2 were insane, 1 neurotic. IV, 19, an epileptic, married twice but had no issue. IV, 21, herself normal, married a hypochondriac (son of third sister's husband by first wife), and had 1 child who was imbecile and 1 who was insane.

III, 6, Jane, is neurotic and married a man of good stock. Of their children 2 are normal and 2 are neurotic with a pronounced dipsomania. Their grandchildren are all normal.

NOTE. On account of the length of the chart it has been cut in two in the middle and the right-hand portion has been placed on the page, below the left-hand portion.

This pedigree contains 22 significant matings (*i. e.*, that yield more than one child). The products of these matings are summarized in Table IX.

TABLE IX

PRODUCT OF VARIOUS MATINGS IN BARR'S PEDIGREE

	Mating Nos.	Offspring N	Ne	F	E	I	X	Still-births
Neurotic×neurotic	4	1	3			1		
Neurotic×neurotic	16	1					3	
Neurotic×epileptic	7	4	2			2		
Neurotic×insane	15	2		1				1
Insane×normal	2	4	4		2			
	10		1			2		
Neurotic×normal	3	2	2					
	5	2	4					
	8	2	2			1		
	11	1	1					
	12			1		1		
	13	7						
	22	2						
Neurotic×unknown	18							2
	20	1	1		1			
Normal×normal	1		2			3		
	6	3	1				1	
	9	2	1					
	14, 17, 19, 21	16						

E, epileptic; F, feeble-minded; I, insane; N, normal; Ne, neurotic; X, unknown.

In Table IX there is no marriage of two insane persons. Where a nervous person marries a neuropath, of 11 known offspring 6 are normal and 5 neuropathic; when two neurotic marry, 2 out of 6 children are normal and 1 insane; when an insane and a normal marry, of 13 children 4 are normal and 2 insane; when a neurotic and a normal marry, of 28 children 16 are normal, 9 nervous, 1 feeble-minded and 2 insane. Even some normal parents (of this strain) have insane or epileptic children. One sees what a variety of gametic conditions may be carried by a "nervous" or even a "normal" person, just as blue eyes may be carried by brown eyed parents, or light brown hair by dark haired parents. A "nervous" person is thus frequently simplex in the factor that makes for mental strength and is apt to carry defective germ cells (Figs. 57–59).

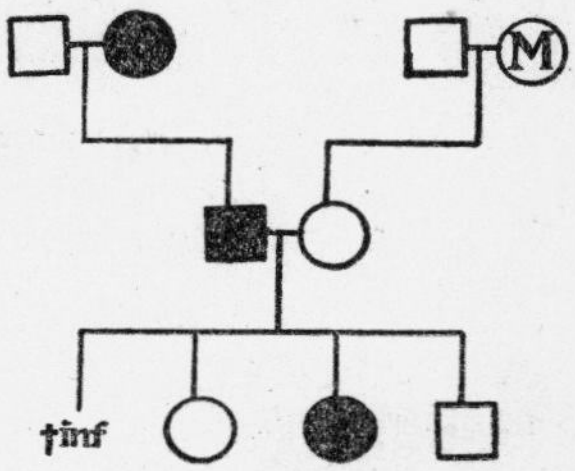

FIG. 57. — Pedigree of "nervous trouble." I, 2, was typically affected and I, 4 suffered from migraine. II, 1, had the same nervous trouble. Of three grandchildren who survive, 1 already shows at 6 years, a tendency toward nervous weakness. F. R; Hug. 1.

c. Cerebral Hemorrhage. — However numerous the causes that weaken the walls of the cerebral arteries or raise abnormally the pressure upon them, there can be little doubt that hereditary predisposition plays an important part. (Figs. 60 and 61). Cerebral hemorrhage is commonly found in the parentage or grandparentage of the mentally

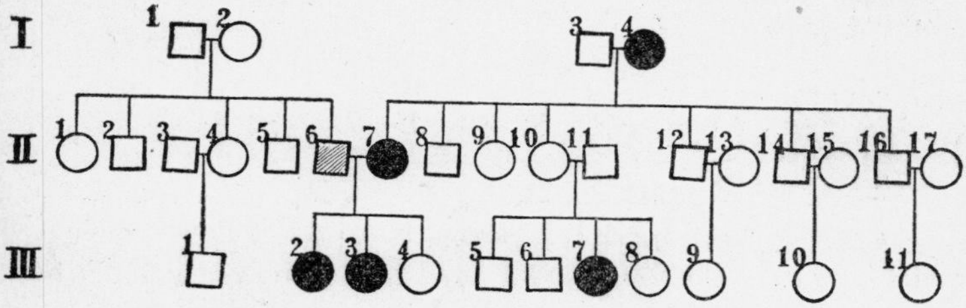

FIG. 58.—Inheritance of nervousness and brilliancy. I, 4, is subject to headaches and nervousness. Her daughter, II, 7, is similarly affected. She married a man, II, 6, who has had temporary attacks of paralysis. One of their children, II, 2, has nervous prostration and one, III, 3, is subject to headaches and nervousness. F. R.; Cla. 3.

weak as well as brilliant. (Fig. 61). See also arteriosclerosis, page 162.

d. Cerebral Palsy of Infancy.—This disease, of obscure origin, affects infants within a few years of birth; it leads

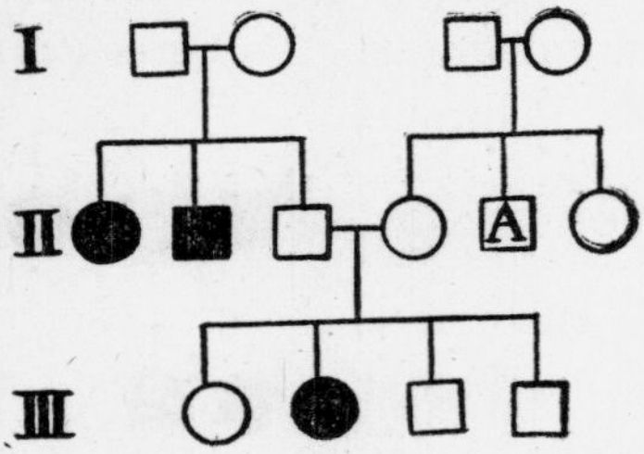

FIG. 59

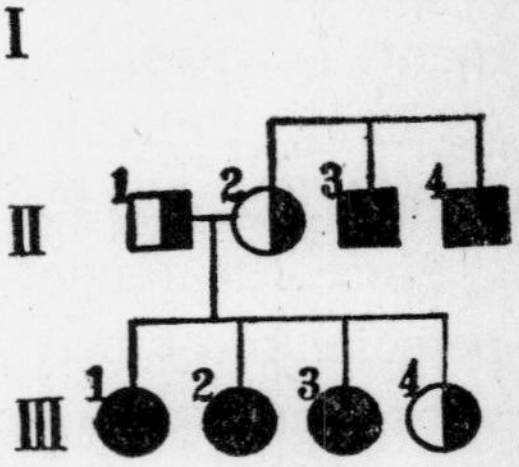

FIG. 60

FIG. 59.—Pedigree of a family with nervous disease. I, 3, was a heavy drinker; I, 4, died of apoplexy after suffering from paresis. The father was normal, but he had a brother, II, 1, who was eccentric and committed suicide, and a sister, II, 2, who was a good linguist but deteriorated mentally. The mother, II, 4, is normal but she had a brother who while a civil engineer and excellent draftsman was alcoholic, and a sister who was a good musician. One child, III, 2, is suffering at 23 from dementia precox. F. R.; Coi. 1.

FIG. 60.—Pedigree of a family with high incidence of cerebral apoplexy. The father and mother, I, 1 and 2, both have apparently a tendency toward cerebral congestion. I, 2, had recently had an attack which was relieved by nasal hemorrhage. Two of the mother's brothers, I, 3 and 4, died after a brief attack of apoplexy. Three of the daughters have died of the same disease at 32, 30 and 46 years respectively; the remaining suffers from cerebral congestion. HARRINGTON, 1885.

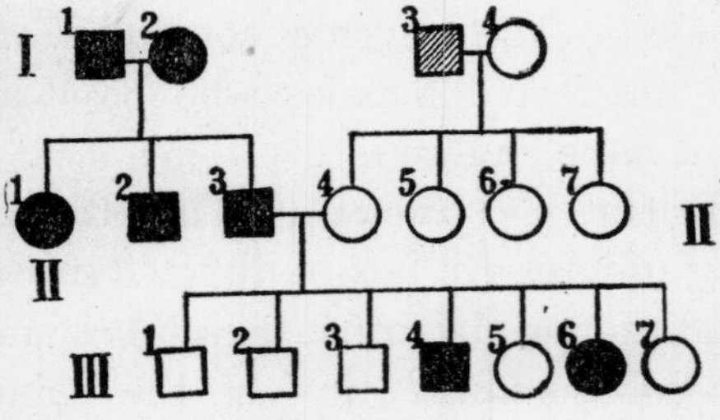

FIG. 61

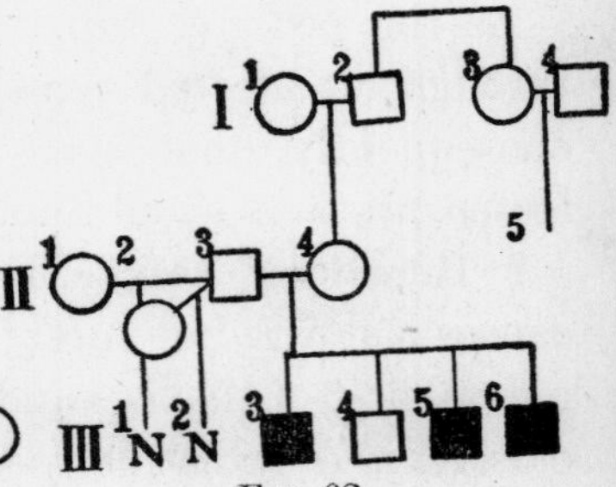

FIG. 62

FIG. 61.—Pedigree of a family with "nerve weakness." The father's father, I, 1, had a "nervous weakness," his wife died at 28 of encephalitis, the mother's father, I, 3, was subject to apoplexy and died of a stroke at 71. The father, II, 3, and all of his fraternity had encephalitis—the father three times—and one died of it, while the others were left with a nervous weakness. The children were not vigorous. III, 1, had always a low vitality and died at 8 years; III, 3, had a low vitality and died at 14 of "congestion of the lungs"; III, 4, was feeble-minded; III, 5, a laborer, suffered much from "bowel trouble"; III, 6, has a nervous weakness; and III, 7, engaged in housework and, with III, 2, is the strongest of the family.

FIG. 62.—Pedigree of a family with cerebral diplegia. The father in the central mating, II, 3, has been three times married. By two of the marriages

to general paralysis of one or both sides and, in later development, is associated with feeble-mindedness. Pedigrees are given by Dercum (1897) Fig. 62, Pelizaeus (1885) Fig. 63, Freud (1893) and others.

Since the tendency is carried by normal persons and since (as in Freud's case) it is apt to occur with consanguineous marriage it is probably due to a specific defect. To avoid the reproduction of the disease, marriage with unrelated blood is essential.

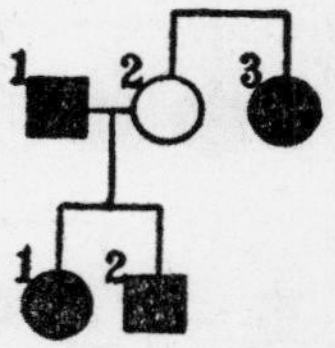

FIG. 63.—Illustrates the pedigree of a man that now has cerebral diplegia who married a woman who had a sister similarly affected. Both children are affected. PELIZAEUS, 1885.

e. Multiple or Disseminated Sclerosis.—This is a diffuse degenerative disease of the spinal cord. It leads to tremors in the arms and trunk, disturbance of speech and eventual paralysis. It is usually not regarded as hereditary but an interesting pedigree showing its appearance in 3 generations has been investigated by Merzbacher (1909), Fig. 64.

As the pedigree table shows, the disease is transmitted through unaffected females. The eugenic conclusion is, consequently, that even unaffected females who have affected brothers should not have children.

f. Hereditary Ataxy (Friedrich's disease).—This disease causes a slowly but surely progressive loss of directed movements, first of the legs and then of the arms; speech becomes elusive and indistinct; scoliosis (curvature of the spine) may appear and the feet become drawn up. These symptoms accompany a degeneration in the upper part of the spinal cord.

he had only normal children, but by the third (to a normal woman who had a first cousin, II, 5, with cerebral diplegia) he had 4 sons of whom 3 were affected with this disease. The eldest, III, 3, was normal until 16 months old, then had general convulsions, after which spastic symptoms gradually appeared, becoming pronounced later. Now he can walk only a few steps and is quite idiotic. The third son was normal until 2 years old, but is now deteriorating after an attack of measles and the youngest, only 2 years old, has just become diplegic and epileptic. DERCUM, 1897.

Some extensive pedigrees of ataxy have been published. One of the most extensive is by Mott (1905). It is reproduced in Fig. 65.

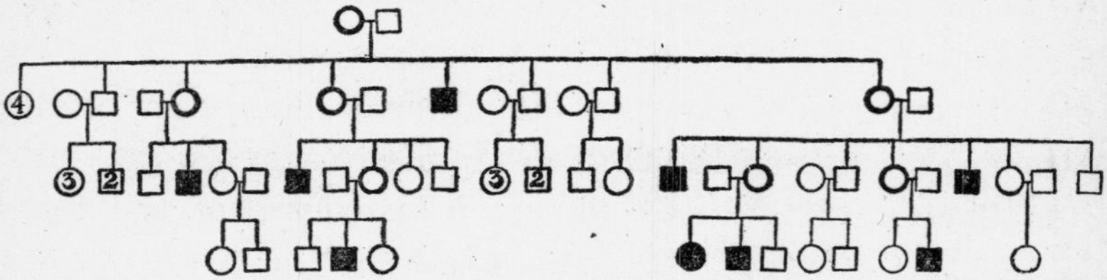

FIG. 64.—Part of EICHOLD-FLEMING-STOSSEL-HERZER pedigree showing multiple sclerosis (black symbols). One notes the skipping of a generation (indicating a recessive trait). The trouble is usually carried by unaffected females (heavy circles) and appears in their sons. Interesting because same family was independently noted by two neurologists. PELIZAEUS, 1885; MERZBACHER, 1909.

Since, as the pedigrees show, normals may have affected offspring the disease is probably dependent, as in insanity, on the lack of something necessary for normal development. The disease seems to be in no way sex-limited (Fig. 65).

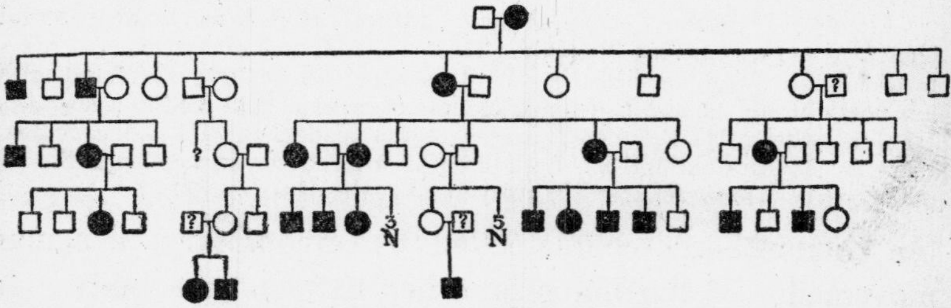

FIG. 65.—Pedigree of a family with hereditary ataxy (black symbols). Consorts not in direct line mostly unknown. Note that affected persons have (for the most part) one affected parent; the trouble is due to the presence of some positive character. MOTT, 1905.

The eugenic teaching is that affected persons and also normals of the affected fraternities should marry only outside the strain. Whether *all* cases of atactic offspring of one normal parent are derived from consanguineous marriage is still uncertain and warrants hesitation in advising the marriage of any atactic person.

g. Ménière's Disease is apparently due to a disturbance in the auditory nerve or its centre. It is accompanied by dizziness and roaring in the ear, often so severe as to force the patient to fall to the ground. Simon (1903) describes a family with these symptoms, consisting of an affected father, son and two daughters. The onset of the attacks varied from the 25th to the 50th year.

h. Chorea (St. Vitus's dance) is a disease of the cere-

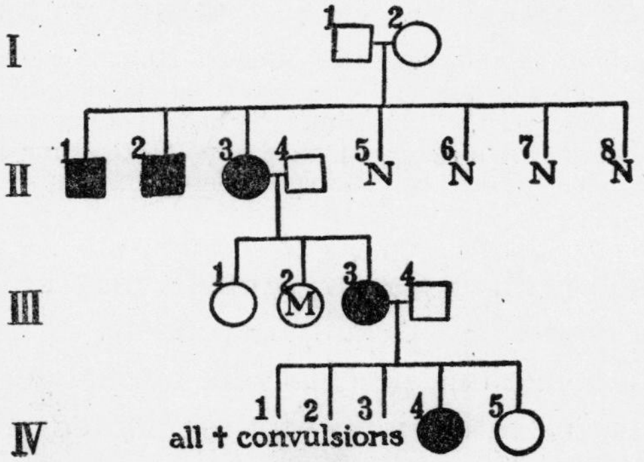

FIG. 66.—Pedigree of chorea (black symbols). II, 1, became affected with chorea at 8 years before his death; II, 2, has suffered many years; 4 other brothers and sisters are healthy. II, 3, became sick at 35 and suffered until her death at 46; she also had a marked loss of memory and died in a hospital. III, 1, is healthy; III, 2, suffers from severe sick headaches. III, 3, has chorea. IV, 4, is 11 years old and has been afflicted with chorea and epileptic fits for past 2 years. Her sister is still healthy at 10 years. JOLLY, 1891.

bral hemispheres characterized by involuntary, irregular movements of the limbs or other parts of the body. It commonly occurs in families with neuropathic make-up. Ordinarily the disease appears in the children and ends in recovery; occasionally it appears only later in life and runs various courses, sometimes ending in death through exhaustion. This disease is commonly sharply separated from Huntington's chorea, but transitional conditions occur. A case cited by Jolly is shown in Fig. 66. In this case nothing is known about the first generation; the second comprises 4 normals and 3 affected persons, 2 males and 1 female. II, 1 became affected with chorea "8 years before his death"; II, 2 "has been affected for many years"; II, 3 became ill with chorea at 35 and suffered until her death at 46. These look like cases of Huntington's chorea. III, 2 suffers from migraine; III, 3 has chorea, IV, 1–3 died at birth of convulsions; IV, 4 at 9 years began to show choreiform movements. These have continued for two years until the present time. This girl also has epilepsy; but her chorea has appeared at the age for St. Vitus's dance.

i. **Huntington's Chorea.**—This is said to be a "rare" disease in Europe, but not so in the United States. It is characterized by appearing typically first in middle life and progressing with ever increasing disorder of movements until dementia and death occur. It affects both sexes about equally. Two pedigrees are given in Figures 67 and 68.

The method of the inheritance of this disease was recognized by its original describer, Dr. George Huntington. He states that those exempt from it cannot transmit it. An examination of the extensive pedigrees shows only one exception to his rule and this a doubtful case. Huntington's chorea is, consequently, a typical dominant trait, the normal condition is recessive; or, the disease is due to some positive factor. The eugenic lesson is that persons with this dire disease *should not have children.* But the members of normal branches derived from the affected strain are immune from the disease.

This disease forms a most striking illustration of the principle that many of the rarer diseases of this country can be traced back to a few foci, possibly even to a single focus; certainly in this case many of the older families with Huntington's chorea trace back to the New Haven Colony and its dependencies and subsequent offshoots. The subject of foci of origin of traits will be discussed more fully later (page 181)

j. Hysteria.—This term is applied to a variety of symptoms that indicate a functional disturbance of the psychic centres usually combined with a derangement of the lower

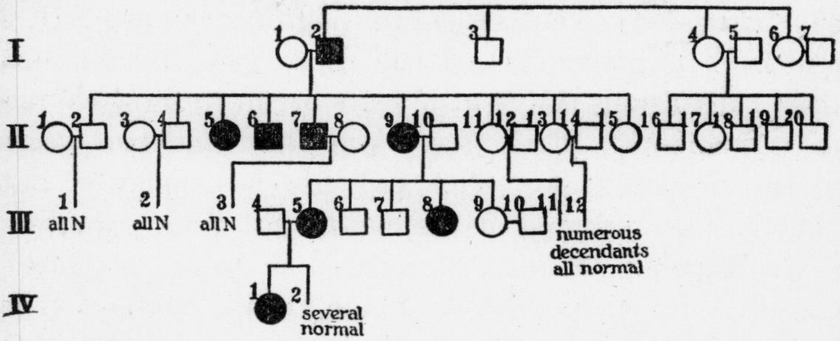

FIG. 67.—Pedigree of a family showing Huntington's chorea. Affected persons (indicated by black symbols) are always derived from affected parents. From original data furnished by Dr. S. E. JELLIFFE; Smi-family.

cerebral or spinal centres. The psychical symptoms approach mania on the one hand and show a more or less complete loss of the moral sense on the other, so that many

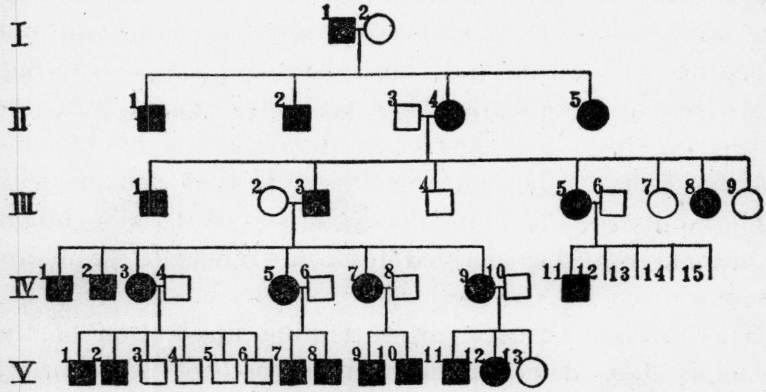

FIG. 68.—Pedigree of a family with Huntington's chorea. All affected persons (black symbols) have at least one affected parent. HAMILTON, 1908, p. 453.

cases of larceny, assault, and sexual immorality are consequent upon this disease. The emotions usually are disturbed. The motor symptoms are frequently profound.

Thus paralysis, or spasmodic contractions, or even convulsions not unlike, if not identical with, those of epilepsy, make their appearance.

The greatest social importance of hysteria lies in its relation to crime and responsibility. A large proportion of "criminals" doubtless are in need of hospital care. The family history of the offender will give the best possible clue to his probable mental condition and, where a "neuropathic blood" is evident, the patient should be segregated, not to punish him but to care for him at the expense of that "society" which still permits his kind to breed unrestricted; and to prevent, or at least to limit, the further spread of his tainted germ plasm.

In studies made on 175 families containing epileptics which the author has had the privilege of making with the coöperation of Dr. David F. Weeks hysteria was frequently found associated with chorea, migraine and a "neurotic" condition in the parentage of epileptics and in the offspring of an epileptic or insane parent married to a normal. It acts like a condition induced by a simplex determiner such that the patient produces some defective germ cells.

25. Rheumatism

Rheumatism, as is well known, is often associated with chorea. An example of such association is given in Figure 69.

A second instructive case is that cited by Cheadle (1900). A man who had subacute arthritis and muscular rheumatism and whose sister died at 8 years of heart disease following acute rheumatism and chorea married a woman who had suffered from acute rheumatism, heart disease and chorea and had had a nephew affected with rheumatic fever and heart disease and a niece with subacute rheumatism. The child of this pair at 9 years of age had chorea in a most severe form, repeated attacks of inflammation of the heart and pains in joints with formation of nodules beneath the skin. Finally the girl died a victim to extreme, uncontrollable rheumatism and chorea.

The exact laws of inheritance in these cases are not clear and eugenic instruction cannot be drawn from them.

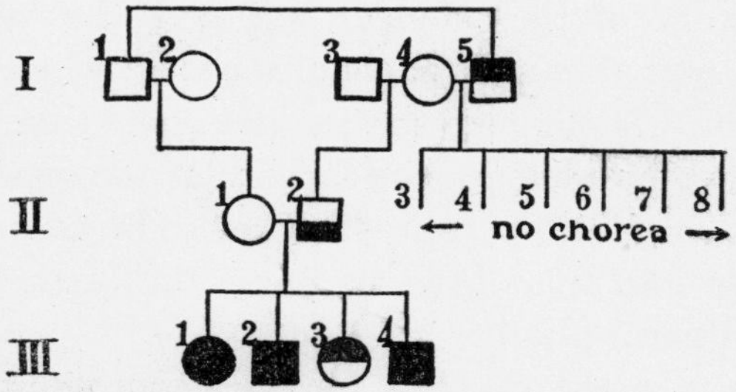

Fig. 69.—Pedigree of family showing chorea and rheumatism. I, choreic at 15 years; still has slight twitchings; II, 2, is not choreic but is subject to migraine and has had several attacks of rheumatism. He has had 2 daughters and 2 sons. III, 1, is 18 years old and since her eighth year has had chronic and severe chorea; at 12 she had an attack of rheumatism and since then attacks of rheumatism and chorea have alternated. Her elder brother, 16 years of age, was attacked a year before by chorea which lasted 2 months; recently has had another attack preceded by rheumatic pains. The third child, III, 3, now 13 years old, has had no rhematism but was first attacked by chorea at 12 and has had other attacks since. The youngest, III, 4, now 11, had a first attack of chorea at 8 years, lasting 2 months; a second attack at 10 and a third recently; in his eighth year he had articular rheumatism. Apert, 1907, p. 235.

26. Speech-defects

While the minor speech defects of stammering, stuttering, lolling, lisping and poltering correspond to no yet recognized abnormality of the central nervous system or organs of articulation, nevertheless, aside from imitation, they clearly have an hereditary basis and while the slighter grades may be cured by practice the more profound disturbances remain a permanent affliction. Especially are these defects found in children of a neuropathic inheritance and, in such, yield the strongest evidence of inheritance.

The exact method of inheritance of stuttering will not

me known until more extensive pedigrees of stuttering ilies have been obtained. Two pedigrees have been tained (Figs. 70, 71).

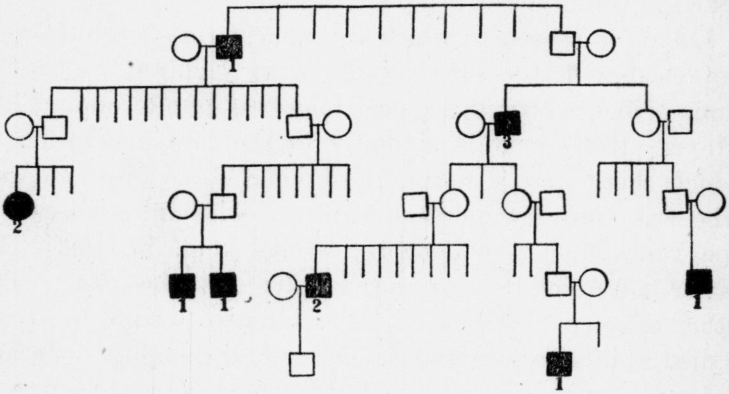

FIG. 70.—Pedigree of a family that contains stutterers (black symbols); 1, stutterer; 2, impediment in speech; 3, impediment, if excited. F. R.; Bar. 4.

Stuttering is seen to affect both sexes. It can hardly be a dominant trait because it is found so often in children of unaffected parents. It *might* be due to the absence of

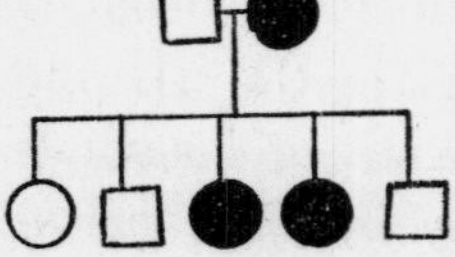

FIG. 71

FIG. 72

FIG. 71.—Pedigree of a part of a family of stutterers (black symbols).

FIG. 72.—Pedigree fragment of poltering family. Affected individuals in black. BERKAN.

some factor if consanguineous marriages were common in these pedigrees.

The trick of repeating short words and syllables is sometimes called poltering. A case of it occurs in three generations and is given by Berkan (Fig. 72). The peculiarity is found in each of three generations; it may of course be assisted by imitation.

Lolling is speech in which the articulatory mechanism is not used with precision, as in young children. There is some evidence that this defect may be a family one. Thus Moyer (1893) records a family in the first generation of which there were a normal sister and three brothers; one who was quite normal in speech, one who did not learn to speak until 6 years old, and one who lolled his life long. The latter had 6 children, all normal save one who lolled. The other affected brother had 12 children of whom, however, 5 died in infancy, leaving 7. Of his four daughters one had defective utterance, while all three boys were defective in speech, although after puberty the defect gradually disappeared. One of these boys has 3 sons, all normal. The case illustrates segregation but hardly suffices to demonstrate the law of inheritance of the peculiarity.

27. Defects of the Eye

Apart from albinism, the effects of which are most strongly felt in the increased sensitiveness of the retina to strong light, the chief optical defects whose inheritance has been studied are as follows; (a) absence of or defect in the iris and displacement of the pupil; (b) reduction in size of the whole eyeball to complete absence; (c) atrophy of optic nerve; (d) cataract; (e) dislocation of the lens; (f) degeneracy of the cornea; (g) glaucoma or excessive production of fluids of the eye; (h) megalophthalmus, or big eye; (i) nystagmus or "swimming eye;" (k) paralysis or imperfect development of muscles of the eye and lids; (l) pigmentary degeneration of the retina (retinitis pigmentosa); (m) night blindness (hemeralopia); (n) color blindness; (o) astigmatism; (p) myopia.

a. Anomalies of Iris.—Coloboma is a defect in the development of the optic cup such that it fails to close completely and leaves an open suture running from the pupil to the optic nerve. The commonest external evidence of

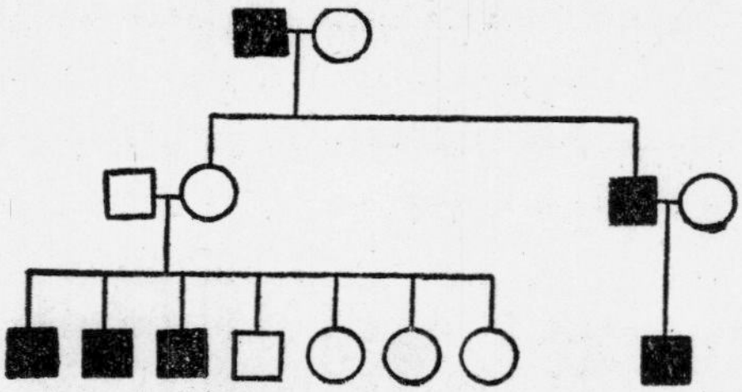

FIG. 73.—A pedigree of a family affected with coloboma. Black symbols stand for affected persons; all are males. A normal female in the second generation transmits the defect to about half of her children, but her sons alone show the defect. STREETFIELD, 1858.

this defect is the incomplete iris; but the lens, retina, choroid coat, etc., may be involved. The cause of the defect is conceded to be an hereditary defect in the developmental impulse (Von Hippel, 1909).

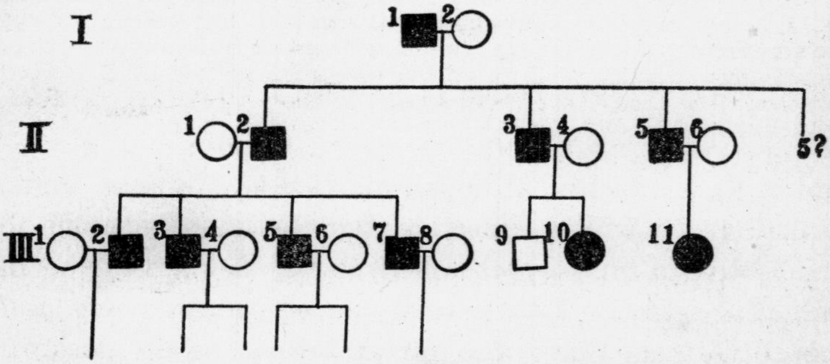

FIG. 74.—Pedigree of a family that shows absence of iridae (black symbols). Here, too, only males show the defect, except for III, 10 and 11. Hypothesis, in this case, requires that II, 4 and II, 6, shall be related to their consorts and carry germ cells with the inhibiting factor. GUTBIER, 1834.

The method of inheritance is shown by the pedigrees (Figs. 73, 74, 75). These lead to the conclusions that the defect is a positive character and is due to an inhibitor of development; the affected male is either simplex or duplex in this inhibitor; the affected female is typically duplex, rarely simplex; unaffected males are always nulliplex, and unaffected females are either nulliplex or simplex.

The eugenic conclusion is: No female with the coloboma defect should have children since *all* sons will be defective in the structure of the pupil. For males with the defect the danger in marriage is also great, for either all or half of the

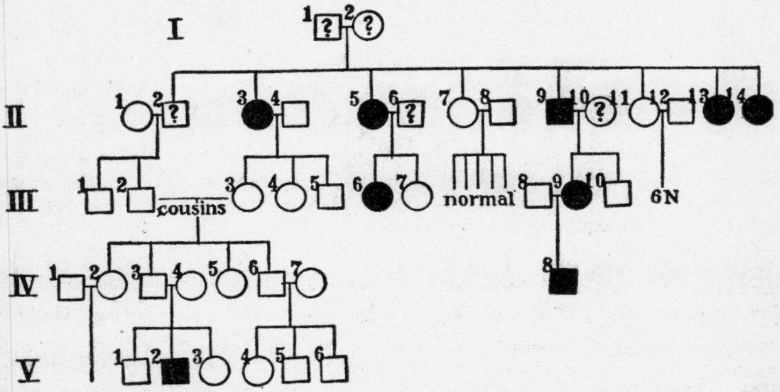

FIG. 75.—This is the pedigree of a family (Payne) with coloboma of the iris. I, 1, and 2 are not definitely known; at least 1 of their sons and 4 daughters are affected. As for the rest, two normal parents have normal offspring. The apparent exception, V, 2, may not be such as the mother, IV, 2, is wholly unknown. The number of affected females in this pedigree is extraordinary. DEBECK, 1886.

sons of such a father, although married to a woman from a normal strain, will be defective, but the daughters will not be defective in this respect unless the wife belongs to a strain with this defect. Two normal persons may marry with impunity except that if the woman belongs to the abnormal strain it may be that half of her sons will be affected.

b. Reduction in size of the Eyeball.—All grades in the size of the eyeball down to complete disappearance are known, but usually only the extremely reduced condition has been studied. Such a condition seems to be due to an inhibitor so that, when present in a marked degree, all offspring shall have it. Both sexes seem to be equally affected.

It is not particularly apt to occur in consanguineous marriages. An illustrative case is given by Martin, 1888 (Fig. 76).

The two sexes are equally affected. A person with the defect in a marked degree will have at least half of the children similarly defective.

It is not, at the moment, possible to say that, when both parents are unaffected the children will all be normal, but there is a strong presumption that such will be the case.

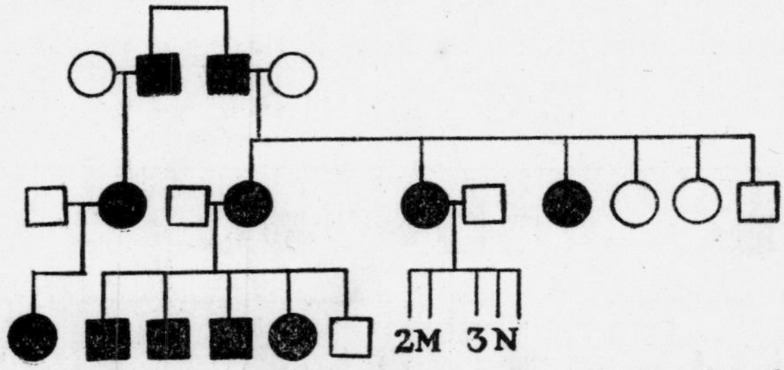

Fig. 76.—Pedigree of a family with small eyeball (microphthalmus). Every affected person (black symbol) that has married has affected offspring. Actually, there are 11 affected progeny to 7 normal; but as frequently happens in practitioner's records, some normal children are probably not recorded. Martin, 1888.

c. **Atrophy of the Optic Nerve.**—This disease usually begins "at about the 20th year with a rather sudden disturbance of the central sight of both eyes while the peripheral parts of the field of vision remain normal." "The course of the disease is generally the same in the same family, so that the prognosis depends in the main upon the degree of malignancy which the malady exhibits in that particular family" (Senator-Kaminer, 1904).

The method of inheritance in this case resembles that of coloboma (except that even duplex females rarely exhibit the trait) and is shown in the ideal scheme of Figure 77 in which the heavy ring means without somatic defect but with defective germ cells.

The eugenic rule is: a normal son of an abnormal male may marry quite outside the family with impunity, but a normal daughter may transmit the defect to her sons. But such a woman may marry with impunity if all of her brothers are without defect and there are more than two of them. A defective male should abstain from having children, for some of his sons, at least, will probably be defective.

d. Cataract.—This is an opacity of the lens which may result from abnormal conditions originating in other parts of the eye or body or they may seemingly originate inside the lens itself, in which case their heredity is marked. Probably more pedigrees of cataract have been published than of any other eye defect. Loeb (1909) refers to 304 families of which accounts have been printed. Of the 1012 children in these pedigrees, 589 were affected, or 58 per cent.[1]

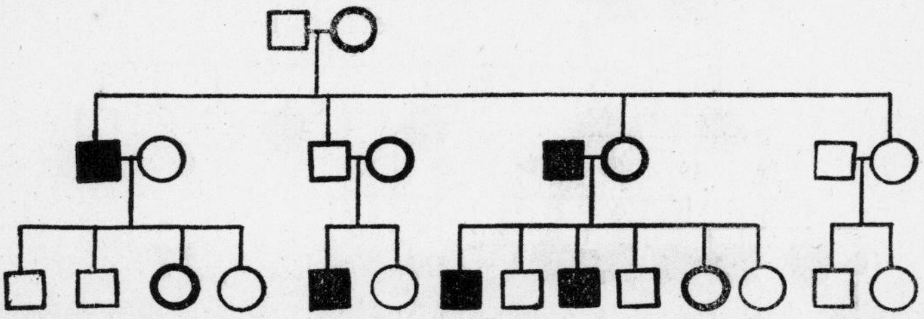

FIG. 77.—Ideal scheme showing inheritance of atrophy of the optic nerve. The solid black squares indicate affected males; the heavy rings represent non-affected females with defective germ cells.

The usual method of inheritance is that of a positive character. Affected individuals have either half or all of their offspring affected, while two unaffected parents will probably not have defective offpsring. However, as cataract usually appears late in life it is not always possible to predict whether the parent will become affected or not (Fig. 78).

The eugenic rule is this:—If either parent has cataract at least half of the offspring will have it also. If a person belongs to a strain that has cataract but is free from it, advice must depend on the nature of the cataract. If in

[1] The report of the medical officer (education) to the London County Council, 1909, contains 9 additional cases.

the family strain cataract appears early, before the age of the person who contemplates marriage, then such marriage may be advised; but if in the given family the cataract occurs late in life it is not possible to predict as to the immunity of the parent, but in that case also, since the potential defect will not greatly interfere with the effectiveness of the children, fertile marriage may not be gainsaid.

e. Displaced Lens (ectopia lentis).—This malposition of the lens always causes distorted vision. Fortunately it is not so common as cataract, for Loeb found only 42 families

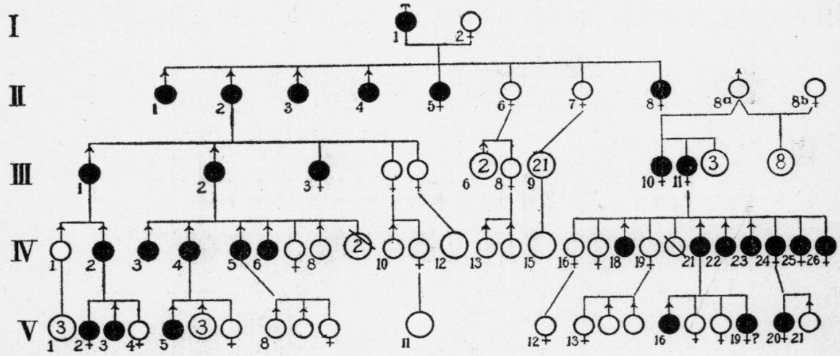

FIG. 78.—Pedigree of "coralliform" cataract. Affected persons represented by black symbols; ♂, male; ♀, female; numbers in circles indicate number of individuals. From NETTLESHIP, 1910.

described, with 150 children, of whom 70 per cent were affected. The details of the condition and the degree of injury to sight vary from strain to strain (Fig. 79).

In this case, also, it appears that the defect is due to some positive factor and that when present in either parent it will be present in about half the offspring; but if present in neither parent it will be absent from all descendants.

The eugenic teaching is clear; persons with displaced lens should have no children; but normal persons of the same strain will not reproduce it in their offspring.

f. Degeneracy of the Cornea.—While several causes of corneal opacity are known that seem not to be hereditary,

18 cases of hereditary degeneration of the cornea are recorded. So far as the studies that have been made go they indicate that persons with such hereditary corneal opacity should not have children but that normal members of such a strain will have normal offspring.

g. Glaucoma.—This is a swelling of the eyeball due to excess fluid in the chambers of the eye. It appears to depend upon the presence of something that prevents the escape of the fluids of the eyeball. In the study of the inheritance of this disease we meet with the difficulty that, like cancer and many forms of cataract, its outset is late in

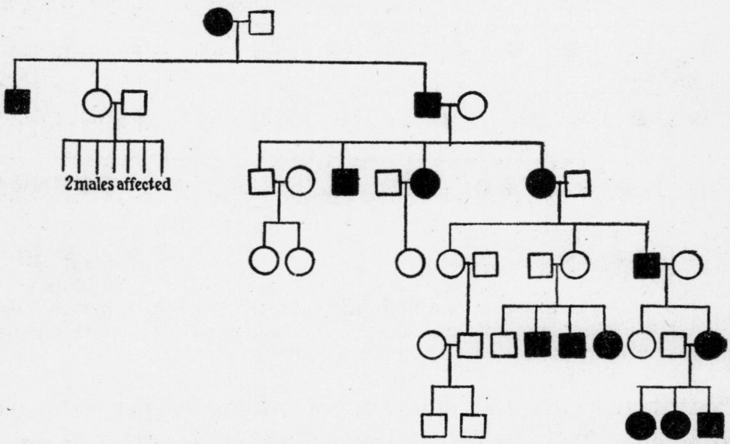

FIG. 79.—Pedigree of a family with dislocation of lens, resulting in imperfect vision, vertigo, flashes of light, etc. The amount of displacement varies in the different individuals. In the third generation 2 individuals are affected in one eye only but in all other cases both eyes are affected. LEWIS, 1904.

life—so that many persons with potential glaucoma die before realizing it. However, the age at onset is variable, in some families high and others low; but in the children the onset is frequently earlier than in the parents; thus, in one family the father shows the disease at 70, his daughters at 45, and 40; in another case father is attacked at 49 and his sons at 18 and 16; again, a father has glaucoma at 60, his 4 children at from 55 to 40; and a mother is affected in one eye at 60 and the other eye at 81, while her 3 children are affected at 60. In one family strain, Von Graefe noticed an unusually long

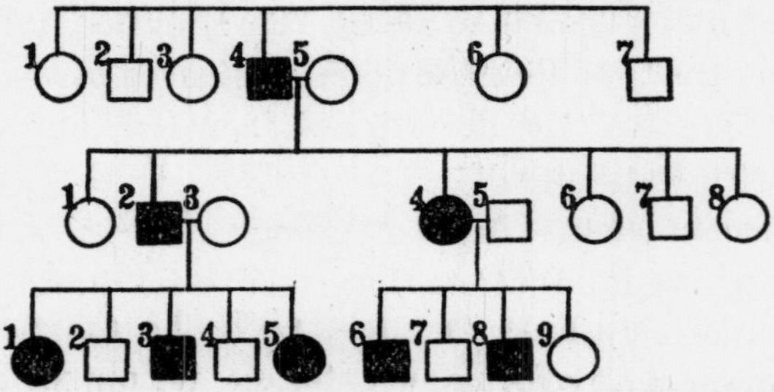

Fig. 80.—Pedigree of family with glaucoma, showing simple dominance of the trait. In I, 4, the disease appeared at 40 years of age; in II, 2, at 28; in II, 4, at 25; in generation III, at 28 to 17 years—an extraordinarily early age. Howe, 1887.

prodromal stage (10 to 15 yrs.), before the fully developed attack. This is one of the special family strains.

Glaucoma is said to have various inciting causes. The type that follows a characteristic inflammation shows the

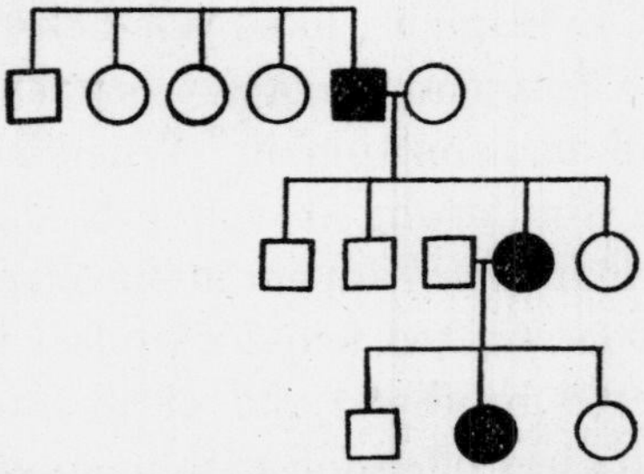

Fig. 81.—Pedigree of family with glaucoma, percentage of incidence of disease small, owing perhaps to early deaths (?). In the first generation the disease began at 71 years, in the second at 40; in the third at between 25 and 30 years. Nettleship.

best evidence of heredity. A pedigree or two will illustrate the method of its inheritance (Figs. 80, 81).

The eugenic teaching is rendered more difficult by the fact that glaucoma usually first appears toward the end of the reproductive period. But certainly affected persons should avoid having children, while non-affected may marry if the disease first appeared in the grandparents at 50 or after. If it appeared earlier it would seem to be prudent for the normal persons to delay reproduction until within ten years of the time that the defect appeared in *their* parents. Then if no trace of the disease has occurred they may have children with impunity.

h. **Megalophthalmus** or protruding eye. A rather rare disease of whose inheritance there can be no doubt, although the exact method of that inheritance is uncertain. Persons with a well marked case had best avoid reproduction.

i. **Nystagmus,** or "swimming eyes." This is due to spasmodic contractions of the eye muscles and may or may not be associated with other defects of the eye. The disorders with which it is most apt to be associated are: strabismus, retinitis pigmentosa, coloboma, albinism, microphthalmus and cataract.

In some of the pedigrees that have been published (Clarke's, 1903), nystagmus, like optic nerve atrophy, is not expressed in the (simplex) females [1] but is expressed in all males capable of transmitting it. When it is unexpressed in the males of the strain, it will probably not (in non-consanguineous marriages) appear in the offspring. But marriages of even non-affected females (unless from large families of non-affected brothers) and of all affected males are pretty certain to yield offspring with nystagmus.

k. **Paralysis or imperfect development of the muscles of eye and lids.**—This includes ptosis, or drop of the upper eyelid; epicanthus, a fold of skin passing from nose to eyebrow over the inner corner of the eye; blepharophimosis, or smallness of opening of eyelids; ophthalmoplegia, or paralysis of eye muscles; strabismus or squinting. Every one of these peculiarities shows clear evidence of heredity.

[1] In other families nystagmus appears also in the females.

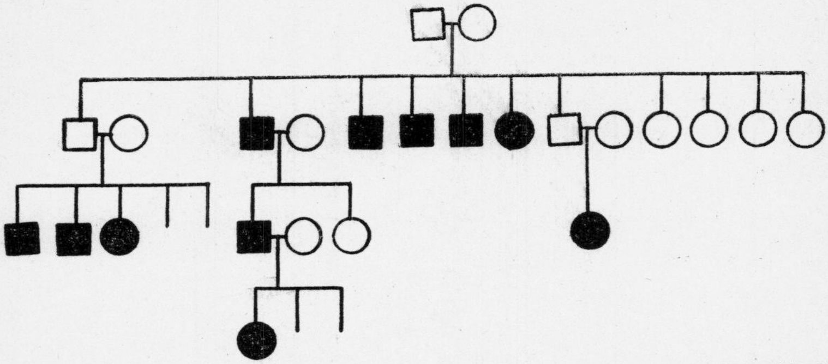

Fig. 82.—Pedigree of a family, every affected member of which (black symbols) has drooping eyelids, a fold over the inner corner of the eye, and narrow eye opening. Vignes, 1889.

One family pedigree is reproduced in Fig. 82. This is remarkable because every affected person showed the same combination of characters, namely, drop of upper eyelid, epicanthus, and ophthalmoplegia.

In Cutler's case (Fig. 83) the parents are first cousins; all affected persons have strabismus. Expectation in this group of cases is that an affected person will have affected offspring but that two normal parents will rarely have offspring with the defect, even though one belongs to the defective strain.

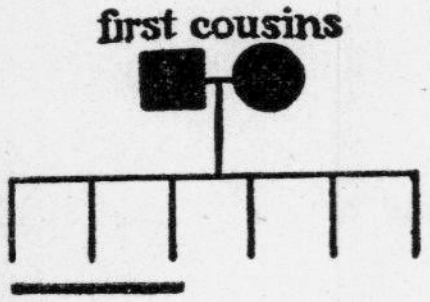

Fig. 83.—Pedigree of a family in which the parents are first cousins and both have strabismus (squint). Three of their 6 children are similarly affected. Cutler.

1. **Pigmentary degeneration of the retina** (retinitis pigmentosa).—This degenerative process is accompanied by an atrophy of the optic nerve and leads to eventual blindness. It is frequently associated with consanguineous marriage, 27 per cent of the marriages which yield it being (according to Feer's list, 1907, p. 14) consanguineous. The method of inheritance is well illustrated by Fig. 84 which is a portion of a chart prepared by Nettleship. This figure illustrates the general law of this disease; namely, that two normal

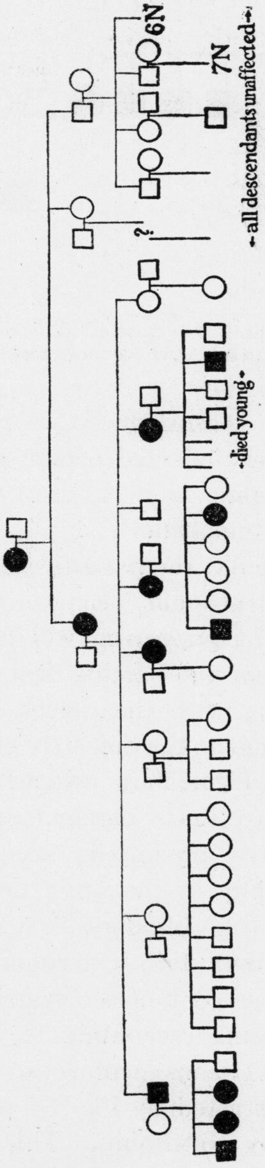

FIG. 84.—A fragment of a pedigree compiled by Nettleship showing method of inheritance of retinitis pigmentosa. Black, affected individuals. Note that two normal parents have only unaffected offspring. NETTLESHIP, 1910, p. 13.

parents produce no abnormal children. The condition that makes for retinitis is something added to the normal condition.

The extent of the degeneration varies with the family. In a pedigree recorded by Leber (Fig. 85) the characteristic, throughout the family, was an increasing dimness of vision accompanied by night blindness; but later the degeneration was stayed.

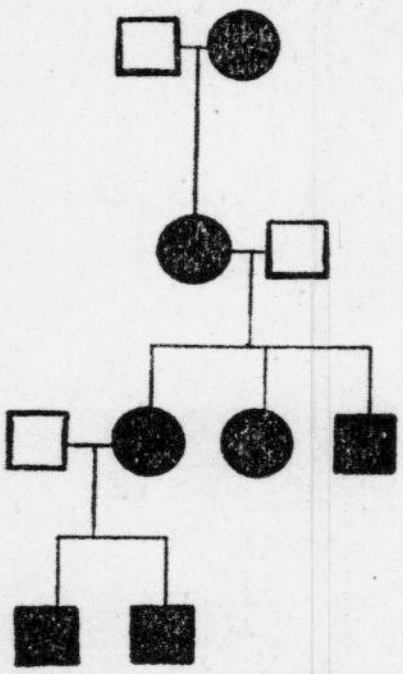

FIG. 85.—Pedigree of retinitis pigmentosa in a family in which the disease becomes checked before blindness becomes complete. LEBER, 1871.

The eugenic instruction is clear. An affected man or woman should not marry even into stock without taint of retinitis. Above all, in retinitis stock, cousins, especially if affected should by no means marry.

m. Night Blindness (hemeralopia).—This disease is accompanied by no loss of perception of form, but at sunset the affected persons must cease working. Artificial light helps little unless very intense. The lamps of the street are of no assistance in guiding these people at night. Eventually, in most strains, the affected persons become totally blind often with a retinitis. This disease is probably due to a defect in the brain and not as has been suggested merely to lack of the visual purple of the retina (Bordley, 1908).

Through the researches of Cunier (1838) and Nettleship (1907) we have a pedigree of a night blind strain that is the most extensive that has yet been compiled for any disease. It includes 2,116 persons. A part of it is reproduced in Fig. 86. Fig. 87 is a pedigree of an American (colored) family furnished by Dr. Bordley.

The disease is due to a positive factor. The normals lack this factor. Usually, however, the factor must be duplex

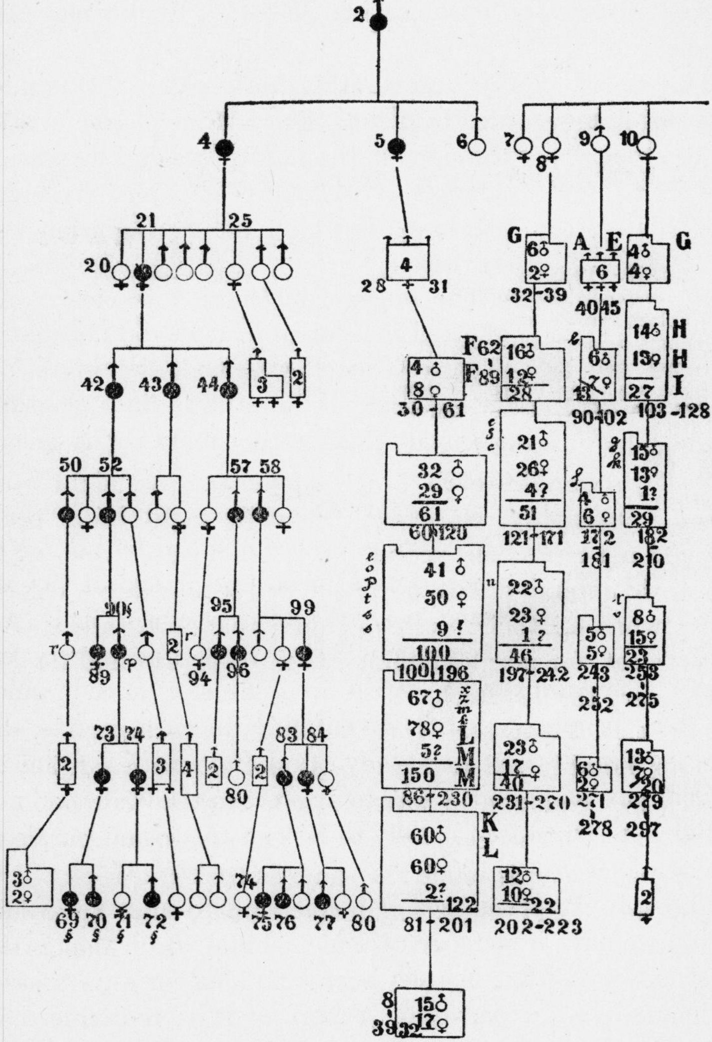

FIG. 86.—Pedigree of chart of an European strain with night blindness (black symbols). The rectangles indicate numerous normal individuals. Two normal parents have only normal children. NETTLESHIP, 1907, from GRÜBER and RUDIN, 1911.

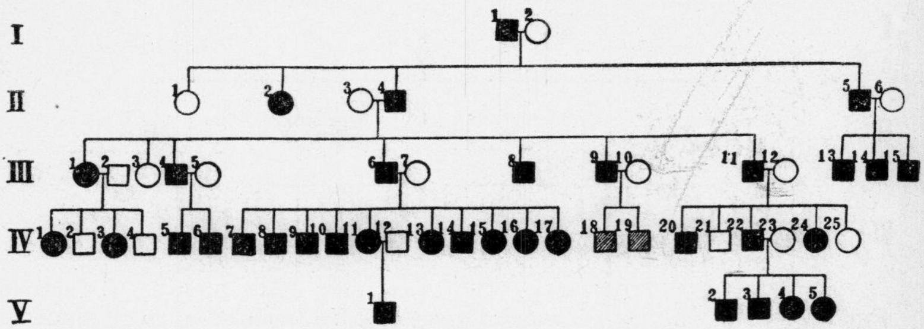

FIG. 87.—Pedigree of night blindness in a negro family, many of whom were personally examined by Dr. Bordley. IV, 18, 19, are doubtful. All solid block symbols stand for affected persons; clear symbols unaffected. The blindness is progressive and ends in death within 16 months after blindness becomes complete. All affected persons have an affected parent. Night blindness is a positive trait. BORDLEY, 1908.

in females in order to develop; but in both Nettleship's and Bordley's families even simplex females have night blindness. Ordinarily, consequently, while night blind people should not reproduce, normal males from such stock may do so with impunity, but normal females may have children only when all their brothers (more than two) are without the defect; for normal females, in most night blind families, *may* carry the disease.

n. Color Blindness.—The inability to distinguish certain colors, notably red and green, is not a rare condition but much less common in women than men (in Europe, 4 per cent males, 0.5 per cent females). The method of inheritance of the condition is much the same as that of atrophy of the optic nerve and night blindness; namely, that color blind males do not have color blind sons but that females free from color blindness may have sons with it (Fig. 88).

The eugenic conclusion is that while color blind males will have no color blind sons and, typically, no color blind offspring of either sex yet their daughters, married to men of normal stock, will have color blind sons.

To the ordinary rule there are various exceptions. Daugh-

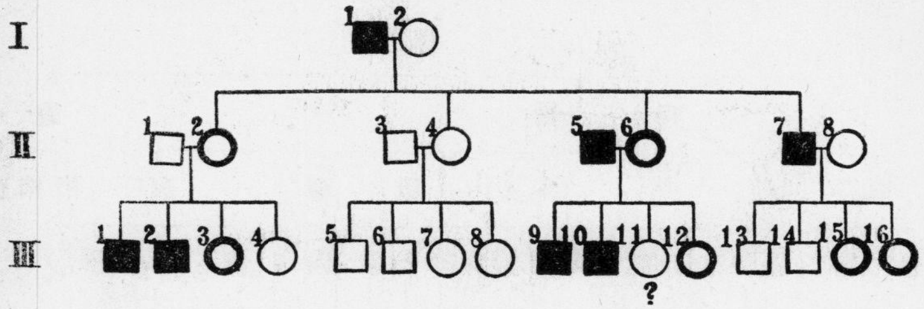

FIG. 88.—Ideal scheme, showing method of inheritance of color blindness. Typically it appears in sons only of simplex females, represented by a heavy ring. The mating II, 5–6, is rare and has not been observed. The nature of III, 11, is also doubtful.

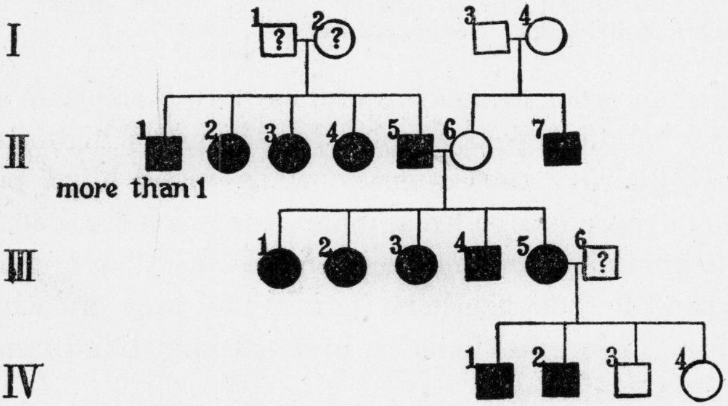

FIG. 89.—A remarkable and exceptional pedigree of color blindness. The fraternity, II, 1–5 (which comprises the grandfather, his brothers, and his 3 sisters), were said all to be color blind. The grandmother, II, 6, had the normal color sense but had an affected brother. The entire fraternity, III, 1–5, including 4 females, has impaired color perception. Details are given about III, 5, as follows: She is about 50 years old, a physician's wife, and a test shows complete confusion of dark green, dark red and brown. While lighter tints are better distinguished, rose and blue are confounded. The sons show exactly the same conditions. REBER, 1895.

ters may inherit color blindness from fathers. At least such is the history given by Reber (1895), Fig. 89; an exceptional history that is not entirely without precedent. In the case of these exceptional families a color blind parent may have color blind offspring of either sex.

o. **Myopia.**—That the shape of the eyeball is largely

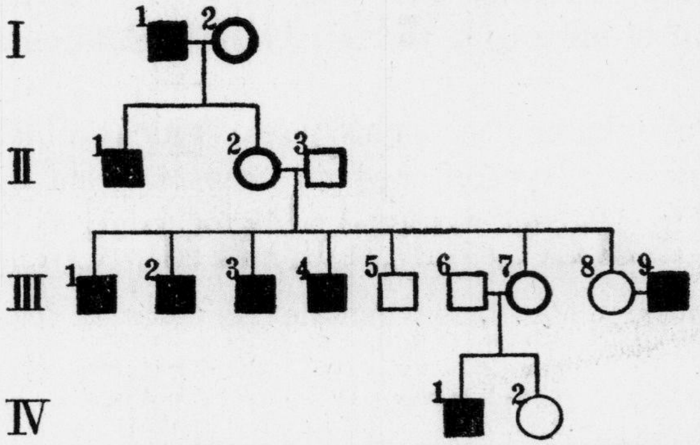

FIG. 90.—Pedigree of a family with myopia. In the first generation the man had myopia and strabismus while his wife was normal. Their son, II, 1, had myopia and died unmarried. His normal sister married a normal man and had 7 children. III, 1 and 2, had both myopia and strabismus; the eyesight of III, 3 and 4, was defective but in what way is unknown. A normal sister, III, 7, had a son with defective sight—probably myopia. From OSWALD, 1911. Note that males only are affected and are derived only from 2 normal parents. Simplex mothers indicated by heavy circles.

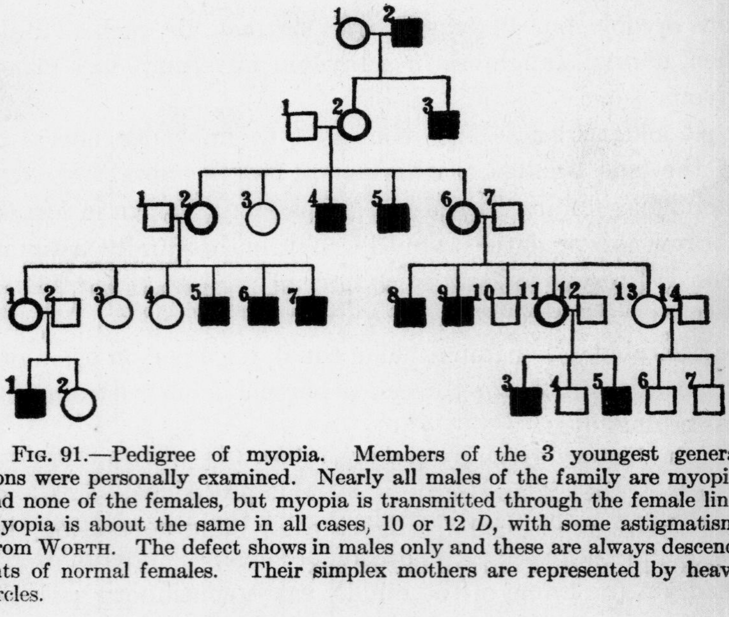

FIG. 91.—Pedigree of myopia. Members of the 3 youngest generations were personally examined. Nearly all males of the family are myopic, and none of the females, but myopia is transmitted through the female line. Myopia is about the same in all cases, 10 or 12 *D*, with some astigmatism. From WORTH. The defect shows in males only and these are always descendants of normal females. Their simplex mothers are represented by heavy circles.

controlled by heredity has been shown by Hertel (1903), as a result of measuring the refraction in children and their parents.

That myopia, or near sightedness, is inheritable has long been known. A typical case has been recorded by Oswald (1911), Fig. 90, and a second pedigree is given by Worth (Fig. 91). In both pedigrees inheritance is sex-limited as in color blindness. A normal female has some, at least, of her

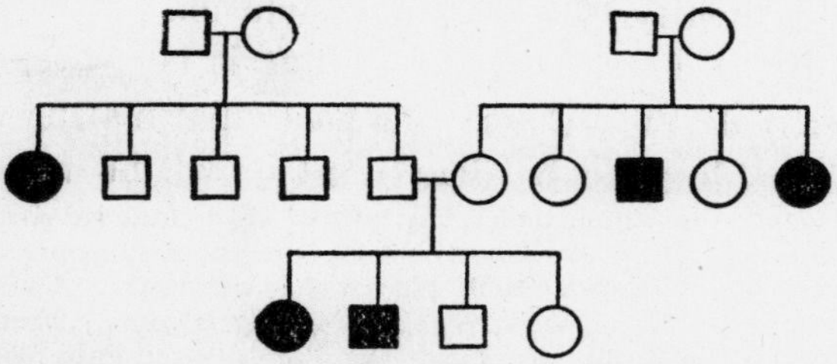

FIG. 92.—Pedigree of astigmatism, affected persons represented by black symbols. F. R.

sons myopic, but all daughters are normal. In such a family, then, normal daughters in a myopic fraternity may expect myopic sons.

p. Astigmatism.—This condition of improper curvature of the lens belongs to the list of family traits. A correspondent submits the pedigree of his family shown in Fig. 92.

From this pedigree it appears that, in this family, astigmatism is a recessive trait, since normal persons may transmit it and since it is equally apt to appear in either sex. It would be desirable, other things being equal, for a person belonging to an affected strain to seek a partner from a strain that has normal eyes.

28. Ear Defects

The ear is the most complicated of the sense organs and though its important elements are deeply hidden in the head yet the lining of the middle ear is continuous with the mucous membrane of the throat—in some respects the most vulnerable portion of the human body. Hence it is subject to the weaknesses of that membrane. On account of its very complexity it is especially liable to exhibit *deformations or deficiencies.*[1] In view of the great variety of changes any one of which may result in deafness it is clear that *deafness* can hardly be a unit defect. Consequently it will not be inherited as a simple character.

The facts justify the *a priori* conclusions. Deafness of certain sorts is clearly hereditary but it is not possible to predict certainly the outcome of a particular mating. Nevertheless something can be done; and it will be worth while to learn what is known of the actual incidence of deafness in the offspring of deaf parents.

Inheritable deafness is of three general types. (a) That due to defects or changes before birth or shortly after, giving rise to *deaf mutism;* (b) *otosclerosis,* or hardness of hearing, with usually progressive symptoms; (c) *catarrhal weakness* of the mucous membranes, rendering them liable to infection with inflammation and suppuration.

a. Deaf Mutism.—This kind of deafness is characterized by its early appearance in life, before speech has been acquired. It is the less likely, consequently, to be due to disease and, as a matter of fact, it is that form which shows clearest evidence of pure inheritance. So clear is the evidence of inheritance of congenital deafness that some coun-

[1] *Politzer* (1807) gives among others the following anatomical causes of congenital deafness: impaired development or absence of middle ear, defects and rachitic deformities of the labyrinthine windows; narrowing of the recess of the round window to a cleft with connective tissue; atresia of the same; atrophy of the cochlear nerve and spinal ganglion in the first turn of the cochlea; abnormalities of the membrance of the otoliths, organ of Corti and ductus cochlearis; faulty development of the sensory epithelium; defects of the crista and sulcus spiralis; lack of development of the labyrinth and of the auditory nerve; malformations of the central nervous system. In addition there are numerous changes in structure due to inflammations.

tries have forbidden the marriage of persons of this class. Yet the inheritance of deaf mutism has been disputed and, indeed, without careful consideration of the separate family histories the method of inheritance seems truly obscure.

The most extensive data on the marriage of deaf are those collected by Fay (1898). He finds that, when both parents are congenitally deaf (Figs. 93, 94), of the 335 matings 25

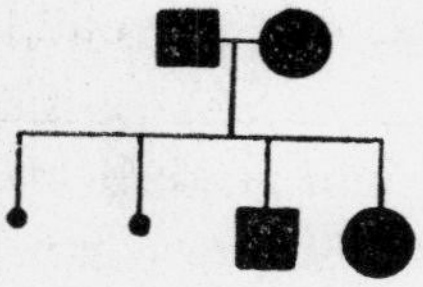

FIG. 93

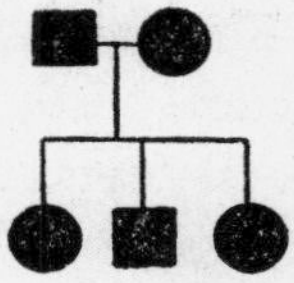

FIG. 94

FIG. 93.—Pedigree of deaf mutism. Parents both deaf; the father at 3 years; the mother before birth. The first two children died shortly after birth; the other two are deaf mutes—one born so; the other following a slight blow on the head. SAINT HILAIRE, 1900, p. 31.

FIG. 94.—Pedigree of deaf mutism. Father mother, and 3 children, all deaf mutes from birth. SAINT HILAIRE, 1900, p. 31.

per cent yield some deaf offspring; and of the total of 779 offspring 26 per cent are deaf. It is clear that such marriages are, in the long run, dangerous. That all children of such marriages are not deaf is doubtless due to the fact that the parents are not deaf in the same way and that one parent brings into the combination what the other lacks. The contrast between the result of marriages of two *congenitally* deaf parents and two who are *adventitiously* deaf is shown by the fact that the latter yield only 2.3 per cent deaf children.

If, on the other hand, the partners belong to the same deaf mute strain, i. e., are related, the percentage of marriages yielding some deaf mute offspring rises to 45, and the proportion of deaf offspring to 30 per cent (Fig. 95). But that is not the whole story, for the closer the relationship of the parents the larger the proportion of deaf children as the following table shows:—

	Per cent deaf offspring
Partners "cousins," degree unreported	19.4
" first or second cousins	34.6
" nephew and aunt (1 family)	75.0

The interpretation of this fact would seem to be that the nearer the relationship the greater the chance that both parents lack the same element and so all of their children

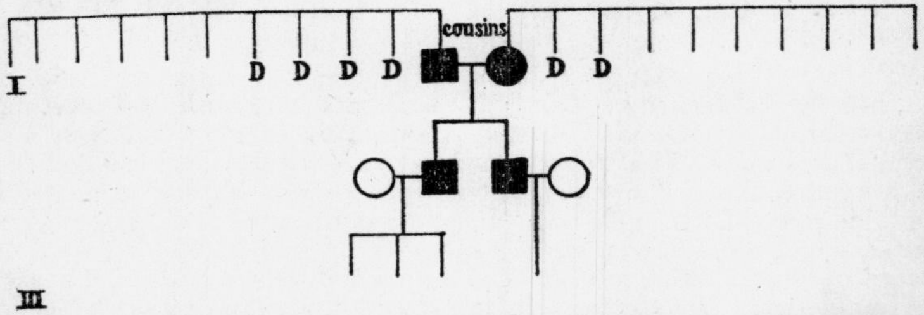

FIG. 95.—Pedigree of deaf mutes. Two deaf mute cousins each belonging to fraternities having several deaf mutes marry one another. Both of their children (II) are deaf. Each child marries a hearing wife and of 4 children all hear. FAY, 1898, No. 2621.

tend to lack it. In Figs. 96 to 100 are given some pedigrees of deaf mute families. They show that, under certain circumstances, probably identity of defect in parents, the children will all be similarly defective.

The studies of Bell (1906) based on the census returns of a large proportion of the deaf population of the United States show the importance of consanguineous marriages in favoring the production of deaf mute offspring. He finds (p. 17) "of the 2,527 deaf whose parents were cousins, 632, or 25 per cent, are congenitally deaf, of whom 350, or 55.4 also have deaf relatives of the classes specified; while among the 53,980 whose parents were not so related the number of congenitally deaf is 3,666 or but 6.8 per cent, of whom only 1,023 or 27.9 per cent have deaf relatives."

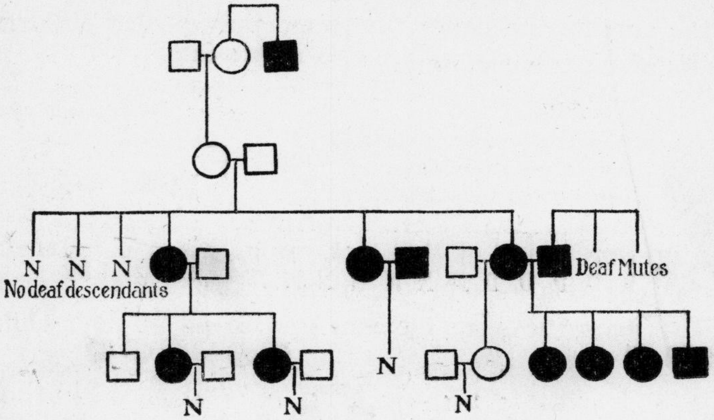

FIG. 96.—Three sisters (Gen. III), deaf mute from birth, had several perfectly normal brothers and sisters. Their mother's uncle had been a congenital deaf mute. The first sister married a hearing man and had 3 children, 1 hearing son and 2 mute daughters, who married hearing men and had only hearing children. The second sister was educated and married an educated mute but died soon after the birth of her normal child. The third sister married, first a hearing man and had a normal daughter whose children were in turn normal. But she married for a second husband a deaf mute belonging to a fraternity with 2 other deaf mutes and all 4 children who survived infancy were deaf mutes. Report, N. Y. School for Deaf and Dumb, 1853, p. 96.

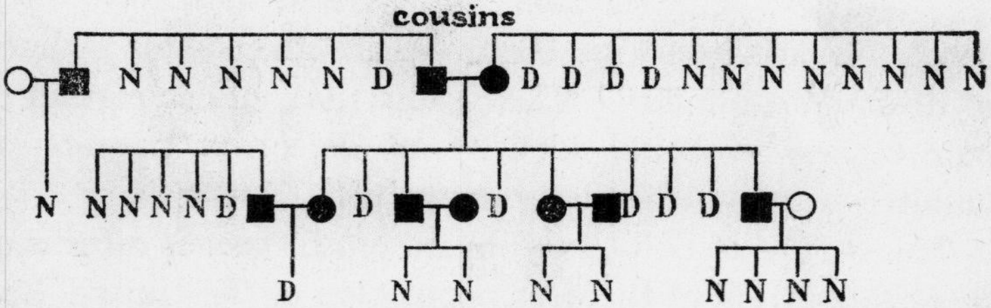

FIG. 97.—Pedigree of deaf mutes—black symbols or *D*. Note the fraternity of deaf mutes derived from the central mating of cousins. Most of those who outmarried, even though their consorts were deaf, had hearing children. FAY, 1898, No. 810.

In view of the foregoing data the first eugenic recommendation clearly is that two deaf mutes should not have children, especially if they come from the same long-settled community or are known to be blood relatives.

If one partner be congenitally deaf and the other have no ear defect and knows of none in his family the chances for deaf offspring are small. In 72 such marriages considered

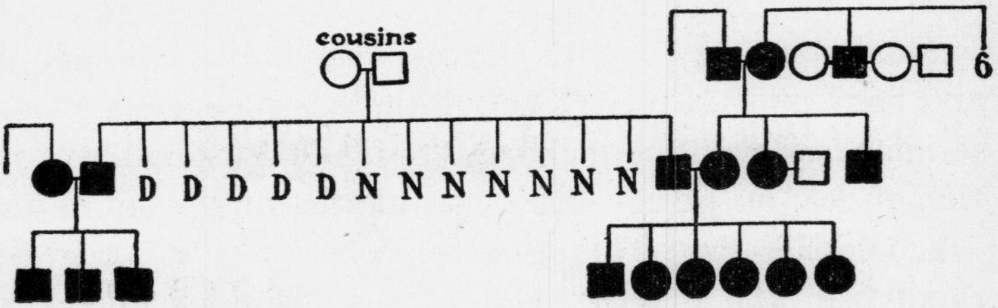

Fig. 98.—Pedigree of deaf mutism. In the first generation 2 hearing cousins marry. They have 14 children of whom 7 are dead. Two of these marry deaf wives belonging to fraternities with other cases of deafness. Of 9 children, altogether, all are deaf. Fay, 1898, No. 7.

by Fay only 5 resulted in deaf offspring. It is quite likely that in some even of these five matings the normal parent had unknown deaf relatives.

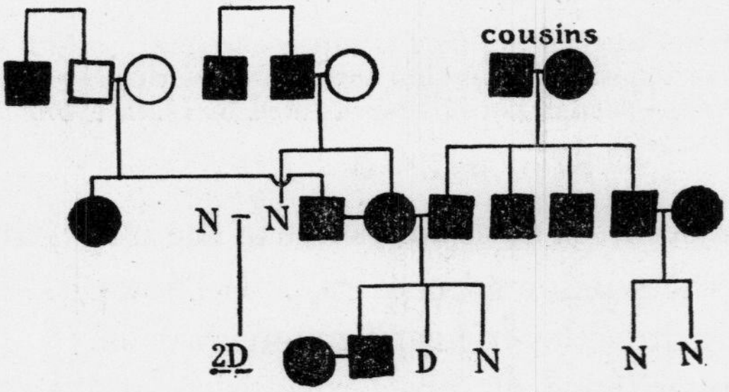

Fig. 99.—Pedigree of deaf mutism. Two deaf mutes, first cousins, marry and have 4 children, all deaf mutes. One of these marries a wife whose father, an uncle and two nephews or nieces were deaf mutes, and two out of three children were deaf mutes. Another child of the original pair married a deaf mute and had two hearing children. Fay, 1898. Nos. 3292, 2260, 442, 3290, 3291, 3234.

But if the hearing partner have deaf relatives then the proportion of resulting fraternities containing deaf mutes increases to 35 per cent.

Even though both partners hear, if they belong to the same strain with a tendency to deafness the liability to deaf offspring is so high as to warrant warning strongly against such a marriage (Fig. 99).

Finally if one or both partners are adventitiously deaf and have no deaf relatives then there is no eugenic obstacle to marriage, for such marriages result in a negligible proportion of deaf offspring—in Fay's statistics only 2 out of 552.

b. Otosclerosis.—This disease consists of a progressive rigidity of the mucous coat of the tympanic membrane;

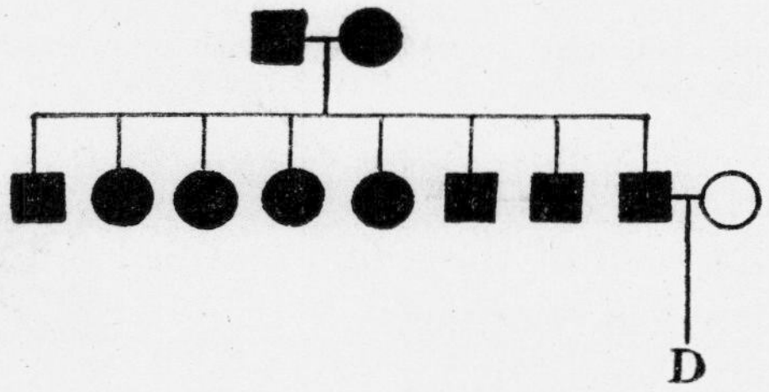

FIG. 100.—Pedigree of "fistula auris congenita." Both of the original pair were affected with a congenital aural fistula, with a fistulous canal anterior and close to the ear; all persons represented by black symbols had a similar fistula. HARTMAN, p. 56.

usually associated with adhesions in the inner ear and alterations of the windows (fenestra). It shows itself in an ever increasing difficulty in hearing conversation.

The inheritance of otosclerosis is a familiar fact. Most persons know families many of whose members become "hard of hearing" as they grow older. The deafness is frequently attributed to climatic causes and this belief is increased by the presence of many cases in the same locality. But it will be found on inquiry that the affected persons are relatives and that their unrelated neighbors are not affected by the same climate. This makes it clear that a severe climate merely brings out the latent weakness of the mucous lining of the ear. Some examples of strains showing otosclerosis are given in Figures 101–104.

An examination of the available pedigrees indicates that otosclerosis is due to a defect—perhaps to the absence of a resistance to infection and inflammation of the lining membrane of the inner ear. Like other defects it is relatively common in the progeny of cousin marriages.

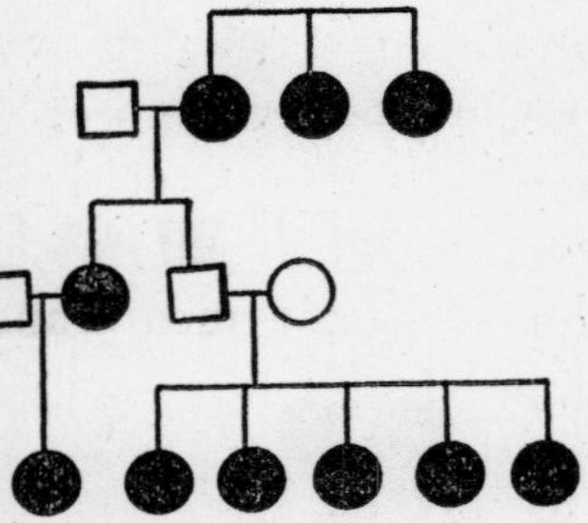

FIG. 101.—Pedigree of otosclerosis. In this pedigree all affected individuals, so far as known, are females. LUCÆ, 1907.

The eugenic indications then are, two persons with a tendency towards otosclerosis should refrain from marrying, as probably all of their children will he hard of hearing. But a person with otosclerosis and an unaffected person of an untainted strain may marry with impunity as their children will probably all have strong hearing.

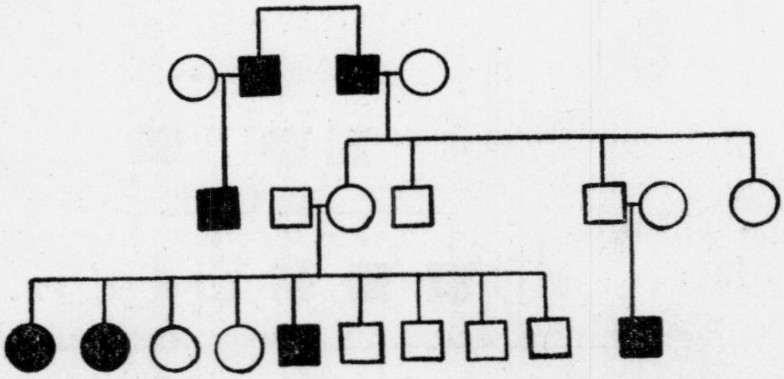

FIG. 102.—Pedigree of a family with otosclerosis. Two deaf brothers marry; one has a single son, who is deaf; the other has four unaffected children. Of these latter two marry consorts who are, so far as known, normal. From one pair three out of nine children are affected; from the other only one child is known and he is hard of hearing. HAMMERSCHLAG, 1906.

c. Catarrhal affections.—That a weakness of the mucous membranes permitting catarrh is hereditary, we shall see in speaking of the weakness of mucous membranes in general, and it cannot be doubted that such a weakness plays a rôle in deafness. Thus Bell (1906) has shown that, in the census returns, over 55 per cent of the deaf children in the country come from parents who became deaf in adult life and he states that this "confirms the conclusion reached upon other grounds that heredity sometimes plays a part in the production of catarrh of the middle ear—the chief cause of deafness occurring in middle life."

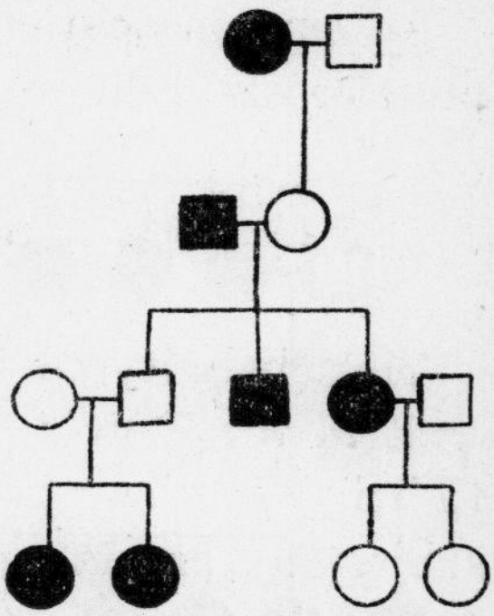

FIG. 103.—Pedigree of otosclerosis. Affected persons (black symbols) for the most part, but by no means always, have an affected parent. LUCÆ, 1907.

29. SKIN DISEASES

The skin is an admirable organ for the protection of the delicate internal parts not only from desiccation but also from the entrance of the numerous parasites that thrive on mammal-

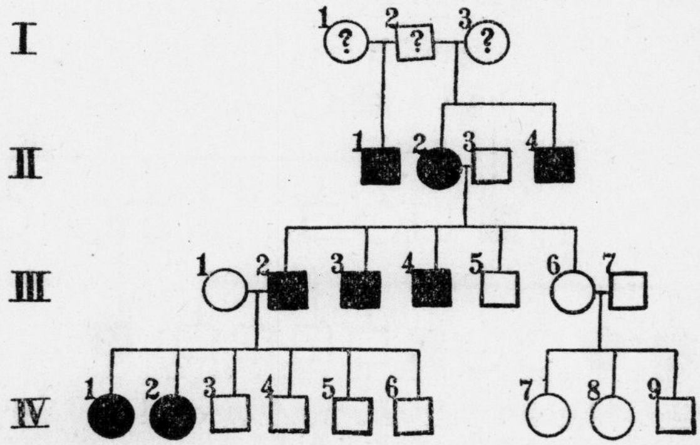

FIG. 104—Pedigree of otosclerosis. The condition of hearing in the first generation is unknown and some of the children in the fourth generation have not reached the age of incidence; thus, IV, 4–6. are 22 to 18 years old and IV, 7–9, are 20 to 14 years.

ian blood and tissues. Nevertheless, its exposed position renders it liable to attack by the various germs that are ubiquitous. Abrasions and the openings of the sebaceous glands and the hair follicles offer vulnerable points. The main reliance of the organism must be its internal means of defense. The efficiency of specific means of resistance is undoubtedly an inherited quality. We find families characterized by low resistance to specific germs of particular diseases.

Thus liability to boils and eczema appears as a family trait in the Dow–1 family. One of the parents is subject to boils and the other to eczema. Of five children three are subject to eczema and one to boils. It seems probable that we are here dealing with a lack of resistance to infection through the skin in both parents, leading to a non-resistance in all of the children. A few cases of inheritance of more specific types of skin diseases are cited below.

a. **Congenital Traumatic Pemphigus** (epidermolysis bullosa).—The children are born with a liability to form fluid filled vesicles after the smallest physical provocation. The excessive vulnerability shows itself in the first month of life and is said to diminish from 40 to 50 years of age and to cease altogether in old age. It is strongly hereditary, often through several generations (5 in Bonajuti's case); it shows also a prevalence in particular families and is rather more frequent in males than females. The slightest injury, blow, pressure, friction or scratching is followed by the formation of a bulla. The bullae are often full of blood and of large size, 5 centimeters or more across and their shape may be irregular instead of round or oval depending upon the nature of the injury. Fingers and nails are often deformed or altogether destroyed. The pathology of the disease is obscure; it seems to be influenced by arsenic (Radcliffe-Crocker, 1903, p. 293).

The case described by Bonajuti is given in Fig. 105. Of an affected parent about half the offspring are affected. Two normal parents usually produce only normal offspring. In case the single known parent is normal and has affected offspring it is presumed that the unknown spouse was affected. On the whole, epidermolysis seems to be due to the presence of a distinct factor, absence of which results in normality.

The eugenic teaching is then that two normals belonging to such a family as that of Fig. 105 may marry with impunity

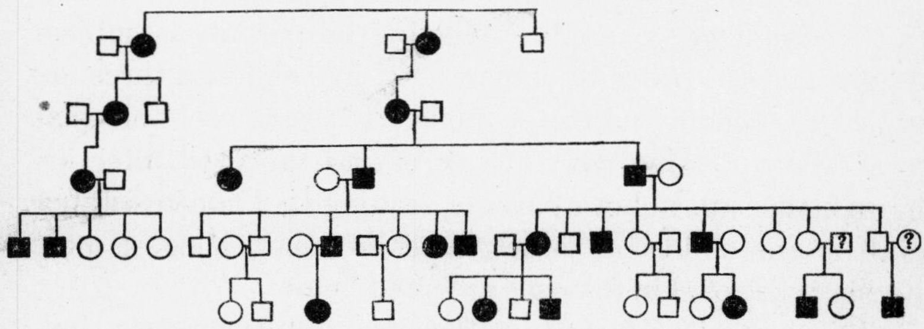

Fig. 105.—Pedigree of a family showing epidermolysis bullosa, behaving like a dominant trait—appearing in each generation. Only in two instances, at the right of the chart, does a case arise from a parent not known to have the trait. Gossage, after Bonajuti.

but that in the case of parents who have, or had in childhood, epidermolysis probably at least half of the children will be similarly affected.

b. Psoriasis (itch).—The question of the inheritability of this disease has been much discussed. Some declare it is due to infection, others deny it. Various experiments have been tried. Schamberg (1908) performed auto-inoculation in 23 cases and got a positive result in only 3. Inoculation into normal human subjects—usually the experimenter's own body—have produced the disease in only one case (that of Dr. Destot). On the other hand in about a third of the cases observed by various physicians psoriasis was recognized as a family disease. The most reasonable explanation is that the disease is due to a parasite to which most persons are immune; and that lack of immunity is an inheritable trait.

Besides skin diseases due to infection there are other abnormal conditions consisting of irregularities or exaggera-

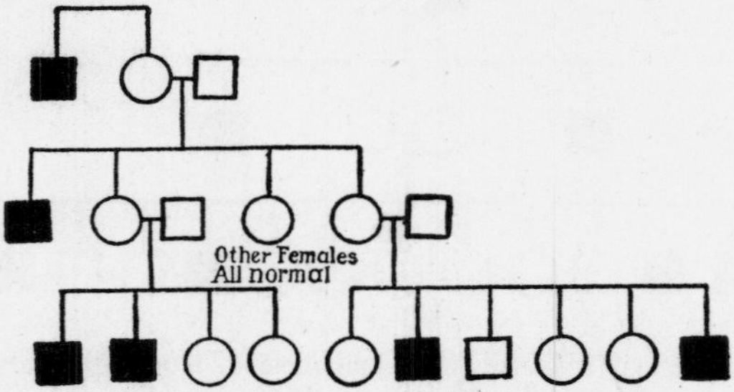

FIG. 106.—Pedigree of ichthyosis. All affected persons are from non-affected females. BRAMWELL, 1903, p. 77.

tions of the process of rendering the outer layer of the skin horny. The liability to these diseases is usually recognized to be hereditary.

c. **Ichthyosis** or **xerosis** (xeroderma).—This is a dryness of the skin in which plates are formed like the scales of a fish. The disease is remarkable because, apparently, it is sometimes limited in heredity by sex and sometimes not,—in different families. At least, in two of the pedigrees (Figs. 106, 108) males only are affected and inheritance is through a normal female. But in other cases (Figs. 107, 109) the females seem to be affected equally with the males and the peculiar skin condition is transmitted either by normal or by affected females. Ichthyosis is especially apt to be found in families in which consanguineous marriages occur and this fact, together with the pedigrees,

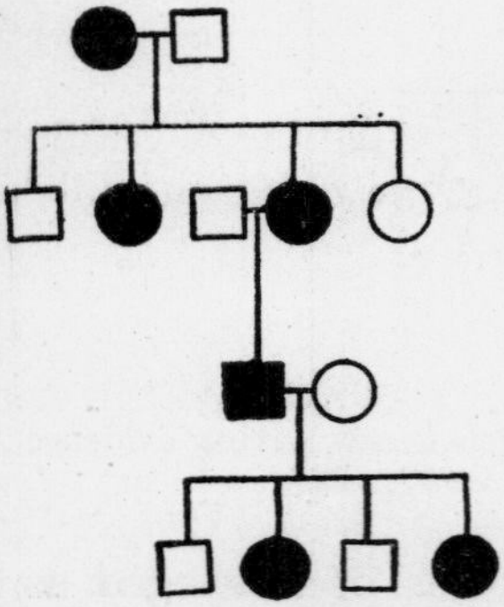

FIG. 107.—Pedigree of ichthyosis, behaving like a positive trait. BRAMWELL, 1903.

suggests that it is due to the absence of some factor that controls the process of cornification of the skin. On this hypothesis a normal person who belongs to an affected family

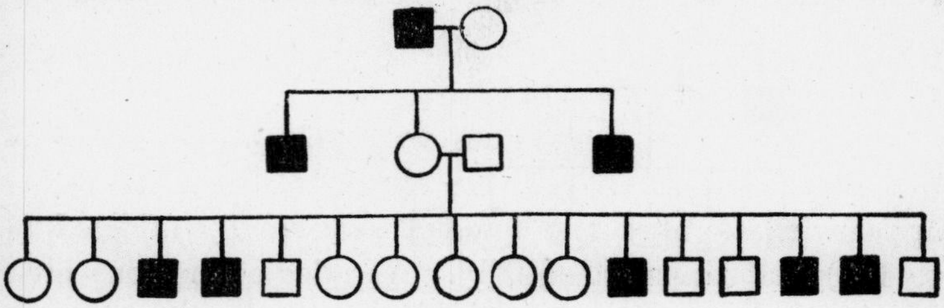

FIG. 108.—Pedigree of a family with ichthyosis. Note that only males are affected. BOND, 1905.

may marry into a normal family with impunity, but cousin marriages are to be avoided.

d. **Thickening of the outer layer of the skin** is a disease that is closely related to the foregoing. In the generalized

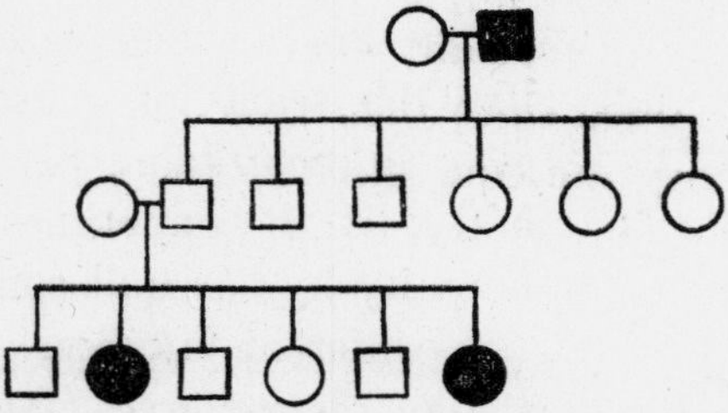

FIG. 109.—Pedigree of a family showing general ichthyosis, giving evidence that it is a positive trait. GOSSAGE, 1907, p. 342.

forms (called hyperkeratosis) infection has been alleged as a cause; but if infection plays a part it seems to be effective only where there is a susceptibility. Evidence for contagion is said to be given by the case where the only two affected children were those who, alone, were nursed by their mother, an affected woman. But, on the other hand, the fact that the mother had the disease proves her susceptibility.

Finally, the peculiar thickening of the palm of the hand and the plantar surface of the foot known as *Tylosis* seems to follow the same rule as keratosis of which it is only a special case. Both males and females are affected and two normal parents, even of an affected family, rarely transmit the defect (Figs. 110, 111).

The records of 45 families with this abnormality have been studied by Gossage. In the 39 that can be used, it appears that males and females are equally affected (166 to 140) and transmit equally. As affected persons always mate with normals, affected offspring are always simplex and expectation is that half of their offspring shall be abnormal. In 28 families 222 children are abnormal and 184 normal. Only one exception appears to the rule that two normal parents have only normal children.

30. Epidermal Organs

Heredity in these organs may be considered under the four heads of glands, hair, nails and teeth. The inclusion of teeth is justified since their true epidermal origin is now recognized; they are equivalent to the scales of fishes, but, in the higher animals, including man, they are confined to the mouth and jaws. On account of the close interrelationship of these four types of organs a modification of one may mean a change in all, and so it is not possible in discussing one of them always to avoid a consideration of another.

a. The Skin Glands are principally the sebaceous and sweat glands, associated functionally with the hair and morphologically with the milk glands. The latter are usually reduced to two in man but cases of supernumerary mammae are not exceedingly rare. This condition is doubtless hereditary for Leichtenstern (1878) refers to the case of a woman with three mammae on the chest who bore a daughter who in turn also had three mammae (though the additional

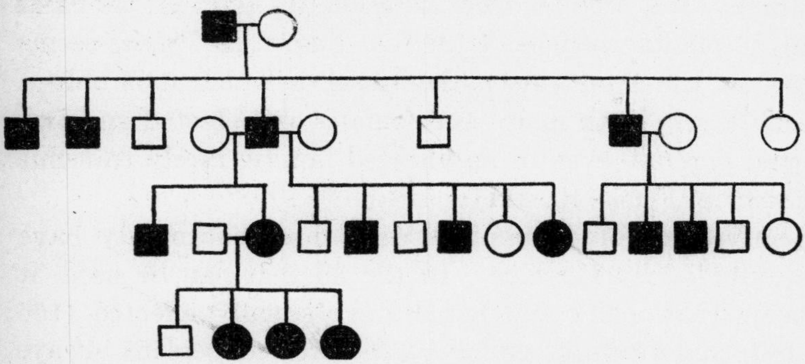

FIG. 110.—Pedigree of a family with tylosis (black symbols). Note that all affected persons have at least one parent affected—showing that tylosis is due to a positive determiner. UNNA, 1883.

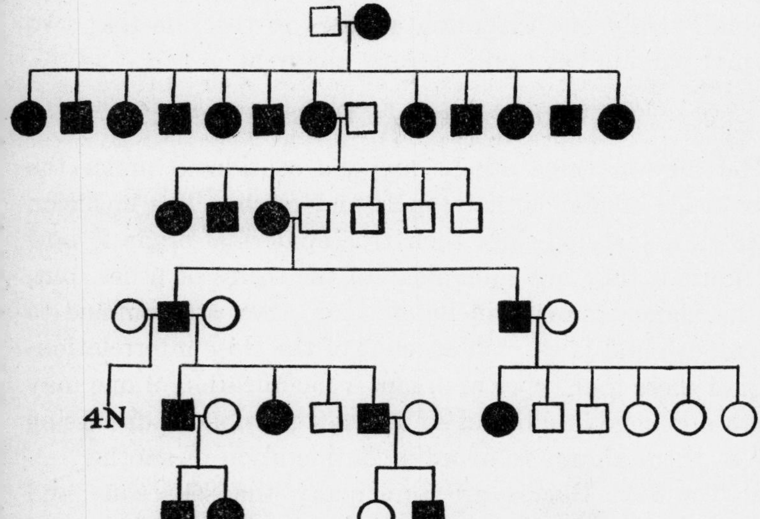

FIG. 111.—Pedigree of a family with tylosis palmae plantaris (black symbols)—proof of its positive nature. 4*N*, four normals. GOSSAGE, after RIZZOLI, 1907.

one was on the thigh), and Iwai (1904) cites many cases of a mother and five to one of several children who possessed supernumerary pectoral nipples.

b. Hair.—Peculiarities of hair, apart from pigmentation are not infrequent as family traits. Thus a family with curled, woolly hair is described by Gossage, the curly condition being clearly dominant over its absence. Hair may be entirely absent even from birth. Such a case is described by Molenes (1890). There was brought to him a girl of 4 years who was hairless from birth until 19 months old. She had a brother who was bald at six and the mother lost her hair at 19. Another case, described in the Medi-chirurgical Transactions, is that of a boy of three who was nearly bald. His sisters had normal hair but his mother had complete alopecia areata from the age of six.

A third case is that described by White who knew a family that came from France to Canada. One grandfather was nearly hairless and the nails were faulty; the parents were normal; but in the next generation of 6 sons and 2 daughters one daughter was almost hairless and the nails abnormal in her and in two sons. This daughter married (presumably a normal man) and had a son who at 19 retains on his scalp the nearly invisible downy coat with which he was born. His only sister has a thick downy scalp-covering quite different from normal hair. One of the uncles of these children has a son of 9 and a daughter of 4; the latter was born entirely without hair or nails. The data are not very full but the fact that normals carry the trait indicates that it may be accompanied by a definite defect in the germ plasm. Baer describes a family of ten children of two normal parents of which one was born hairless and has continued so while three were born with heavy hair but lost it; in two cases at 14 days and in one at 9 months.

The *form of the hair* may show family peculiarities. Thus, in some cases, it is thickened at intervals resembling a string of beads—hence called "monilithrix." A pedigree of a family of this sort has been recorded by Anderson (Fig. 112). Unaffected parents apparently yield only normals and abnormal parents are usually simplex, so that about half of the offspring have the new character.

The facts of inheritance of curliness have been considered on page 35.

Hair-coat Color.—Ordinarily the hair of the scalp is of uniform color but in man, no less than in horses, a piebald condition is possible. This shows itself in locks of white hair in the midst of a prevailing brown or red. This spotted condition is due to a definite positive factor, even as in the coat of mice, and two parents who lack spotted hair-coat will have only uniform-coated children. This is illustrated

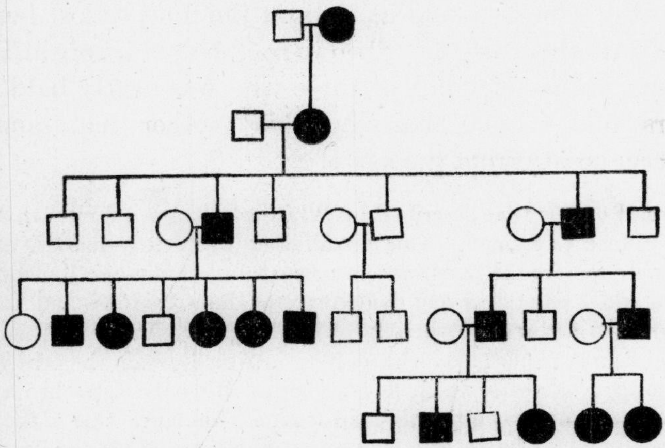

FIG. 112.—Inheritance of monilithrix—a positive character. Black symbols represent affected individuals. ANDERSON.

in the pedigree (Fig. 113) from Gossage. The hair-coat also varies in thickness and that this quality runs in families can hardly be doubted (Fig. 114).

c. **Nails.**—Hereditary nail defects are almost always associated with hair defects, as in the cases of hair peculiarities already described. One family pedigree must suffice for nail and hair defect (Fig. 115).

d. **Teeth.**—As is well known each half of either jaw has typically 2 incisors, 1 canine, 2 bicuspids and 3 molars. To this formula there are, however, exceptions and these exceptional conditions may run in families. Thus McQuillen records a family in which father, son and grandson lacked the lateral incisors of the upper jaw, a second son had them exceedingly dwarfed and some of *his* children had them so stunted that they were unsightly. The absence of the last

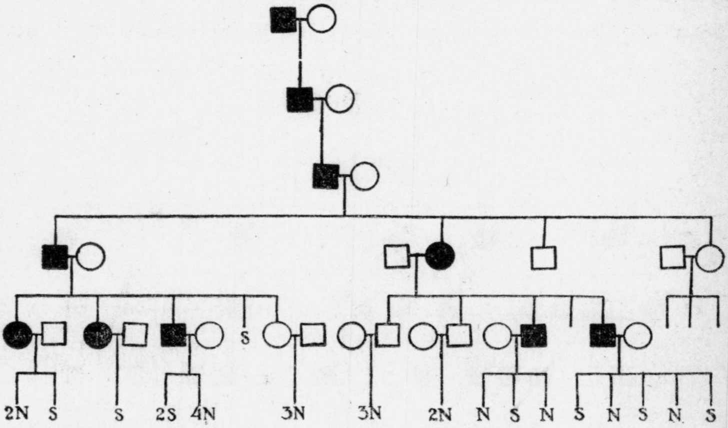

FIG. 113.—Pedigree chart, showing inheritance of spottedness in human hair covering—"congenital lock of white hair." Affected persons in black symbols. *S*, spot in hair-coat, sex unknown. GOSSAGE, after RIZZOLI.

molar is perhaps the commonest variation but no good evidence of its extended occurrence in families is at hand.

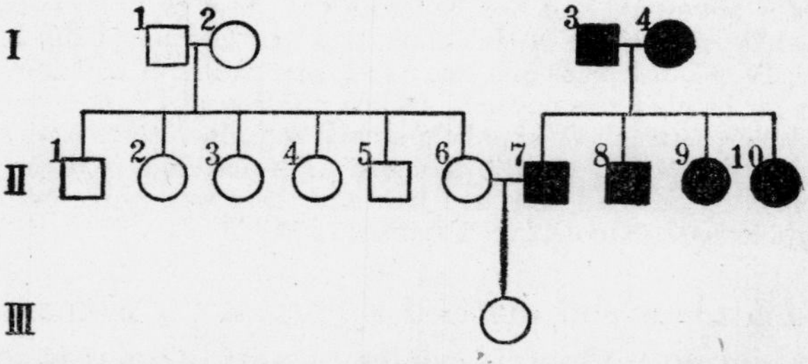

FIG. 114.—Pedigree of heavy hair-coat. I, 3, heavy growth of hair on head and face; I, 4, heavy growth of hair on head; II, 7, 8, heavy growth of hair on head and face; II, 9, 10, heavy growth of hair on head. F. R.; Tin. 1.

Entire absence of teeth is occasionally found as a family trait—there are said to be several such families in America but they have not yet been studied in detail. Guilford

(1883) records the case of a woman who never had teeth nor hair. Her sister was normal but her son was edentulous, and hairless. The sister (by an undescribed consort) had 18 children who grew up. Of these, one is edentulous while some of the others have failed to erupt all of their teeth.

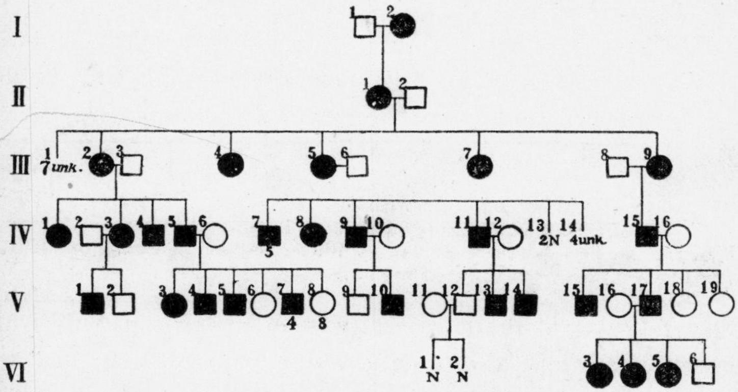

FIG. 115.—Pedigree of a family with peculiarities of hair and nails. I, 2, wife of PIROUT, poorly nourished nails and hair; II, 1 wife of QUIMBEL, *born* Rouen, 1775, poorly nourished nails and hair; III, 2, mar. DELAF, bald with bad nails; III, 4, bald, bad nails; III, 5, DELAU, bald, bad nails; III, 7, bald, bad nails; III, 9, bald, bad nails; IV, 1, bad nails; IV, 3, bald and bad nails; IV, 4, chestnut hair, bad nails; IV, 5, bald and bad nails; IV, 7, stands for 5 boys who were bald and had bad nails; IV, 8, a girl who is bald and has bad nails; IV, 9, rachitic in childhood, bad hair and nails; IV, 11, bad nails and hair; IV, 15, bad nails and hair; V, 1, had bad nails and hair, he died insane but his brother was normal. Of the children of IV, 5, 6, three had bad nails and hair, four (V, 7) were bald as well and nine others were normal. Of the children of IV, 11, 12, two had bad nails and hair. Of the children of IV, 15, 16, two had bad nails and hair and there were three granddaughters similarly affected. NICOLLÉ et HALIPRÉ, 1895.

The edentulous son married a normal (?) woman and had eight children. One, 14 years of age, who was examined, had many teeth undeveloped; another, at 16 years of age, had only 14 teeth when 28 were to be expected. Further data are necessary to determine whether or not imperfect development of the dental arcade is due to a genuine defect in the germ plasm.

Abnormalities in excess number of teeth are also found. Tomes refers to the occurrence of "well defined additional lingual cusps in the upper molar" in both "father and his

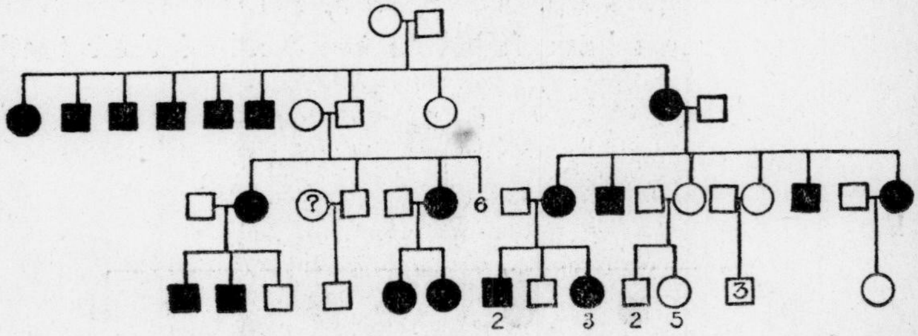

Fig. 116.—Pedigree of family with faulty enamel of the teeth—"brown teeth." Numbers below, or inside of, symbols indicate the number of individuals of the sex and condition of teeth. With one possible exception affected persons have at least one affected parent. Spokes, 1889.

children." An American family with whom the writer has corresponded has a double set of permanent teeth as a family trait.

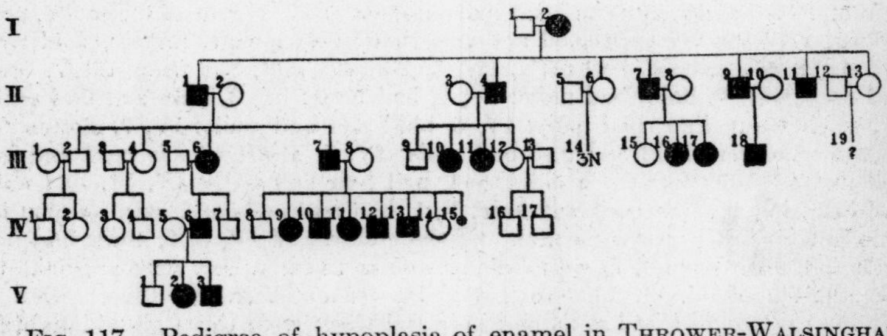

Fig. 117.—Pedigree of hypoplasia of enamel in Thrower-Walsingham-Chessum family of Ware, England. I, 2, original parents of strain; II, 1, at the age of 84 two stunted teeth in the upper jaw; III, 6, two stunted upper teeth; III, 7, at 51 years has the fourth upper right and fifth lower teeth broken down; IV, 6, some teeth never erupted; some broken down; IV, 9, at 30 some teeth small, some never erupted. This dental peculiarity appears only in the offspring of an affected parent, consequently it is a positive trait. Turner, 1907.

More complete are the studies made on families with *faulty enamel* of the teeth. In Fig. 116 is given the case of "brown teeth" due to faulty enamel. In Fig. 117 is given

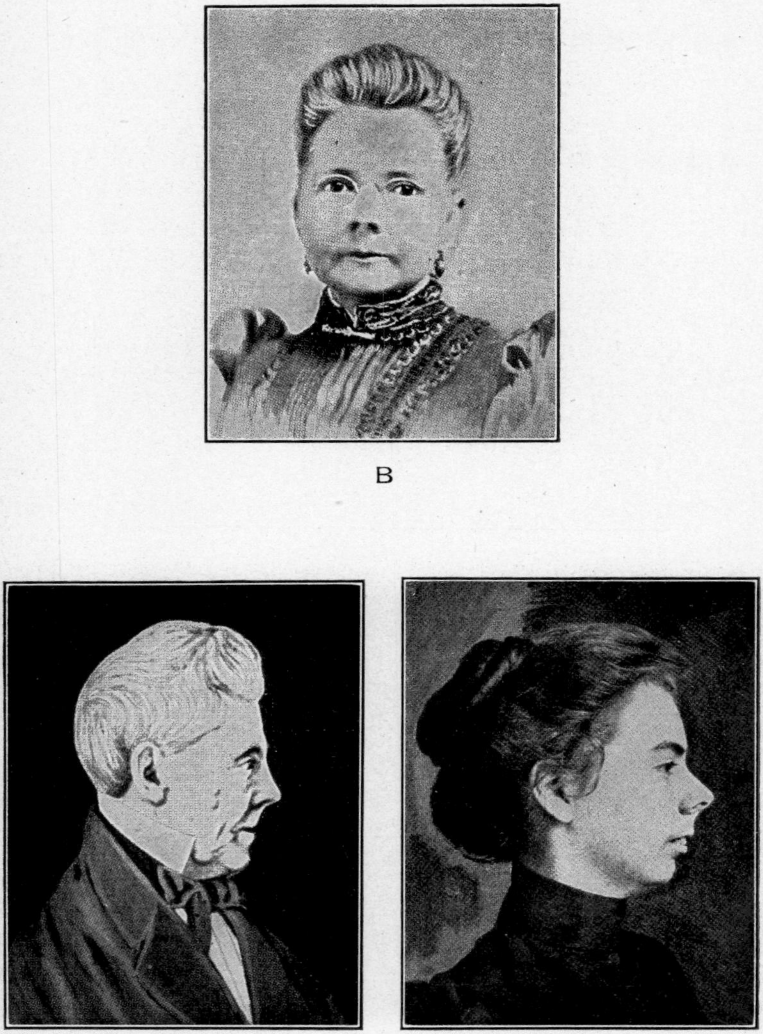

FIG. 118.—A case of reappearance of peculiarities in the features of three generations; namely, upturned nose and receding lower jaw. *A*, the grandfather; *B*, his daughter; *C*, his granddaughter. V. H. JACKSON, Orthodontia, 1904.

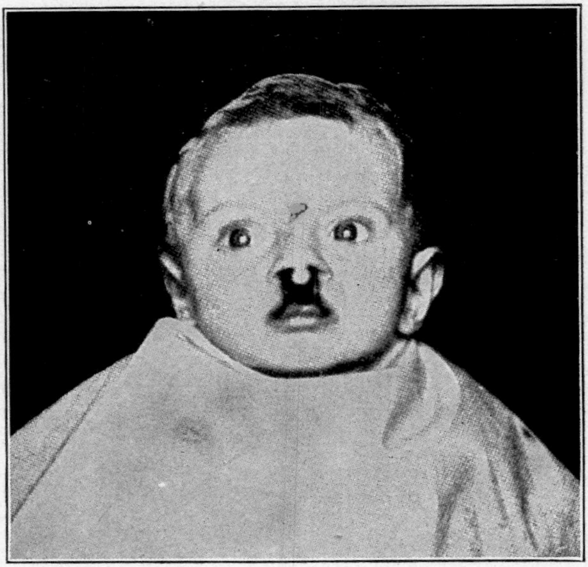

FIG. 119.—Case of harelip at one year of age. R. W. MURRAY, "Harelip and Cleft Palate," 1902.

a second case of insufficient enamel together with failure of some teeth to erupt. In these cases the abnormal condition seems to be due to some additional factor, inhibiting, as it were, the normal development of the enamel.

There is a close relation between the form of the jaw and peculiarities of dentition. That the form of the jaw is inheritable is nicely shown in figure 118.

e. Harelip and Cleft Palate.—These are intimately associated deformities, due to a more or less complete failure of the foundations of the upper jaw, which are paired, to grow completely to the middle line of the roof of the mouth. If the failure to close is in front harelip results, if behind cleft palate or merely cleft uvula. Occasionally both cleft palate and harelip may be present (Fig. 119).

A number of fairly extended pedigrees have been published (Rischbieth, 1909) yet they are not as critical as one would like (Figs. 120, 121), particularly, the consorts are

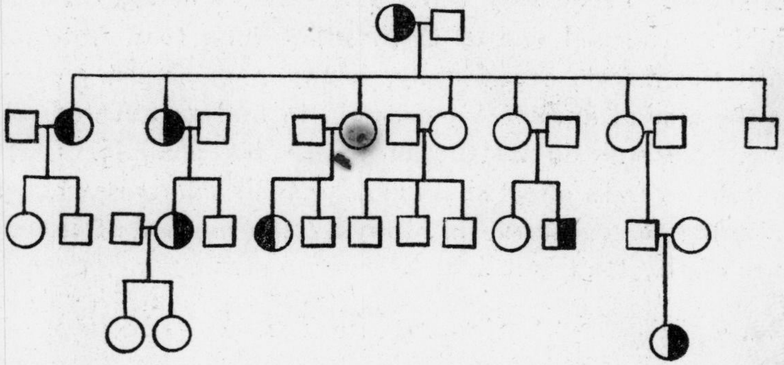

FIG. 120.—Pedigree of a family with harelip (right half of symbol dark) and cleft palate (left half dark). Frequently the affected persons descend from affected parents. APERT, 1907, after SCHMITZ.

rarely given. One can say, however, that the defect seems not to be sex-limited. So often are some of the children

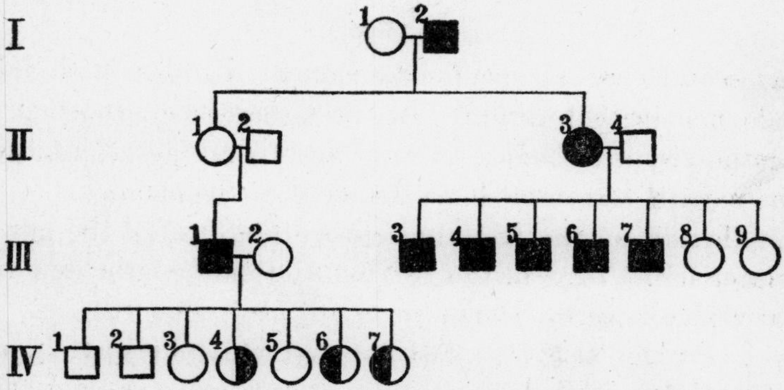

FIG. 121.—Pedigree of harelip (solid black symbol) and cleft palate (half black symbol). The type of defect is not constant. I, 2, simple fissure; II, 3, bilateral fissure; III, 1, palatine fissure; III, 3–7, lip fissures; IV, 4, harelip with cleft palate; IV, 6, 7, palate cleft without harelip. This particular pedigree is interesting because of an alternation of the affected sex in successive generations. SCHMITZ, 1904.

of one affected parent defective that the first impression is that the trait is dominant. But, if so, two normals should not have affected offspring—but this is just what is alleged commonly to happen. These cases, however, deserve careful study. Frequently when both parents of the defective child are normal one of them will belong to a fraternity with the defect; occasionally, however, one must go back to the second ancestral generation to find an affected relative. No eugenic instruction is, as yet possible. Correspondence from affected persons, or their relatives, who will volunteer to coöperate in studying the method of inheritance of this trait is solicited.

31. Cancer and Tumor

The question of "inheritance of cancer" has been much discussed and nothing but difference of opinion has resulted. This is largely due to the bad formulation of the problem. In the first place, if, as seems probable, the stimulus to cancer growth is an inoculable something—germ or ferment—it does not follow that the consequence of stimulus is not determined by an inheritable factor. It is known that certain strains or families of mice are uninoculable while others will acquire cancer upon inoculation. The question is, are there human strains that are easily and others with difficulty inoculable? The whole question is complicated by the fact that cancer is a disease of middle or later life. Thus in the census for 1900 we find that the heavy incidence of deaths from cancer occurs between 40 and 80 years (84.4%). The detailed distribution is shown in Table X. Here we see that the death rate of cancer (as compared with deaths from all causes) reaches its highest point at between 50 and 60 years, but that absolutely more deaths occur from that disease between 60 and 70 years. On account of this heavy mortality late in life many who are inoculable never reveal the fact, owing to their death before the cancer age. If cancer is communicable,

TABLE X

DISTRIBUTION OF DEATHS FROM CANCER IN AGE GROUPS

At death period	40–49	50–59	60–69	70–80
Per cent of all deaths from cancer	17.1	24.4	25.8	17.1
Proportion of cancer deaths to all deaths at that age period	8.3	11.2	10.1	7.0

like typhoid fever, still not all who are non-resistant will die from cancer because some will not become inoculated. The answer to the question of the "heredity of cancer" is not to be sought in mass statistics—in the correlation of

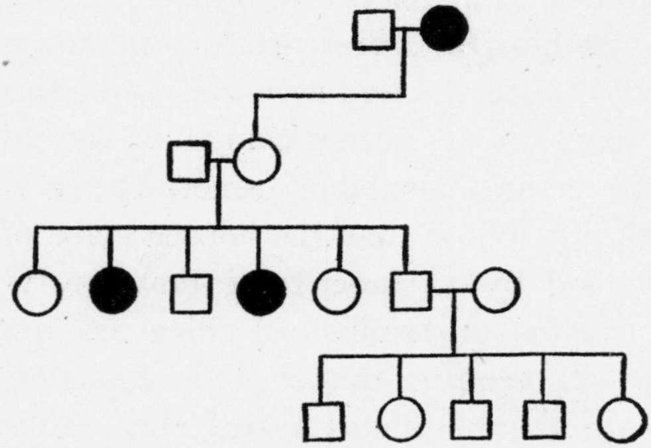

FIG. 122.—Pedigree of cancer. In the first generation cancer is admitted. In the second it is not known to have occurred, but the father died at 71 of a somewhat mysterious disease. In the third generation were two cases of cancer (one "bone cancer"). The fourth generation contains persons who are still young.

deaths from cancer between parents and children, but only by a careful analysis and comparison of individual families. One then sees in many families no deaths from cancer among 10 to 20 persons dying at cancer age, while in other families there will be 2 or 3 or even 4 deaths from cancer among those dying at the cancer age (Fig. 122). Thus in a pedigree that lies before me, half of those who have died at 35 years or over have died of cancer or tumor or have been operated on for cancer (4 cases in all) and two others have been operated on by a cancer surgeon, but details were not furnished. Two others in the family are suspected of having died of the disease. Now such families as these are by no means rare and this is the basis for the conclusion that there is a family liability to cancer.

Moreover, there is a specificity of the disease in each particular family. In one family non-resistance shows itself in the females in cancer of the breast, in another, in cancer of the uterus, in another in cancer of the intestine. Silcox (1892, Fig. 123) gives a fragment of a pedigree showing that a father, four daughters and a granddaughter all probably have sarcoma of the eyeball; and Broca records the case of a woman and three daughters who, at about the same age, possessed fibrous formation on the breast. Considering the few pedigrees of cancer families extant and the large number of organs subject to cancer these cases of cancer in the same organ strengthen materially the view of specific inheritability.

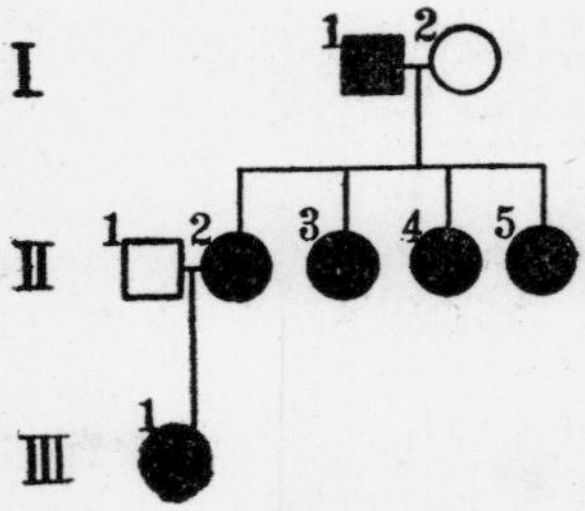

FIG. 123.—Fragment of a pedigree showing a specific inheritance of sarcoma of the eyeball. All persons indicated by black symbols are similarly affected. SILCOX, 1892.

That certain "benign" tumors are hereditary is indicated by various records in the literature. Thus Atkinson cites the case of a man whose body was covered with countless tumors varying in size from that of a canary seed to that of a pullet's egg. His sister and their father were similarly affected. The disease is not a common one in this form and this fact gives its high incidence in this family the greater weight as evidence that internal conditions have at least molded the form taken by the disease.

32. Diseases of the Muscular System

Since most muscular response is controlled by the nervous system it is frequently difficult to determine whether a peculiarity of muscular response is due chiefly to the one organ or the other. The classification of these diseases is therefore somewhat arbitrary.

a. Thomsen's Disease is a rather rare one in most localities. It is characterized by lack of tone and prompt re-

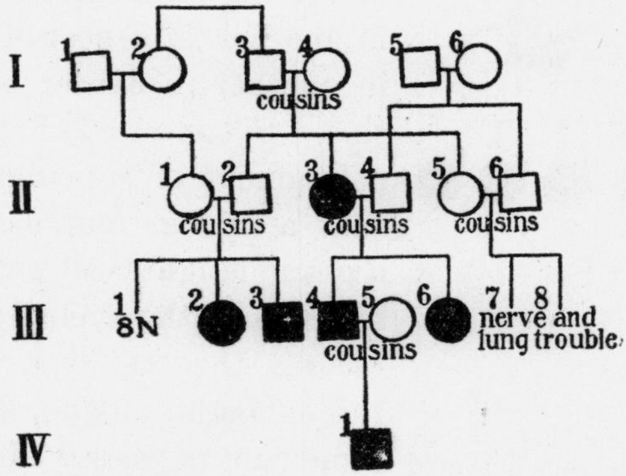

Fig. 124.—Pedigree of Thomsen's disease. Appears in cousin marriages even from unaffected parents; hence due to a defect. Bernhardt, 1885.

sponsiveness in the voluntary muscles. A striking pedigree has been recorded by Thomsen (Fig. 124). It shows a remarkable reappearance of the disease in the offspring of cousin marriages and this indicates that the disease is due to some sort of a defect whose nature has yet to be elucidated. The clear eugenic advice is *outmarriage*.

b. Certain Muscular Atrophies appear to be secondary to diseases of the nervous system while others seem to originate in the muscles themselves, without corresponding defects in the nervous centers. In a family described by Herringham (1885) sometimes all appendages, sometimes the arms only,

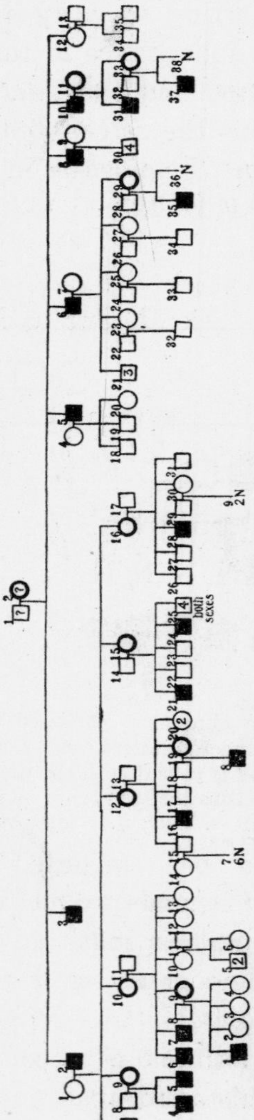

FIG. 125.—Pedigree of muscular atrophy in SEAR-FACER family of England. I, 2, said to have been crippled; II, 2, was affected in arms and legs and died at 70 of apoplexy; none of his children were affected but several of his grandchildren were; IV, 4, died of consumption, hands affected; IV, 5, had progressive weakness in legs and wasting in hands; IV, 6, has weakness and wasting in appendages; IV, 7, at 20 years, feet getting bad; a son of IV, 9, is weak on his feet at 6 years; the legs of IV, 17, began to waste at 10, hands now getting weak; 1 of the 5 children of IV, 19, is badly affected at 12 years; IV, 21, disease began at 21, feet arched; IV, 24, at 16 years, legs much wasted, feet much arched, walking difficult. Males only affected and only when they are son of unaffected fathers and simplex mothers; IV, 36, represents 4 normal persons. The other black symbols stand for affected persons, of whom no further details are given. HERRINGHAM, 1888.

underwent a slow atrophy starting as early even as the twelfth year. The method of inheritance in this family is striking. Only males are affected and they, as well as the unaffected females, may transmit the defect; but unaffected males have no affected children. Femaleness in this family is incompatible with atrophy. (Fig. 125).

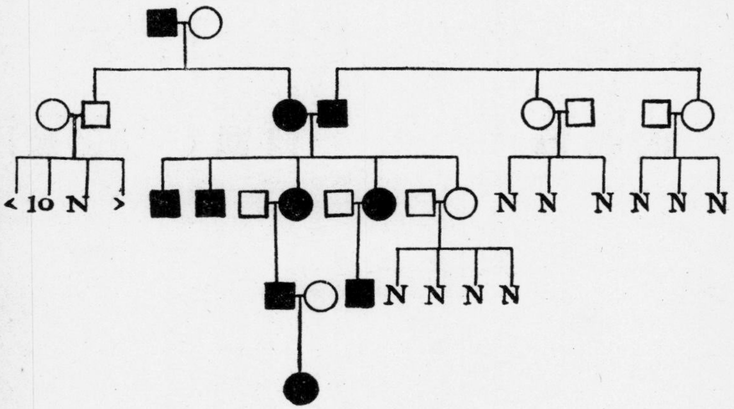

FIG. 126.—Pedigree of a family of tremblers. Affected persons (black symbols) are derived from at least 1 affected parent, and 2 normal parents have only normal offspring. Trembling is thus due to the presence of a special character. From DEBORE and RENAULT, 1891.

c. A family of *tremblers* has been recorded by Debore and Renault. In this family all normals produce only normal offspring while two affected parents may have a normal child. The pedigree deserves no great stress since details are lacking (Fig. 126).

d. Hernia.—Man's erect position is accompanied by physical dangers from which his quadruped ancestors were free, for in man the weight of the viscera has largely to be borne by the pelvis and lower abdominal wall. The erect position has subjected the muscles of the inguinal region to a peculiarly rigorous test. They often fail and an inguinal hernia is the result. Such hernias usually are consequent to a strain but the strain merely reveals, and does not cause, the weakness.

That such weakness or liability to hernia is inherited admits of little doubt. Just how, there is hardly sufficient data

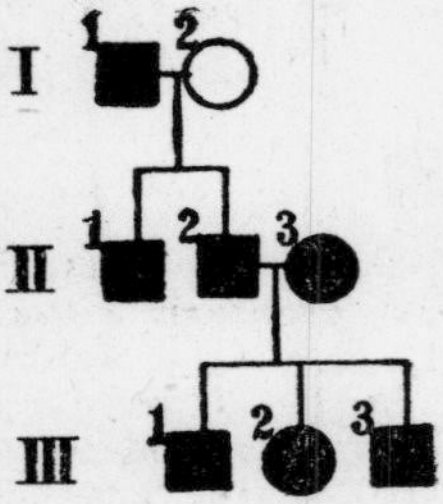

FIG. 127

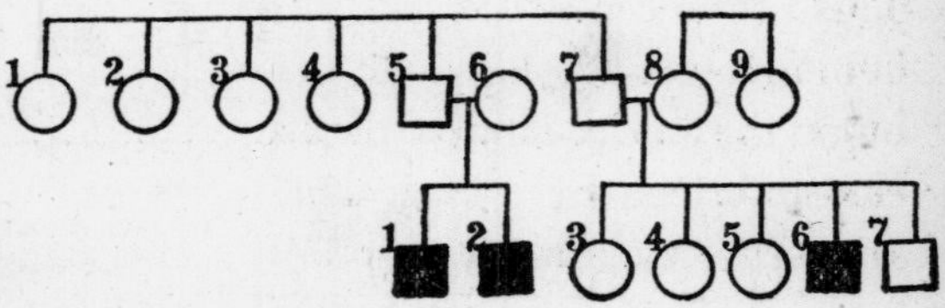

FIG. 128

FIG. 127.—Pedigree of inguinal hernia. Probably only affected persons (black) are shown. All males have a right handed scrotal hernia and both affected females have a femoral hernia. COUCH, 1895.

FIG. 128.—Pedigree of inguinal hernia (black symbols). F. R.; Rei. 3.

to determine with certainty. It is probable that a weakness from both sides of the house will yield only weak offspring. This is indicated in Figs. 127, 128; all males have a right handed scrotal hernia and both affected females have a femoral hernia.

33. DISEASES OF THE BLOOD

These are generally classified into two groups; the anemic and the hemorrhagic; in both, the evidence of an inheritable tendency is clear.

a. Of the Anemic Diseases, *chlorosis* is the commonest, is found almost exclusively in females, and occurs frequently enough in many or all of the females of one family to render it probable that eventually it will be found to accompany a distinct inheritable weakness.[1] A careful study of pedigrees is highly desirable.

[1] Potain (Article, Anemia, Dict. encycl. des sci. med.) says "The children of a chlorotic woman are often all chlorotic—and in certain cases even the male children do not escape."

b. Progressive pernicious anemia.—This is a relatively rare disease which has been little studied from the standpoint of heredity. A case described by Bramwell (1876) is suggestive (Fig. 129).

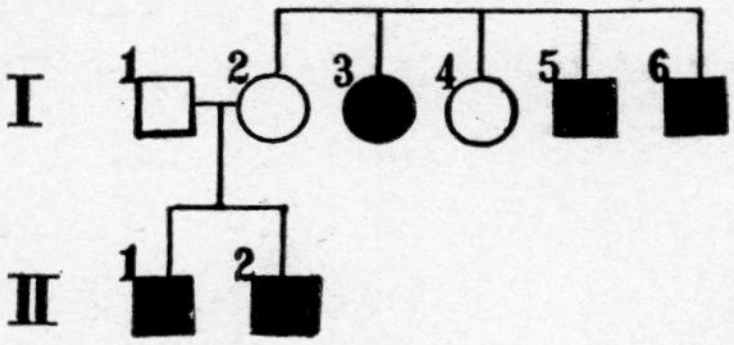

FIG. 129.—Pedigree of a family with progressive pernicious anemia. The mother, I, 2, died of cardiac weakness and chronic diarrhea; it is uncertain in how far a tendency to anemia was responsible for the result. I, 4, died of a heart trouble which was not further diagnosed. The other three members of the fraternity died of anemia. Both children, II, 1, 2, were affected with progressive anemia. BRAMWELL.

c. Nosebleed (epistaxis) — This representative of the hemorrhagic diseases of the blood may be a family disease, characterized by its frequency and severity and occasionally by its fatalness. In some of the fraternities from an affected parent all, in others about half, of the children are affected. An example is the family described by Babington (1865). Unfortunately no facts are given about consorts (Fig. 130). In this case most of the persons were violently affected. The fact that no cases are recorded from normal persons in so far raises the suspicion that the disease is due to the presence of a positive trait, which should tend to make persons having a violent form of the trait hesitate about having children.

d. Telangiectasis.—Nosebleed is often associated with red spots in the skin from which bleeding may occur. This condition is called telangiectasis; its behavior is well illustrated in Figs. 131, 132. Like epistaxis it seems to be a dominant trait, so that normal children who outmarry will probably have no affected offspring.

e. Hemophilia.—This remarkable condition is characterized by a proneness to hemorrhage and by difficulty in blood-clotting, so that a hemorrhage once started is stopped with difficulty. Families with this peculiarity (fortunately not very frequent) are known as "bleeders." In such fam-

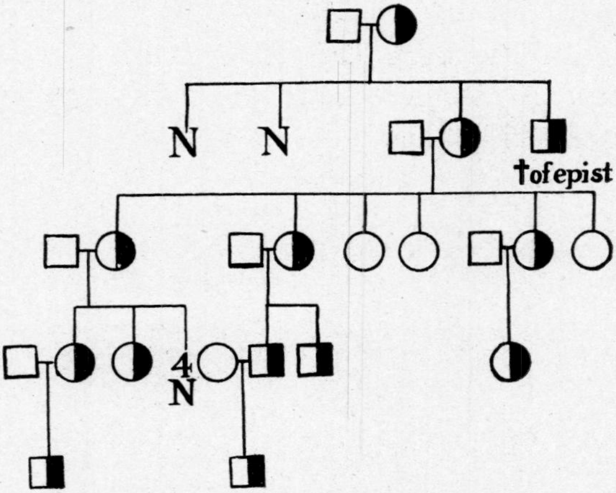

FIG. 130.—Pedigree of a family showing epistaxis or nosebleed. Affected persons indicated by half shaded symbols. All affected persons arise from an affected ancestor. *N*, normal. Consorts unknown. BABINGTON, 1865.

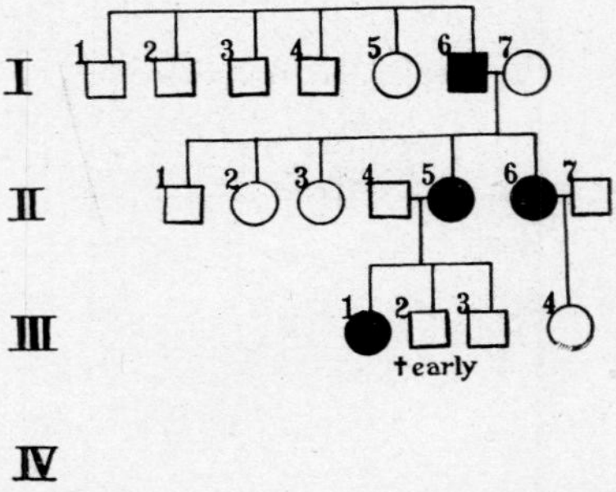

FIG. 131.—Pedigree of family showing multiple telangiectasis. Affected persons (solid black) from affected parent only. I, 6, had "spots" on face, subject to vomiting and to nosebleed, from which latter he died. II, 5, spots appeared at between 38 and 48 years, epistaxis increased and led to her death. Her daughter, III, 1, is gaining telangiectasis but the younger son at 20 years shows no sign of trouble; II, 6, has red spots that first appeared in her 27th year and are extending.

ilies there are more than fifty times as many affected males as females. In general as age advances, the severity of the hemorrhages diminishes and finally they cease altogether.

As in other diseases so in hemophilia special variants appear in particular families. Thus among some of the de-

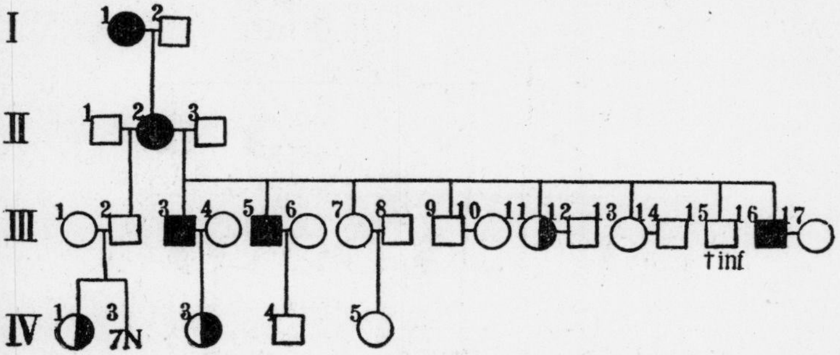

FIG. 132.—Pedigree of multiple telangiectasis. I, 1, is an English woman who was subject to epistaxis (nosebleed) and had red spots on her face; her daughter, II, 2, 60 years old, has a number of bright red angiomata distributed over face, ears, lips, tongue, mucous membrane of mouth, and inner surface of all 4 eyelids. During last 6 years has had recurrent attacks of epistaxis. By her first husband she had a son and 8 grandchildren of whom 1 suffers from epistaxis. By her second husband she had 8 children of whom III, 3, has had epistaxis since 8 years and 2 small "spider naevi" on left cheek and has a child of 11 who suffers from epistaxis; III, 5, has nosebleed and 3 small spots on cheek; his son is normal as yet; III, 11, has epistaxis; III, 16, has slight attacks of epistaxis but no spots visible. WEBER, 1907.

scendants of the early settlers of Sullivan Co., Pennsylvania, occur "nine-day bleeders." "After the wound is received, instead of healing a sort of core, of very dark color, composed mostly of coagulated blood forms in the wound, which in about nine days opens, and the blood begins to flow as if from a freshly severed artery. It usually continues to bleed about two weeks, or until the patient is thoroughly exhausted, when the "core" falls out and the wound heals. Binding up the wound does no good. The only death known to have occurred through bleeding is supposed to have been caused by binding the wound lightly to stay the flow of blood."

That hemophilia has an hereditary basis is generally conceded and the conclusion would not be weakened were a specific hemophilia germ some day demonstrated. The particular method of inheritance is well illustrated by Fig. 133 of the Sullivan County strain. The males alone are af-

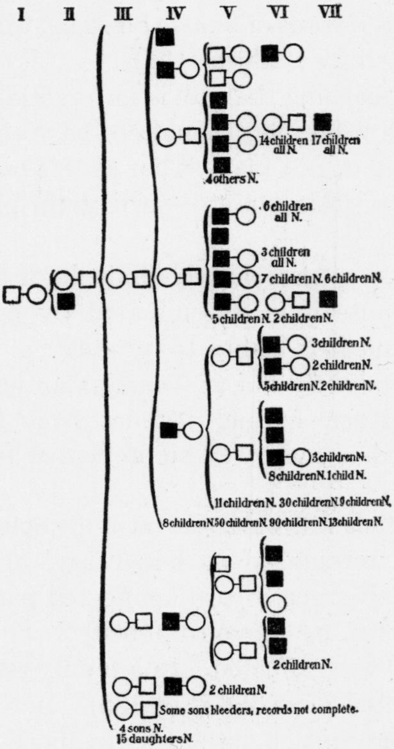

Fig. 133.—Pedigree of the Sullivan Co., Pa., bleeders. Roman numerals at top of columns indicate generations. Of the two symbols connected by a horizontal line that at the left is the direct descendant, that at the right the consort; the bracket includes their children. Only males are bleeders, and bleeding children are derived always from non-bleeding females of the family. Pardoe, 1904.

fected. No male of the family, whether affected or not has affected offspring so long as he marries outside of the family. Hence, all "bleeding" children are derived from the females of the family.

Fig. 134 gives the pedigree of the family Mampel from Kirchheim near Heidelberg (Lossen, 1905), and Fig. 135 is the pedigree of a family that settled in Carroll Co., Maryland,

and has since spread over the country. It is remarkable because it contains records of female bleeders, whose occurrence has been doubted by Bulloch (1911).

The eugenic teaching that holds for practically all families is clear. Sisters of bleeders should not have children. Males whether bleeders or not may, so far as this trait goes, marry and reproduce with impunity—their germ plasm is free of taint of hemophilia.

Hemophilia is a particularly difficult disease to control in descent because it is disseminated by normal females. On this account it is liable to produce a community of bleeders as it formerly did at Tenna, Canton Graubunden, Switzerland. Even normal females from the old world families of bleeders may well be prevented from landing in America.

f. Splenic Anemia with enlargement of the Spleen.—This condition, usually recognized as hereditary, not infrequently appears in the offspring of two unaffected parents. In such a family reported by Bovaird (1900) 2 children out of a fraternity of 10 were affected. In a family reported by Brill there were affected 3 out of 6 (Fig. 136). In both families together there were, then, 5 out of 16. In another family, when one parent is affected, of 15 children of whom details are known, 5 were certainly affected, two doubtful and 8 were normal. Of the two matings involved one is consanguineous (Wilson, 1869, Fig. 137). Though the data are still meager the result favors the view that the liability to splenic anemia is due to the absence of some factor that usually gives strength. A person having or fearing such a defect should marry into a normal strain. It may be added that Gossage (1908, p. 321) suggests that splenic anemia is due to the presence of some dominant factor so the matter must be regarded as still unsettled.

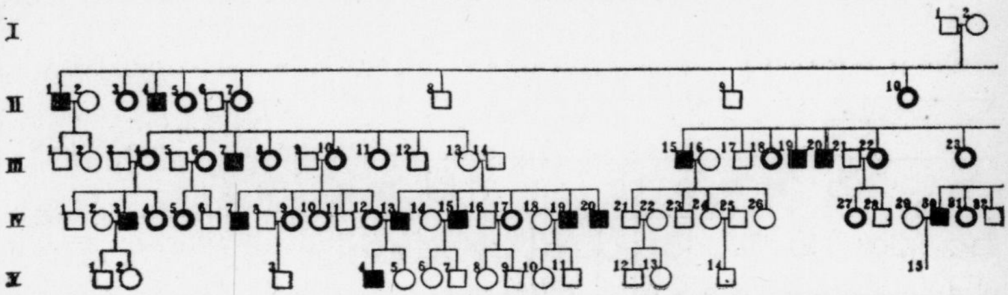

FIG. 134.—Pedigree of hemophilia in the MAMPEL family, originally of Kirchheim near Heidelberg, Germany. Black symbols indicate bleeders; it is seen that they are males only, but they, in turn, have no bleeding sons.

34. DISEASE OF THE THYROID GLAND

This may lead to a variety of effects, cretinism, goitre, myxedema, exophthalmic goitre, etc. Many of these show evidence of an inheritance of the liability to thyroid degeneracy.

a. Cretinism.—This is characterized by arrest of growth, by large pendulous abdomen, poor teeth, coarse, scanty scalp hair, mongolian face, feebly developed genitalia, and marked impairment of intelligence. The thyroid gland is often absent and a goitre frequently present. The distribution of the disease is interesting. It appears chiefly in mountainous countries where close intermarriage is more likely to occur than on the plains. Thus it abounds in Switzerland and is said to occur in some parts of Scotland. It is a cause of deportation when it occurs in immigrants to this country. That it is hereditary admits of no doubt. Aosta, at the southern base of Mount St. Bernard, was once a great breeding place of cretins, since their marriage there was permitted. For some years they have been segregated and kept from marrying and now, we are told, they are nearly all gone (Jordan, 1910).

b. Goitre.—That goitre frequently occurs repeatedly in families is well known; but in how far this is due to common sources of infection is still disputed. Buschan states that

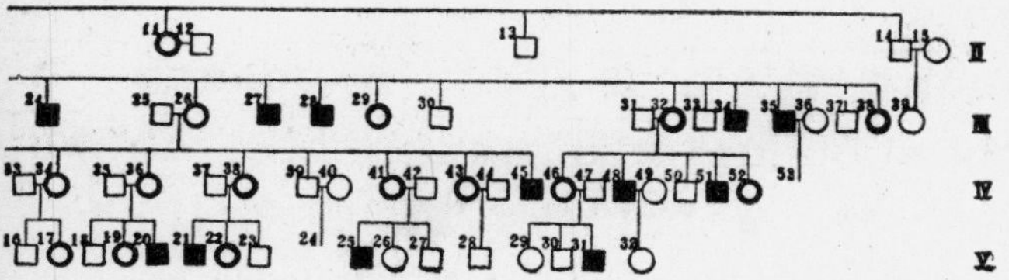

Heavy ringed circles are normal females who transmit the trait. LOSSEN, 1905. The details of LOSSEN's paper are translated in the "Treasury of Human Inheritance," Parts V and VI, pp. 267–271.

family histories of goitrous patients usually show a neuropathic ancestry. A pedigree from Buschan is given in Fig. 138.

c. **Exophthalmic Goitre.**—This peculiar condition is characterized by an enlargement of the thyroid gland, protrusion of the eyeballs, and extreme nervousness. It more commonly affects women than men. Although, in the country as a whole, it is not common yet it is more prevalent in some districts than in others, doubtless owing to the interrelationship of the members of the district with heavy incidence of the disease.

The disease is common in females; yet it is not inherited strictly in sex-limited fashion. It is, however, clearly inherited; as certainly as epilepsy, with which it is not infrequently associated. Not many family pedigrees seem, however, to have been studied (Fig. 139).

35. Diseases of the Vascular System

This system consists, in the narrow sense, of the heart, arteries and veins. Less is known about heredity of defects and diseases of such an internal system because it is so inaccessible to observation and study in the living person. Nevertheless we shall see that "blood tells" in respect to the traits of this set of organs.

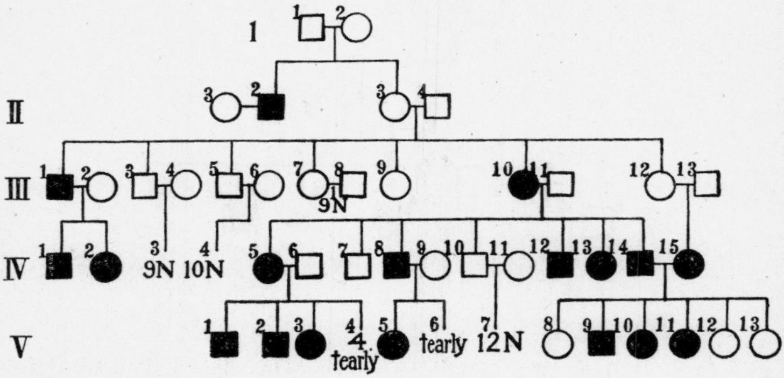

FIG. 135.—Pedigree of a family of "bleeders"—the K. family, located in and about Carroll Co., Maryland. Their son, II, 2, was a bleeder but died without issue. The eldest son, III, 1, of the daughter was a bleeder from 18 up to 45 years, "often bled till he fainted." He had 2 unaffected brothers and 3 normal sisters but 1 sister, III, 10, was "a bleeder until 40." He had a son, IV, 1, who was a very bad bleeder from 18 until toward middle life and a daughter, IV, 2, who often "bled until she fainted" and eventually died of dysentery. All 19 children of the 2 normal brothers were normal and 9 children of the normal sister, III, 7. The affected sister, III, 10, had 3 sons and 2 daughters who were affected. IV, 5, is stated to be "a bleeder" and had by an unaffected husband 2 bleeding sons and 1 bleeding daughter besides 4 others who died of scarlatina. Her brother, IV, 8, had a daughter, V, 5, who was a bleeder until 15, and then died of a hemorrhage of the lungs consequent upon tuberculosis. There were other children all of whom died young of scarlatina. The normal brother, IV, 10, had 12 normal children. The next 2 had no offspring. The youngest son, IV, 14, began to bleed while an infant, grew worse until he was 25 and has since improved. He married a cousin who is also a bleeder and they have 6 children. Three of the daughters have not bled as yet. V, 9, has been a bleeder since he was 8 months old and bleeds until he faints; V, 10, has been a bleeder since she was 8 months old and V, 11, bleeds occasionally but not very severely. Original data, contributed by Dr. J. H. STICK.

a. Heart.—That congenital heart defects are hereditary has long been known and the striking evidence for it has been brought together by Vierordt (1901). His summary deserves translating entire: "Friedberg mentions 3 sons suffering from cyanosis (due to imperfect structure of heart) from one father, 2 from his first, 1 from his second marriage; likewise Foot records 3 cases in one family; Haillet reports on 4 children with open foetal canals (in the heart)

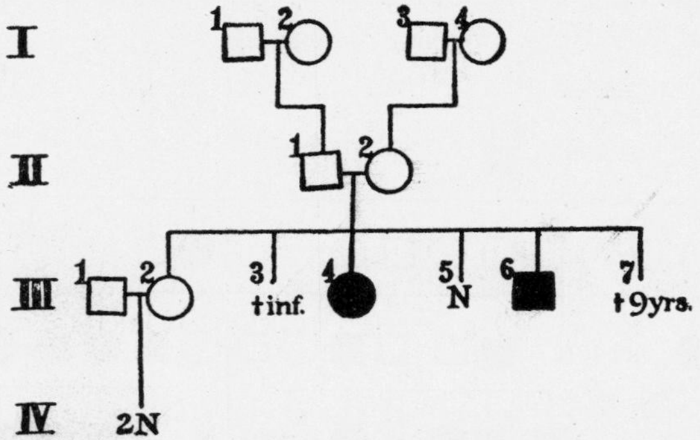

Fig. 136.—Pedigree of a family with splenic anemia. I, 1, died at 73 of gall stones; I, 2, died at 94 from a fall; I, 3, died at 72 of pneumonia; I, 4 died at 38 from childbirth; II, 1, died of pneumonia and II, 2, is in perfect health at 62 years. In the third generation all are well except that III, 3, died in infancy of diarrhea; III, 4, was well until an enlargement of the spleen occurred, which has continued; III, 6, 30 years old, suffers a continued enlargement of the spleen; and III, 7, died at 9 years of an enlargement of the spleen. Brill, 1901.

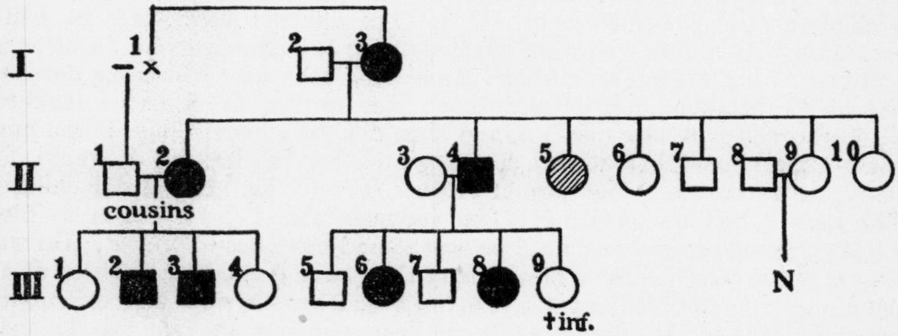

Fig. 137.—Pedigree of splenic anemia. A. P., I, 2, has a form of nervous deafness but otherwise healthy until attacked by diabetis mellitus. His wife gained sallow complexion and enlarged spleen at 33 years. Of their children one, II, 2, had enlarged spleen, at 7; she married a cousin and had 2 boys with projecting spleen. A son, II, 4, is subject to epistaxis and fainting spells; since 35 years old his spleen has been enlarged; he has 2 affected girls; II, 5, became deaf at 4; she is becoming sallow, but the spleen is not palpable. II, 6, is slightly deaf. Wilson, 1869.

from one marriage; Strehler of a rachitic woman who bore 5 cyanotic children, 3 boys and 2 girls; the father (who later died of phthisis) has by a second wife a normal daughter. In Kelly's case of transposition the mother had borne 11 children of whom one died at 5 months from congenital heart disease. In the case of Schmaltz, that of a seven year old boy, the father and father's mother had heart defect.

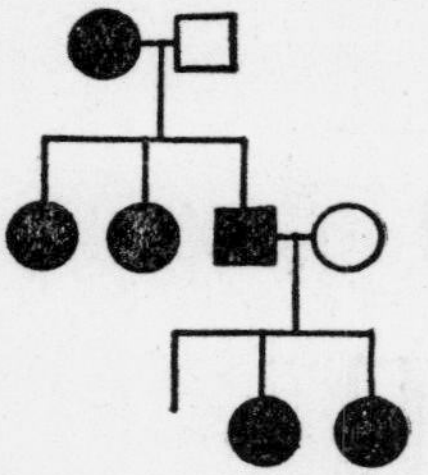

Fig. 138.—Pedigree of goitre. Affected persons come from at least one affected parent. Buschan.

The patient of Potocki who, 29 years old, died of brain abscess and had a pulmonary stenosis with closed septum and defect of the interauricular septum, descended from a mother with a congenital heart disease. Rezek observed 8 cases of heart disease in 4 generations of one family, including 2 congenital defects; the mother probably having got her heart disease from the grandmother (Fig. 140). Two sisters afflicted with ichthyosis congenita, descended, according to Leuch's report, from a mother who suffered from a defect of the bicuspid valve; the oldest

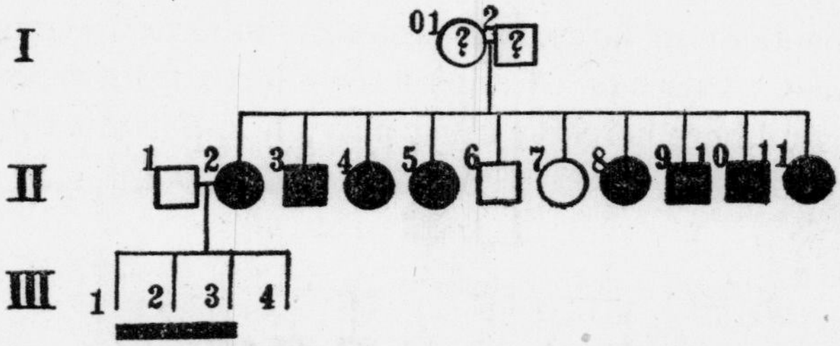

Fig. 139.—Pedigree of a family showing heavy incidence of exophthalmic goitre. III, 1, 2, 3, also affected; sex unknown.

child, the son, had also congenital heart disease. . . . Eger found in 12 cases of congenital heart disease, three times lues patris as well as consanguinity of the parents." To these cases it would be possible to add almost indefinitely. "Heart disease" is very common, but it does not fall upon individuals at random, but prevailingly upon strains with an inherent liability or weakness (Figs. 140–143).

b. Arteriosclerosis.—While degeneration of the wall of the arteries is ascribed to numerous inciting causes there can be no doubt that the cerebral hemorrhages, even of old age,

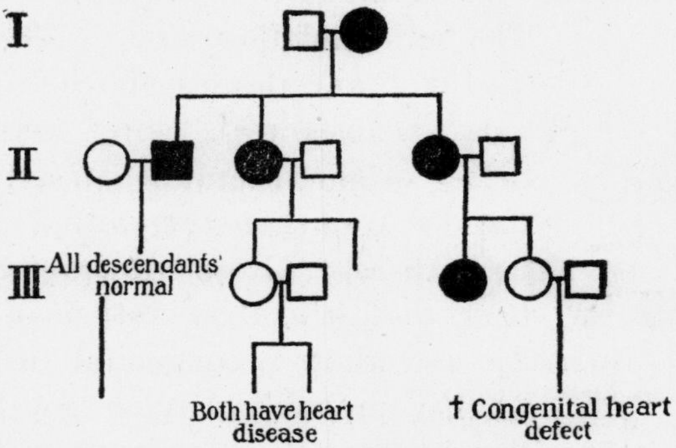

FIG 140.—Pedigree of heart disease. I, 2, probably had heart disease, II, 2, 3, and 5 had heart disease. The descendants of II, 1, 2, are normal for two generations. Those of II, 3, 4, are healthy but 1 of them has 2 children with heart disease. II, 5, has a daughter and a grandson who died of congenital heart defect. REZEK from VIERORDT, 1901.

are dependent in large part upon an inherited strength or resistance. Cases of arteriosclerosis have been reported in infants and here heredity must play an important rôle.

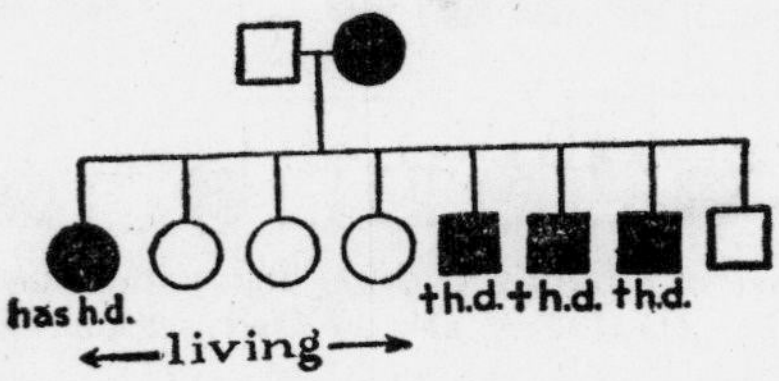

FIG. 141.—Pedigree of "heart disease."

36. DISEASES OF THE RESPIRATORY SYSTEM

The respiratory organs, including the passages to it that are lined by mucous membranes, are the weakest part of our body. This is probably because our remote ancestors, at the beginning of the vertebrate series, were aquatic animals and we land animals have not yet become fully adjusted to life in the air. The dry, dusty and often germ laden air is a difficulty with which our mucous membranes can hardly grapple; little wonder that they, and the whole body, so often succumb.

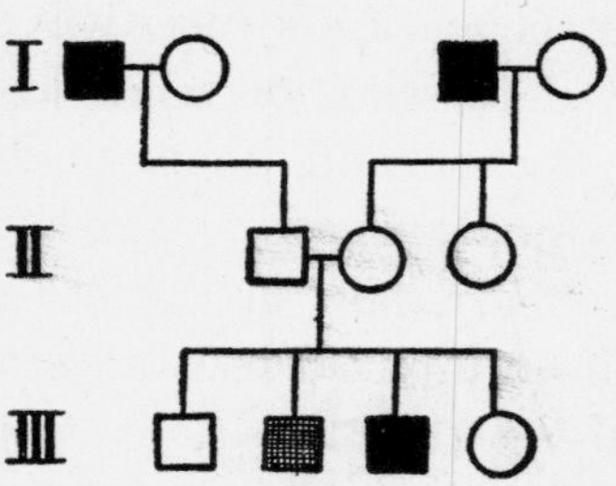

FIG. 142.—Pedigree of heart trouble. The father's father, I, 1, died of anguina pectoris at 69 years; and the mother's father, I, 3, died of ossification of the valves of the heart at 59. Father and mother are living and said to be well. Of their children, III, 3, died of heart disease at 9 months and another, III, 2, had temporary heart trouble. F. R.; All. 1.

Of the diseases of the lungs the most fatal is tuberculosis. We know that it is induced by a germ and that if there is no germ there will be no tuberculosis of the lungs. The first impulse of the modern sanitarian is to eliminate the germ. But this is a supra-herculean task; for germs of tuberculosis are found in all cities and in the country amongst most domesticated a n i m a l s. The germs are ubiquitous; how then shall any escape? Why do only 10 per cent die from the attacks of this parasite?

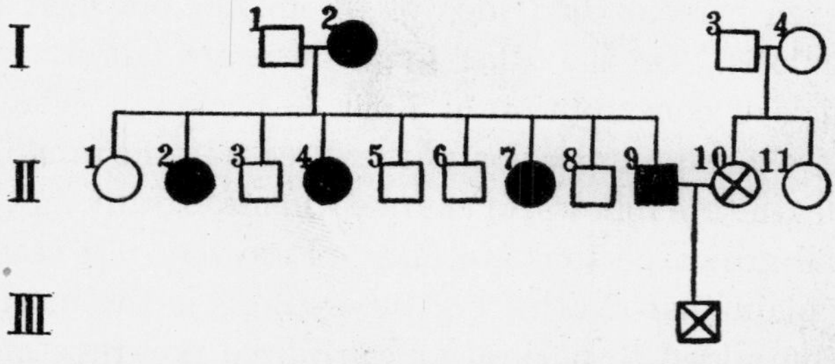

FIG. 143.—Pedigree of family with heart disease and migraine, I, 2, died of heart disease at 72 years; II, 2, 4, 7, died of "heart disease;" II, 9, died of "heart failure" at 59 years, hardworking physician; III, 1, suffers from migraine; her mother is a semi-invalid from migraine. F. R.; Bra. 1.

The answer is given by autopsies and the experiences of many physicians. Autopsies show that nearly all mature persons have the germs of tuberculosis in their lungs, but, for most part encysted and, perhaps, even completely destroyed.

Those who die of tuberculosis are those whose bodies have not been able successfully to combat the germs—their bodies have lost in the battle. Family physicians know cases where under bad conditions, overwork, depression of mind and body their patient will begin to decline and, then, under more favorable conditions begin to build up again. The battle wages now in favor of the one side, now of the other. The result depends quite as much on internal resistance as virulence of the germ.

That families vary in their internal resistance is well known. Dr. Coolidge of the Lakeville Sanitarium, Massachusetts, tells me that he classifies his patients on the basis of their resistance as measured by their response to good treatment in the first few days; and he states that the old New England families now show a relatively high resistance to tuberculosis as compared with recent immigrants.

The Family Histories that have been placed in my hands show the same thing. Though one in ten die of tuberculosis it was not difficult to pick out ten families in each of which about ten persons had died of whom not one had died of tuberculosis. On the other hand there are families with an incidence of consumption of 75 or 80 per cent. That this is not merely communication of the disease in the families with high death rate follows, of course, when we grant that practically all grown persons are infected anyway. It seems perfectly plain that death from tuberculosis is the resultant of infection added to natural and acquired non-resistance. It is, then, highly undesirable that two persons with weak resistance should marry, lest their children all carry this weakness.

Pneumonia.—Since the germ of pneumonia is a normal resident of our throats, the disease is not due merely to infection; but to a weakening of a natural or acquired resistance. Our Family Records show again and again the heavy incidence of pneumonia in certain families causing the death even of infants (Fig. 144).

Likewise a general weakness of the mucous membranes,

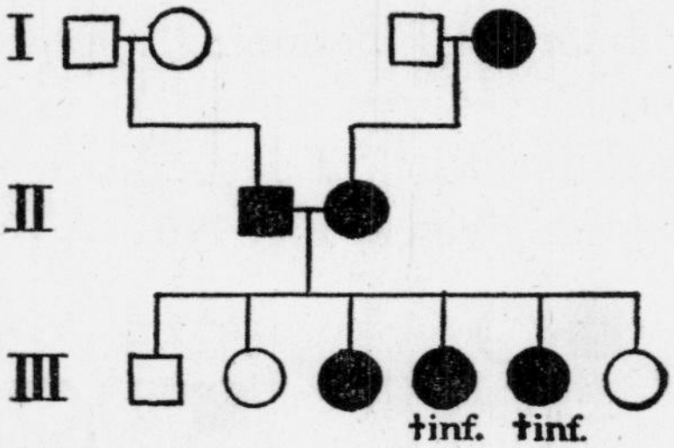

FIG. 144.—Pedigree of a family with tendency toward lung disease. I, 4, died of pneumonia at 82 years. II, 1, had an attack of pneumonia which terminated in tuberculosis from which he died at 43 years. His wife, II, 2, died at 62 years of tuberculosis. Of their 6 children 3 are still living; the others all died of pneumonia, 2 in early childhood. F. R.; Mor. 1.

leading to catarrh, adenoids, tonsilitis, deafness, bronchitis, etc., seems clearly to run in families. Such a case is illustrated in Fig. 145.

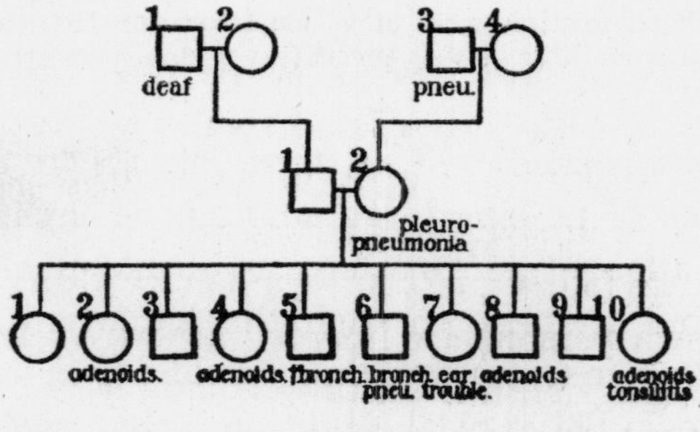

FIG. 145.—Showing "inheritance" of throat and ear weakness in a family. F. R.; New. 1.

37. DISEASES OF THE ALIMENTARY SYSTEM

The diseases of the alimentary tract are so largely due to bad habits in eating, exercising and attending to the demands of nature that most physicians consider a possible hereditary basis relatively unimportant. It is, to be sure, recognized that the "nervous temperament" may be largely responsible for disordered digestion by disturbing the ordinary secretory functions. So, likewise, it is probable that there are family characteristics which favor peculiarities of the liver resulting in its abnormal functioning. Especially jaundice and gout may have hereditary basis. An example of family pedigrees with high incidence of dyspepsia and more specific alimentary troubles is given in Fig. 146.

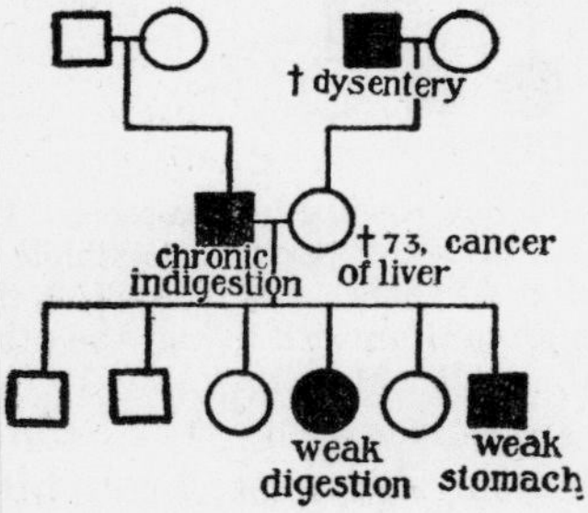

Fig. 146

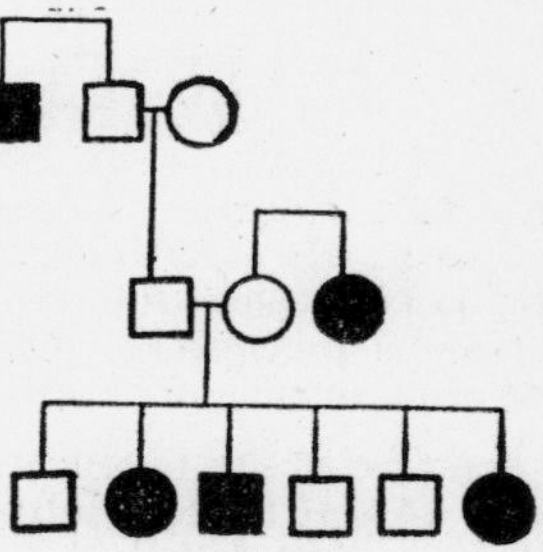

Fig. 147

Fig. 146.—Pedigree of digestive weakness. F. R.; She. 1.

Fig. 147.—Pedigree of diabetes mellitus (black symbols). In this case the parents of affected offspring are not themselves affected; the trait is due to the absence of something that is present in normal persons. Bramwell, 1908, p. 265.

a. Diabetes Insipidus.[1]—This term has been applied to the symptoms of passing large amounts of greatly diluted urine. The affected persons have to drink much water to meet the rapid drainage through the kidneys. Numerous families are known that show this peculiarity in several close blood relatives. The typical condition is that two unaffected parents, even of diabetic strains, will have only normal children; diabetic offspring have at least one diabetic parent. This would indicate that diabetes is due to a positive factor (Fig. 148). Nettleship (1910) points out that age of incidence tends to diminish in successive generations.

[1] The hereditary behavior of diabetes mellitus or "sugar in urine" has been less studied. (Fig. 147).

The eugenic teaching is that persons with diabetes insipidus will probably have some diseased children, but unaffected persons, even of diabetic origin, will probably have only normal children.

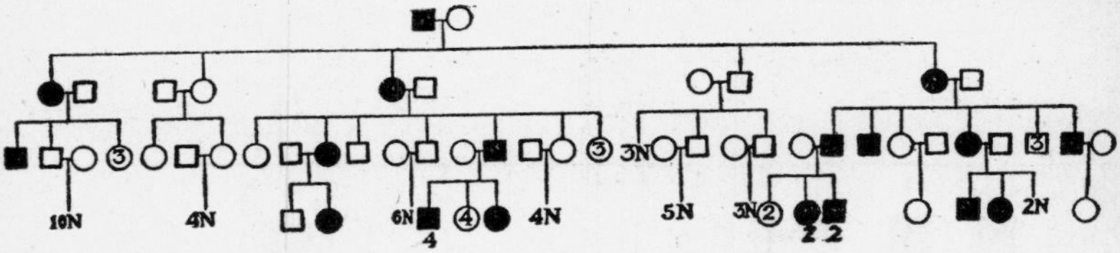

FIG. 148.—Pedigree of a family with diabetes insipidus. Affected persons (black symbols) are derived only from affected parents—thus diabetes is a positive trait. GOSSAGE, 1907.

38. DISEASES OF EXCRETION

Since the urine is the main stream carrying waste products of metabolism from the body it gives the best evidence of disorders of metabolism, hence much attention has been directed toward its study. Some of its peculiarities are known to be family traits.

a. Alkaptonuria.—This condition is marked by the constant excretion of homogentisic acid which darkens upon oxydation so that the urine darkens after passage; it is not injurious to the individual and has no special eugenic interest except as it illustrates the law of heredity. The transmission of this trait has been studied by Garrod (1902). The disease is a rare one and, apparently, occurs only in the offspring of two persons belonging to alkaptonuric strains. This condition is most easily met in cousin marriages and, as a matter of fact of the 17 alkaptonuric fraternities studied 8 were offspring of first cousins. When neither parent of an alkaptonuric fraternity is alkaptonuric about 1 in 4 of the children have the peculiarity. It appears then that alkaptonuria is due to the absence of a condition found in other (normal or ordinary) persons; and it is lost in the product of marriage of an alkaptonuric and a normal person.

b. **Cystinuria and Cystin Infiltration** are both family diseases though so rare that the method of inheritance has not been precisely determined.

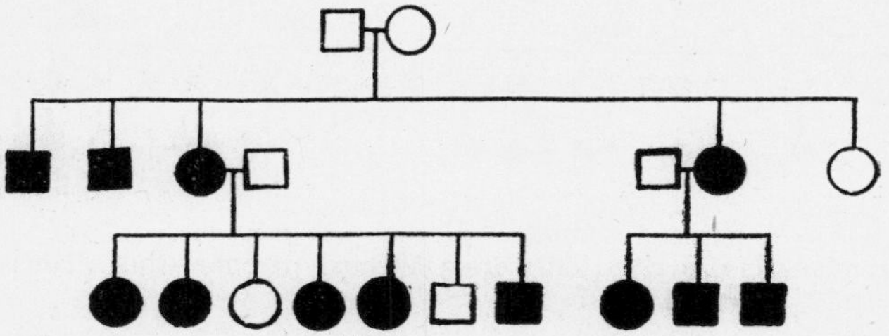

FIG. 149.—Pedigree of a family showing hematuria (red urine). Affected persons (black symbols) are descended from an affected parent, evidence that hematuria is a positive trait. GUTHRIE.

c. **Hematuria,** or red urine, may also be a family characteristic as the pedigree chart worked out by Guthrie shows (Fig. 149).

d. **Urinary Calculi.**—This is frequently hereditary. A pedigree recorded by Cluble (1872) illustrates this fact, though it does not give sufficient data to determine the law of inheritance. He says:—"During the last four or five years I have cut three of his sons [i. e., of the Lowestoft fisherman] at the respective ages of 2, 3, and 8. Two of the stones were lithic acid, one apparently lithate of ammonia. The father and mother of the lads always have lithic acid sediment, often gravel, deposited from urine. Their grandfather passed one stone, their grandmother seven. A great uncle was cut for stone. There are six uncles and four aunts who suffer from fits of gravel or from gravelly or sedimentary lithic acid deposits; and a cousin, an uncle's child, gets rid of urinary calculi."

e. **Gout.**—The hereditary tendency to gout is generally

recognized—a pedigree recorded by Garrod illustrates the fact. A man who has very severe gout is married to a woman who when 70 years old began to suffer from it. They had 7 children; all have suffered from gout, 5 have died from gout and its various complications; the other two are still living.

39. Reproductive Organs

a. **Cryptorchism,** or retention and atrophy of testicles. This condition, a semi-"hermaphroditic" one, is characterized by the fact that the normal descent of the testis into the scrotum fails to occur. A pedigree of a family exhibiting this condition is given, in Fig. 150. In the third generation one boy out of four is normal. This trait is probably inherited just like hypospadias.

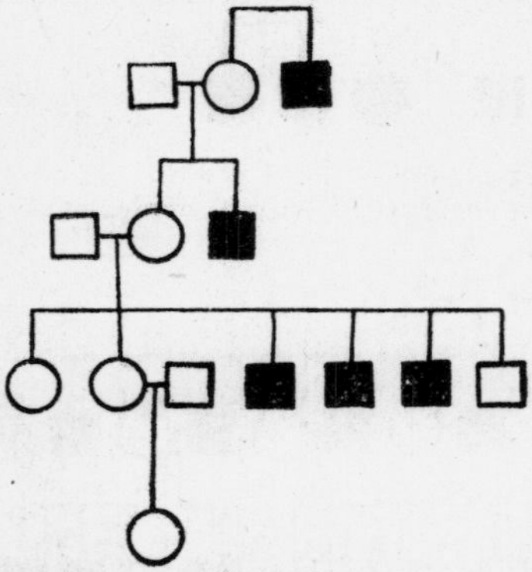

Fig. 150.—Pedigree of cryptorchism. Affected persons represented by black symbols. On account of the sterility of the males all affected persons are derived from sisters of affected persons. All affected persons are natural eunuchs. Bronardel, p. 169.

b. **Hypospadias.**—Like the last this is evidence of an imperfect development of the external secondary sex characters and possibly indicates an imperfect stimulus to sex dimorphism. The defect is characterized by the more or less complete failure of the male genital papilla to close along the median raphe up to the apex of the glans. An affected man may have by a wife who belongs to a normal strain some or all of his sons affected. His normal daughters may have abnormal sons even when the father belongs to a normal strain. It seems that there is an inhibitor to complete sex-differentiation in the males. Usually males who show no trace of the inhibitor when married into a normal strain have normal sons. But occasionally apparently normal fathers in whom the "inhibitor" is inactive may have abnormal sons (Fig. 151.) The eugenical conclusion is that females belonging to hermaphroditic (hypospadic or cryptorchitic) strains, if married, will probably have at least half of their sons defective, particularly if they have defective brothers; but normal males of such strains may marry females from unaffected strains with impunity.

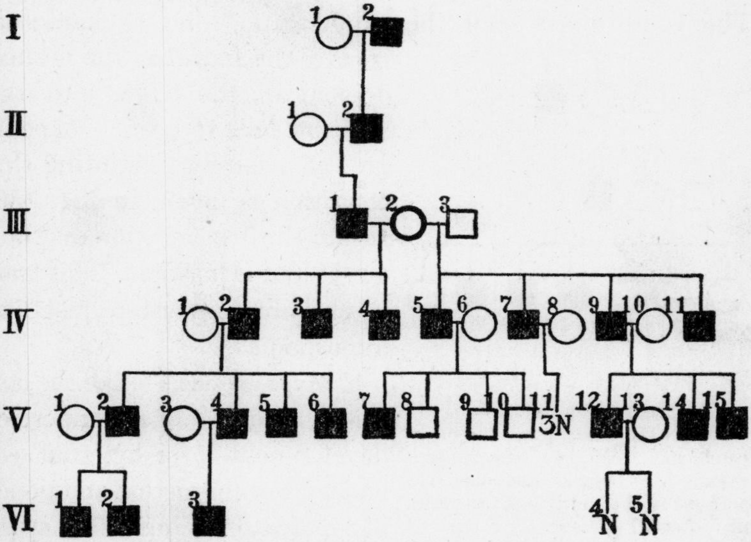

FIG. 151.—Pedigree of hypospadias (black symbols). Inheritance from affected males and unaffected females, III, 2. LINGARD, 1884.

c. **Prolapsus of the Uterus and Sterility.**—Corresponding in a way with incomplete development of the male reproductive organs is the prolapsus of the uterus in the female. This is also definitely inherited but the trait is never transmitted by affected females since they are sterile (Fig. 152).

40. SKELETON AND APPENDAGES

Since the size and form of the bodily frame are greatly influenced by the skeleton the heredity of these features is

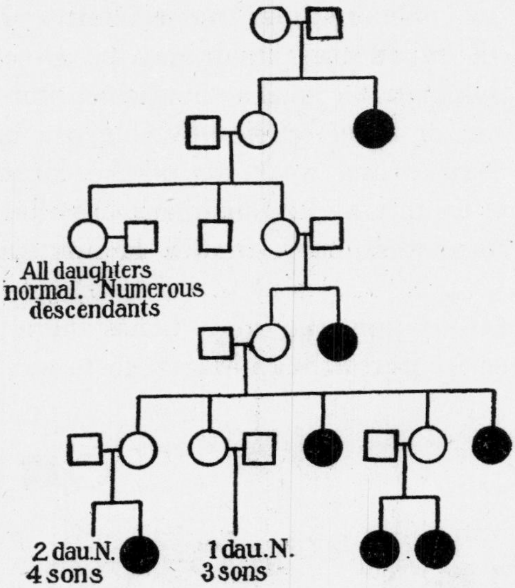

Fig. 152.—Pedigree of a family showing prolapsus of the uterus (females) and sterility. Inherited like the *absence* of a character, with probable consanguinity in marriage. Bronardel, 1900.

usually due to an inheritance in the processes that go to determine the form and size of the skeleton.

a. **Achondroplasy** is characterized by relatively short limbs, a condition in man like that in the Ancon sheep, dachshund and some bull-dogs. The condition is rare and so we have few if any full pedigrees but enough is known to indicate that it is inherited, as in the case cited by Pouchet and Leriche (1903), Fig. 153, and it is probably due to an abnormal positive factor.

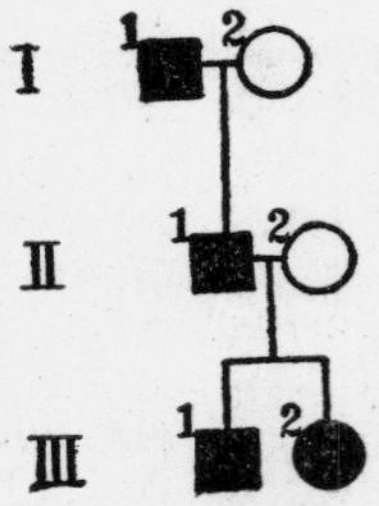

Fig. 153.—Pedigree of achondroplasy (black symbols). Pouchet and Leriche, 1903.

b. **Scoliosis.**—The dissymmetry of the trunk accompanied by a curved "spine" is a fairly common condition. That there is an hereditary tendency to it cannot be doubted in view of its frequent occurrence two or more times in one family. Either father or mother of an affected child may be affected; or they may have symmetrical spines themselves but have an affected brother or sister. The offspring are born with an hereditary laxness and weakness of the constituent parts of the spinal column and its ligaments, so that the column easily falls into lateral curves under the influence of secondary causes.

c. Exostoses.—Upon the long bones there occasionally develop osseous outgrowths known as exostoses. The method

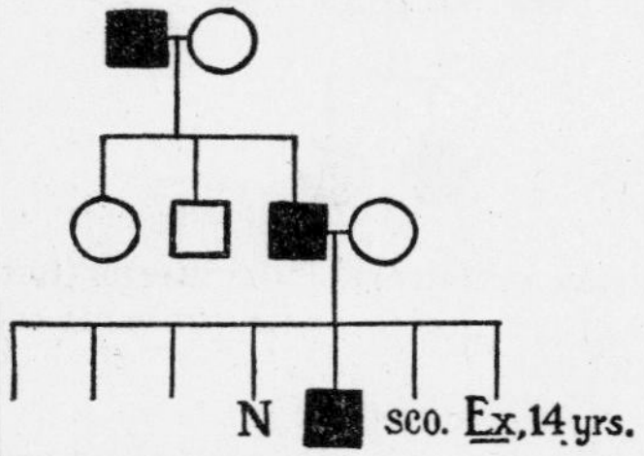

FIG. 154

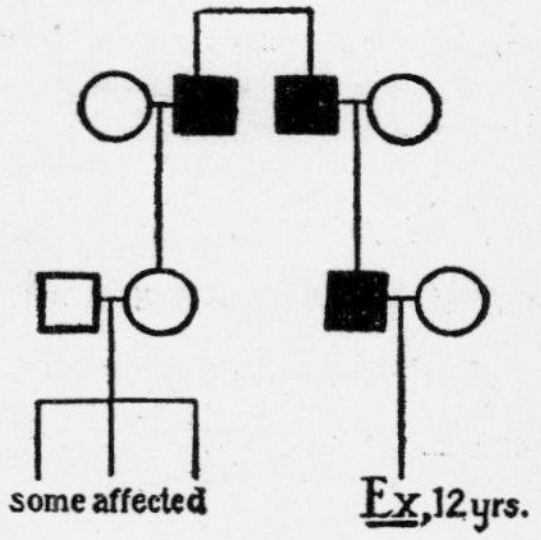

FIG. 155

FIG. 154.—Pedigrees of exostoses on the long bones. Affected individuals represented by black symbols. *Ex,* exostoses, sex unknown; *sco,* scoliosis or spinal curvature. TEISSIER and DENECHAM, 1905.

FIG. 155.—Part of a pedigree of exostoses on the long bones that have been traced through 6 generations. *Ex,* exostoses, sex unknown. MERY and METAYER, 1905.

of inheritance of the tendency to produce such growths is indicated by pedigrees given in Figs. 154, 155.

d. Absence of Clavicles.—The collar bones, or clavicles, are occasionally imperfectly developed and the tendency to this result shows itself in several members of one family. This is well illustrated by a case described by Carpenter (1899) Fig. 156. The high incidence of the abnormal condition in this family suggests that the defect is due to a positive inhibitor.

e. Congenital dislocation at the thigh bone—pelvis joint.—This is a peculiarity that usually runs in families. It is doubtless due to a laxness in the ligaments by which attach-

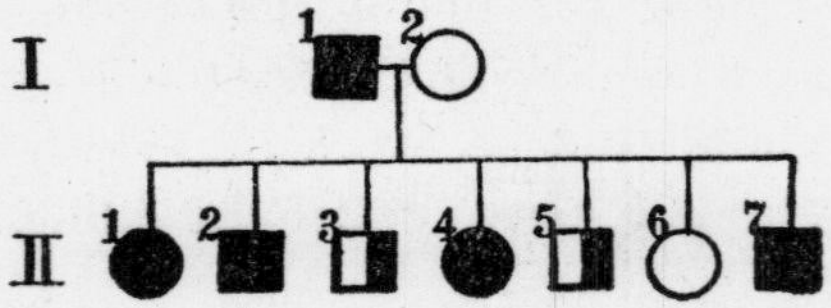

FIG. 156.—Pedigree of absence of clavicles. The father, I, 1, has deformed clavicles. By a normal wife he has 7 children affected as follows: II, 1, has a slightly deformed clavicle; II, 2, has a deformed right clavicle; II, 3, has normal clavicles but a prominent transverse process of the last cervical vertebra; II, 4, has clavicles nearly absent and also the clavicular portion of the great chest muscle; II, 5, has a peculiar kink in the clavicles; II, 6, is normal; II, 7, has a deformed right clavicle. CARPENTER, 1899.

ment is made. Several pedigrees have been worked out by Nareth (1903) of which one is reproduced here (Fig. 157).

No evidence appears as to the amount of consanguineous marriage except in one case. The pedigree looks like one

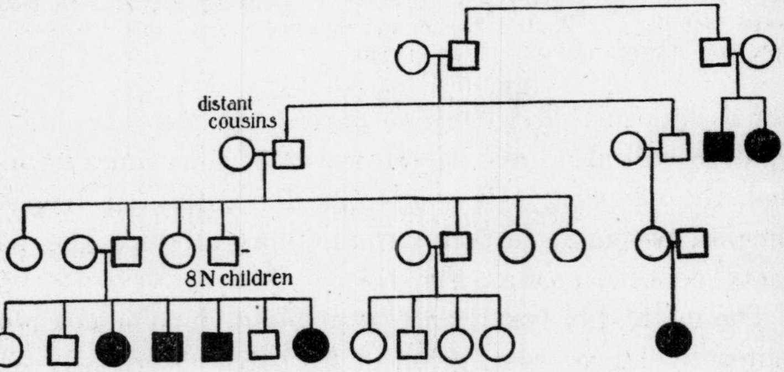

FIG. 157.—Pedigree of a family showing congenital dislocation of the hip. Affected persons (black symbols) descend from unaffected, suggesting that the condition is due to a defect. SENATOR and KAMINER, 1904.

of albinism and suggests that congenital dislocation is a defect. In that case the marriage of related persons, even though normal, is to be discouraged, but an affected person by marrying into new blood may expect normal offspring.

f. Polydactylism.—The peculiarity of supernumerary fingers and toes is one that is inherited in nearly typical fashion. I have worked extensively on polydactylism in fowls and there can be little doubt that the character behaves in the same way in man. The extra toe is due to an addi-

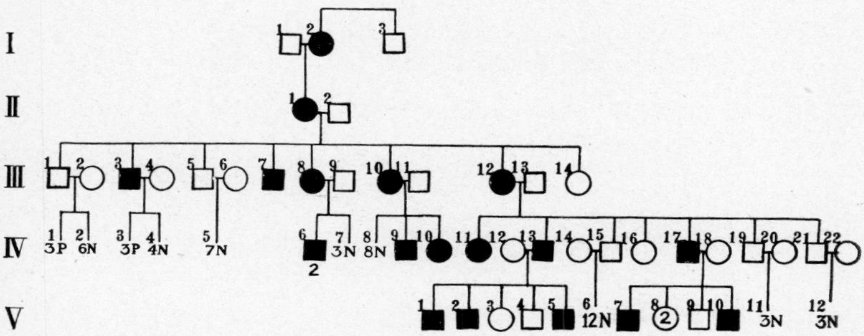

FIG. 158.—Pedigree of polydactylism. Affected persons represented by black symbols. III, 3, has six toes on each foot; III, 8, has six toes on each foot; III, 10, extra fingers on each hand; III, 12, extra fingers on each hand; V, 1, five fingers and thumb on each hand; V, 2, supernumerary digits on both hands and feet; V, 5, extra toes, both feet; V, 7, harelip, cleft palate, web between each big toe; V, 10, 5 fingers and thumb on each hand, 6 toes on each foot, web between all toes. LUCAS, 1880.

tional unit so that when one parent has the extra toe the children will also have it. However, it sometimes happens that the offspring fail to produce the extra toe; but such persons, becoming in turn parents, may produce the polydactyl condition again (Fig. 158).

The method of inheritance of polydactylism is well represented by Lucas' case, given in Fig. 158. Here only when one parent was polydactyl were there polydactyl offspring, excepting in the progeny of the oldest son of the third generation. This son is said not to be polydactyl and is recorded as normal. If the record is correct his case is one of failure to dominate of the polydactyl determiner.

The eugenical conclusion is: polydactyl persons will have at least half of their children polydactyl. Those quite free

Fig. 159.—A case of polydactylism. The boy's father has 12 fingers and 12 toes, but the extra fingers are boneless. Besides the boy figured, who is like his father, there is 1 son with extra toes, 1 with extra toes and an extra finger on the left hand only. One sister has extra toes only. The other 5 children were normal in respect to the number of toes and fingers they bear. Through the kindness of Professor C. A. Scott.

from the trait, though of the polydactyl strain, will probably have only normal children.

g. Syndactylism.—The union of the bones and tissues of two or more digits into one mass is found in many animals including man. I have studied it in hundreds of fowl. It is inherited there, as no doubt also in man, in such fashion as to permit the conclusion that syndactylism is due to a factor that extends the web *paripassu* with the development of the digits. On this hypothesis the normal hand or foot lacks the factor and two normal persons (even of a syndactylic strain) will not show the abnormality in their offspring. This expectation is indeed realized in most of the pedigrees published; as for instance in that of Parker and Robinson (1887, Clin. Soc. Trans., Vol. XX., p. 181), Fig. 160.

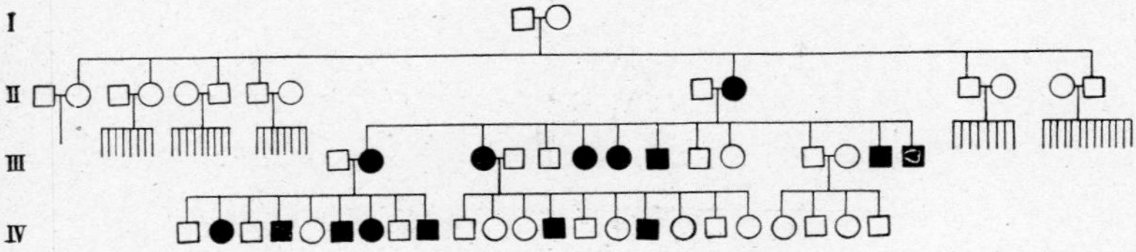

FIG. 160.—A pedigree of syndactylism, or "split foot." All affected persons are from an affected parent; hence the trait is a positive one. Little is known about the condition of the digits in the first generation. PARKER and ROBINSON, 1887.

The general conclusion is that, while a syndactyl individual will transmit his trait, normals from a syndactyl strain have little chance of doing so.

h. Brachydactylism.—This is a condition of shortened digits due to the presence of only two segments to the digit—so that all fingers are like thumbs. The middle phalanx is usually a more or less rudimentary bone attached to the base of the distal phalanx. Inheritance follows the laws of syndactylism. Two normal parents produce only the normal condition; no generation is skipped.

i. Other deformities of the hands.—From time to time other digital peculiarities have been recorded and these are usually strongly inherited. Thus Dobell has described a family in which the hands are double jointed, all joints thick, ring and little finger crooked from the last joint. The peculiarity is distinguishable at birth. The law of inheritance is the same as for syndactylism; viz., normal parents have no offspring with the defect; but one affected parent tends to transmit the defect to half (rarely all) of his offspring (Fig. 161). The tendency of the great toe to grow under the others occurs in at least one family strain (Fig. 162) and is apparently inherited like double jointedness. Another case of family deformity of the digits is given by Carson (Keating's Ency. III, 935). Here there is an absence of the

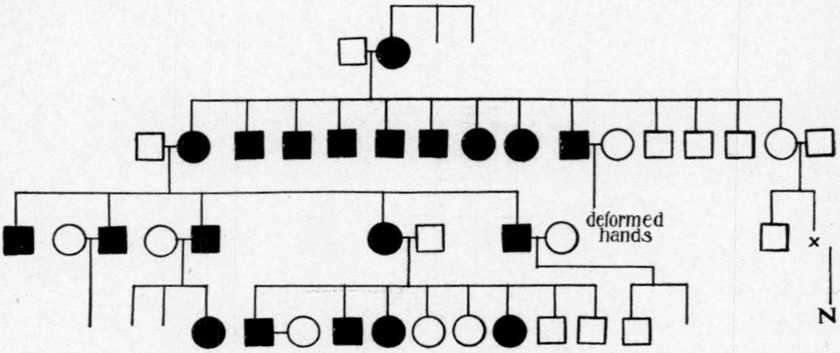

FIG. 161.—Pedigree of family with double jointed hands, all joints thick, ring and little fingers crooked from the distal joint. Affected persons marked by black symbols. DOBELL.

distal phalanx and part of the median phalanx from all fingers of both hands, the thumbs being normal. Here again the defect had not skipped a generation, i. e., was not transmitted by normals. It has been known in the family

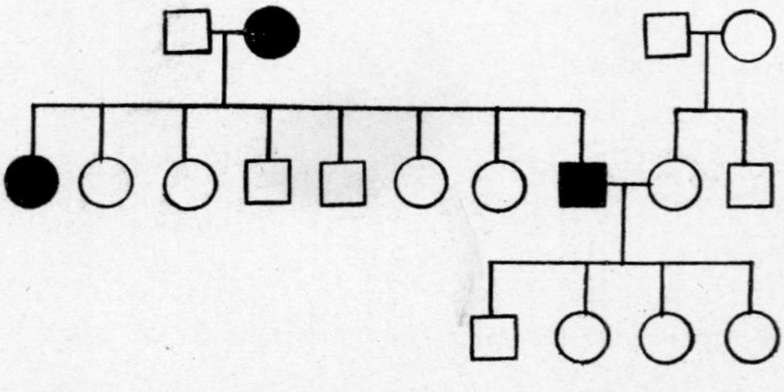

FIG. 162.—Pedigree of tendency of great toe to grow under others (black symbols represent affected persons). F. R.; Ov.

for over a century. Foot (Difformités des Doigts, p. 80) tells of a family in which for three generations the peculiarity has appeared of possessing only the fifth finger. The second and third fingers are represented in these individuals by the metacarpal bone only and the other two fingers are entirely missing. This is, of course, a case of syndactylism, with inheritance of a specific type. In a case cited by Marshall (Trans. Soc. Stud. Disease in Children, III) in which for

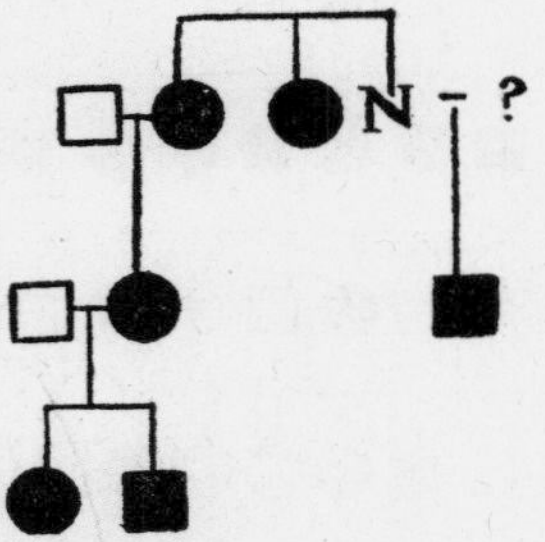

FIG. 163.—Fragment of a pedigree of a family showing hereditary club-foot in 3 generations. So far as it goes this pedigree suggests that the condition is due to a positive character. DREW, 1905.

five generations this peculiarity appeared, each finger stopped short at the proximal phalanx and the thumb was ill developed. Drew has recorded a case of club-foot in three

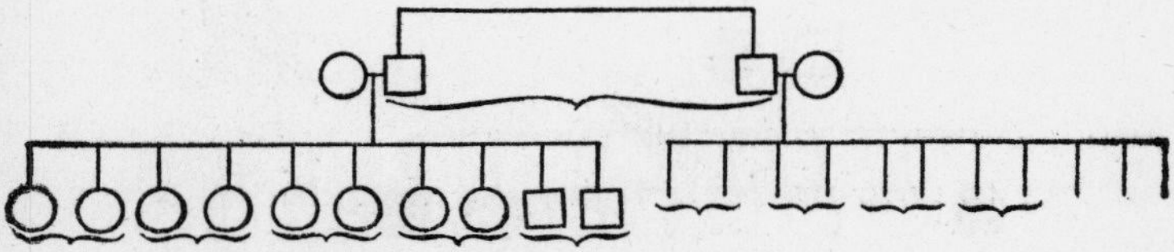

FIG. 164.—Pedigree of a family of twins. Two twin brothers married. The first had 10 children, all born as twins; 4 pair were daughters and 1 pair were sons. Seven of the daughters are married and 4 have produced twins at the first birth, nothing is known of the others. One of the sons is married and has 3 single children. The second brother (first generation) had 8 children born as twins and 3 born singly. STOCKS, 1861.

generations (Fig. 163). It is astonishing what a variety of inheritable variations, that are often minute, are shown by the hand and foot. The data are too limited to give assurance as to the law of inheritance in each case.

41. Twins

It is well known that twin production may be an hereditary quality. Thus the Dorset race of sheep is characterized by the tendency to bear twins. In man, too, strains are known where plural births are the rule. Remarkable cases are re-

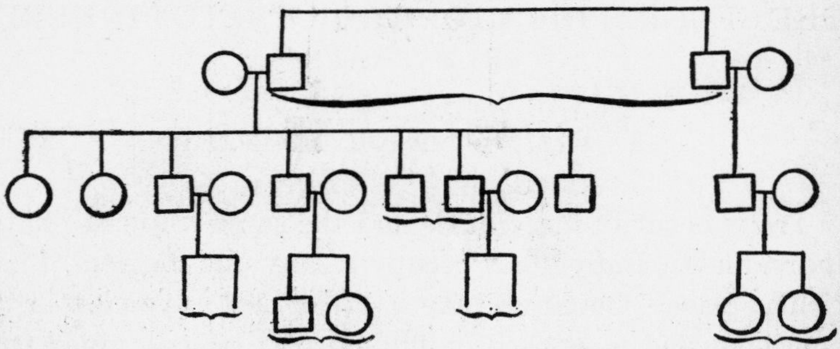

Fig. 165.—Of 2 twin sons one has a pair of twin sons and 5 single born children; the other had 1 son. The former has, through his sons, 3 pair of grandchildren; the latter 1 pair. Wakley, 1895.

corded by Stocks (1861, p. 78), see Fig. 164, and by Wakley (1895, p. 1289). See Fig. 165.

In the foregoing cases inheritance of the twinning capacity is through the males only, and this is true in some strains of sheep. However, other human strains are known with the tendency to twin-production passing along the female line.

CHAPTER IV

THE GEOGRAPHICAL DISTRIBUTION OF INHERITABLE TRAITS

1. The Dispersion of Traits

Traits occur in individuals and the same traits in related individuals. Individuals occupy at any one moment a particular place. Could we take a sort of bird's eye view of the continent and were each individual that bears a given trait conspicuously marked, we should have a perfect picture of the geographic distribution of the trait. Had we such a picture for each day of the hundred thousand odd days since America began to be settled and were they to pass in review as in a cinematograph, then we should see the reproduction and dissemination of the family trait in question. Such a view would show us the traits coming across the ocean from European centres, settling in a place or flitting from point to point, reproducing themselves at a place and continuing to increase there for generations while throwing off individuals to move far athwart the face of the country and to settle down as new proliferating centres. We should see two persons with the same defect coming together as a married couple and proliferating in a few years a number of new individuals with the same negative characters. Or we should see an individual with the defect uniting with a person without it and ending there the trail of the defect. Or, on the other hand, a positive trait, like cataract, hemophilia, or Huntington's chorea, would move about, settle in a spot, multiply itself into many individuals either all of one sex or of both sexes, as the case may be; and these individuals, moving apart, would form new proliferating centres. In the multiplication of negative and positive traits we would see this plain difference—that negative traits multiply most in long established and stable communities where much inbreeding occurs, while positive traits are increased by emigration, as a fire is spread by the wind that scatters firebrands. If, on the other hand, the negative traits be scattered the chance of mating with the same defect is diminished and the trait is not reproduced. Conversely, a country characterized by much inbreeding will have a population that is affected prevailingly by negative traits with a slight tendency for positive traits to increase; while a country that is settled by a restless people will show a small percentage of negative traits and a high percentage of positive ones.

That the picture of the dissemination of traits that I have drawn is not exaggerated but corresponds to the empirical facts is proved by the evidence of many studies. Thus Alexander Graham Bell (1889) finds that not only the deaf mutes of Martha's Vineyard but "groups of deaf mutes who have never been near Martha's Vineyard, trace up to" the blood of James Skiff. A genealogist with unusual intelligence and breadth of interest has traced a "bleeding" tendency from a Hannant who came from Norfolk, England, and whose progeny settled in Sullivan County, Pennsylvania, and created there a colony of bleeders; and by emigration has started new colonies in Minnesota, South Dakota, and California. Students of Huntington's chorea find many of their widely scattered cases tracing back through Delaware County, New York, to the sources of its early population at East Hampton, Long Island, or to that sister settlement of the New Haven Colony, Fairfield County, Connecticut. Even students of crime have traced the disturbing element of a large area to a single focal point; "the Jukes" were traced back to Max living in a lonely mountain valley and the "Ishmaelites" of Indiana were traced back through Kentucky to Virginia and probably to the cutthroats and prostitutes which England spewed out upon, and against the protests of, the Virginia colony in the latter half of the seventeenth century (Butler, 1896). So too a family in New Jersey of over 600 persons, more than three-fourths of them defectives have been derived, by Goddard and his field-workers, from a single pair. These are examples, merely, of a universal fact, that the more strikingly inheritable traits may be followed back generation after generation to a few focal points.

And the focal points of this country have been transported here from abroad. A settlement worker in New York City inquired into the meaning of a particularly unruly and criminalistic section of his territory and found that the offenders came from one village in Calabria—known as the "home of brigands." Of the weary but hopeful thousands of immigrants who weekly (almost daily) enter the port of New York how many are destined to bring in traits for good or evil, that are to proliferate and to affect the future of this country for better or worse! For we must not forget the good. The germ plasm of an Austrian who migrated to the United States three generations ago has produced a race of yacht builders who enable this country to maintain its supremacy in the sport of yachting. From the germ plasm (in part) of an extraordinarily talented but erotic woman who migrated to America in the early part of the seventeenth century have arisen statesmen, college presidents, men of science, great philanthropists from New England to California in extraordinary numbers. From an Irish pair who came to the wilderness of Virginia nearly two centuries ago have descended vice presidents, cabinet officers, admirals, generals, governors, senators and congressmen in great numbers. In these cases the good was not "interred with their bones."

2. Consanguinity in Marriage

The customs of civilized nations oppose certain limits to marriage, almost universally bar the marriage of nearest kin, and have given to the word incest a connotation so loathsome and so emphatic that it is appreciated by practically every normal civilized person. It will be interesting to consider for a moment how wide-spread is this taboo.

First of all it must be said that the union of brother and sister or of parent and child as recognized spouses is not unknown. Various reputable observers report that among the Weddas of Ceylon, probably on account of the sparsity of the population and the isolation of families, the marriage of brother and younger sister is permitted by local custom (Virchow, 1881). In ancient times the marriage of parent and child was not opposed by custom in Persia (Heath, 1887, p. 65) and perhaps in other Eastern countries.

Such customs are to-day, however, highly exceptional and against social ideals. But the line between permissible and non-permissible unions is variously drawn. Thus we are told (Nelson, 1899) that the Eskimos of Behring Strait favor the union of first cousins or even closer relatives on the general ground that in time of stress and hunger the blood tie will be found stronger than the marriage tie to hold the family together. Among other natives of North America a paternal uncle and niece might marry but not a maternal aunt and nephew. However, the North American Indian, on the whole, has strong sentiments against close intermarriage. Also among Africans and the South Sea Islanders cousin marriages are, in general, taboo; and among the Malays "consanguinity, even the remotest, constitutes an important obstacle to marriage." We read of the Islanders making voyages to other islands and carrying off maidens for wives. In India and China marriage of persons within the patronymic is against social ideals.[1] European ideals are largely a legacy of Roman law. Here the purely formal and legal relations constituted as much of an obstacle as blood relationship. A stepchild should not marry his mother nor a father-in-law his daughter-in-law. Only recently has a relic of these legal and non-biological interdictions been removed in England by the repeal of the law prohibiting a man from marrying his deceased wife's sister.

Such wide-spread social barriers to close intermarriage, even among the children of nature—one might almost say *especially* among them—indicates if not an instinctive repugnance to, at least an apprehensiveness toward, such marriages. We have still to inquire if there is any biological basis for such apprehensiveness. The answer to this question has been furnished in many places in the earlier part of the book. Defects in the germ plasm tend to reveal themselves in the offspring of cousin marriages but tend to disappear entirely in the children that are derived from outmatings. On the other hand, undesirable positive traits that are absent from both parents will not reappear in the offspring even though the parents be cousins. One can easily imagine a strain without any important defect, so that a consanguineous marriage would, for generations, be uninjurious to the offspring; but such strains are doubtless rare. We are told that in the family of the Ptolemies and in the royal family of the Incas the marriage of brother and sister repeatedly occurred but, as a friend of mine says, "Where are the Ptolemies and Incas now?" The conclusion seems

[1] The foregoing summary of marriage limitations is based chiefly upon the compiled data of Ploss-Bartels: Das Weib.

FIG. 166.—Rows of maize, each from a single ear of corn. The central row (labeled) is from a 16 row-to-ear race *self-fertilized for five years*. Row to left of center, self-fertilization prevented for six successive years. Row to right, a first cross between long self-fertilized strains.

clear that, while in certain strains consanguineous marriage may not lead to defective offspring, in most families it will, at least after a few generations. This is well illustrated in corn-breeding where self-fertilization leads to rapid loss of productivity and vegetative vigor (Figs. 166, 167).

Let us now consider some of the statistical results gained from a study of consanguineous marriages in a large population. In 1858 Dr. Bemiss reported to the American Medical Association on a collection of 833 consanguineous marriages producing 3,942 children or an average of 4.6 children per marriage. Of these children 28.7 per cent are said to be defective, 3.6 per cent are deaf mutes, 2.1 per cent blind, 7 per cent idiots, 1 per cent insane, 1.5 per cent epileptic, 2.4 per cent deformed, 7.6 per cent "scrofulous" (i. e., probably

FIG. 167.—The piles of ears of corn on the right and left are from seed ears which had been self-fertilized; the pile in the middle from a seed ear in which self-fertilization had been prevented. This figure and the preceding were contributed by Dr. G. H. SHULL.

tubercular) and 22 per cent are said to have "died young." In some data gathered by Dr. Howe (1853) 17 consanguineous marriages produced 50 per cent idiots; in the data of Dr. Mitchell (1866) 7.5 per cent were insane, and 1.4 per cent deaf mutes. Other observers record consanguineous marriages without deaf mutism, others without idiocy, others with less than 1 per cent of insanity. Voisin (1865) tells of the isolated community of Batz where 5 marriages of first cousins and 31 of second cousins has occurred without a case of mental disease, deaf mutism, albinism, retinitis pigmentosa or malformation appearing. These varied results are to be expected. Consanguineous marriage *per se* does not create traits; it permits the defects of the germ plasm, that may not appear in the parents, to reveal themselves in the offspring.

If there is no insanity or albinism in the stock consanguineous marriage will not bring it out; and, strictly, it is not at all consanguinity that brings the trait out but the increasing liability that consanguinity affords to the mating of two similarly defective germ cells.

The variety of the product of consanguineous marriage is well brought out when we compare localities. Thus consanguinity on Martha's Vineyard results in 11 per cent deaf mutes and a number of hermaphrodites; in Point Judith in 13 per cent idiocy and 7 per cent insanity; in an island off the Maine coast the consequence is "intellectual dullness"; in Block Island loss of fecundity; in some of the "Banks" off the coast of North Carolina, suspiciousness, and an inability to pass beyond the third or fourth grade of school; in a peninsula on the east coast of Chesapeake Bay the defect is dwarfness of stature: in George Island and Abaco (Bahama Islands) it is idiocy and blindness (G. A. Penrose, 1905). There is thus no one trait that results from the marriage of kin; the result is determined by the specific defect in the germ plasm of the common ancestor.

The question is often asked, How common are consanguineous marriages? What proportion of marriages are between kin? This question is so ill-defined that a reply is hardly possible. When we recall the enormous number of our ancestors resulting from the fact that the number (theoretically) doubles in each earlier generation, so that there are more than a million in the twentieth ascending generation, and more than a billion in the thirtieth, then we see that *some* degree of consanguinity in the parents is to be expected. There are hardly two persons of European origin who are more distantly related than thirtieth cousin —or who do not have a common ancestor of the time of King William I of England. Indeed, how improbable it is that there are many persons of "pure" European stock whose line of descent has not received contributions from Ethiopia within the last millenium—when we stop to consider the slaves, not only white and yellow but also brown and black, that were brought to Rome, became free there and contributed elements to the population of Italy and to all Europe.

Returning from this digression, we may recognize that, however vague scientifically the term consanguineous may be, popularly, it means related as first or possibly as second cousin. This is, of course, from the standpoint of modern heredity, an absurd limitation of the term since fifth or tenth cousins may carry the same ancestral traits. Our question may then be transformed in this fashion: What proportion of the population marries within the grade of fifth (or tenth) cousin? The answer to this question for the United States as a whole would require a special census, and the proportion, expressed in a single figure would have little significance. Much more important is it to know for each of several small communities the grades of relationship of consorts; and the association of degree of consanguinity with physiographic and other barriers.

3. Barriers to Marriage Selection

Barriers, indeed, to free and wide marriage selection favor consanguineous marriages, and for the same reason they favor the formation of races of men with peculiar traits, even as it has long been recognized that they facilitate the formation of races of plants and animals, by permitting newly-arisen traits to infect, as it were, the entire population and thus to form a new species. The barriers may be classified as physiographic and social.

A. *Physiographic Barriers*

Physiographic barriers are for man, a land animal, stretches of water, such as parts of the ocean, sounds and bays that separate from the mainland, and even broad rivers; also mountain ridges or heights of land. All such barriers restrain exogamy, or marriage outside the family, and favor consanguineous marriage or endogamy.

a. Barrier of Water.—Of oceanic islands the Canaries, Azores, Bermuda, the Bahamas and the Lesser Antilles are examples. In the case of the South Sea Islands the half aquatic nature of the inhabitants has reversed the usual order and made the sea a means of intercommunication. On our own coast we have striking examples of semi-oceanic islands with evidence of consanguineous marriage (Fig. 168).

At Miscou Island on the Northeast coast of New Brunswick there is said to be much intermarriage. The population "is partly English and partly Arcadian French and each race has kept pretty much to itself so they are closely intermarried within the same race."

The islands off the Maine coast show much consanguineous marriage. Thus in Small's (1898) History of Swan's Island it is stated that the amount of intermarriage of persons of the same name in Mount Desert Island, Gott's Island and Swan's and Deer Islands makes genealogy confusing. For example, take the Gott family as shown in Fig. 169; or a family from Swan's Island (Fig. 170). Even more marked examples are furnished by outer Long Island and the islands opposite Jonesport, Maine.

One sees how little opportunity is afforded in such pedigrees for the coming in of new blood. Little wonder that among these descendants of some ancestor who probably carried inferior mentality are some intellectually dull ones.

At western Martha's Vineyard Dr. Alexander Graham Bell (1889, p. 53) has made a careful genealogical study of the inhabitants. "I found," he says "a great deal of intermarrying and a great many consanguineous marriages." Concerning this locality Dr. Withington (1885, p. 26) says:

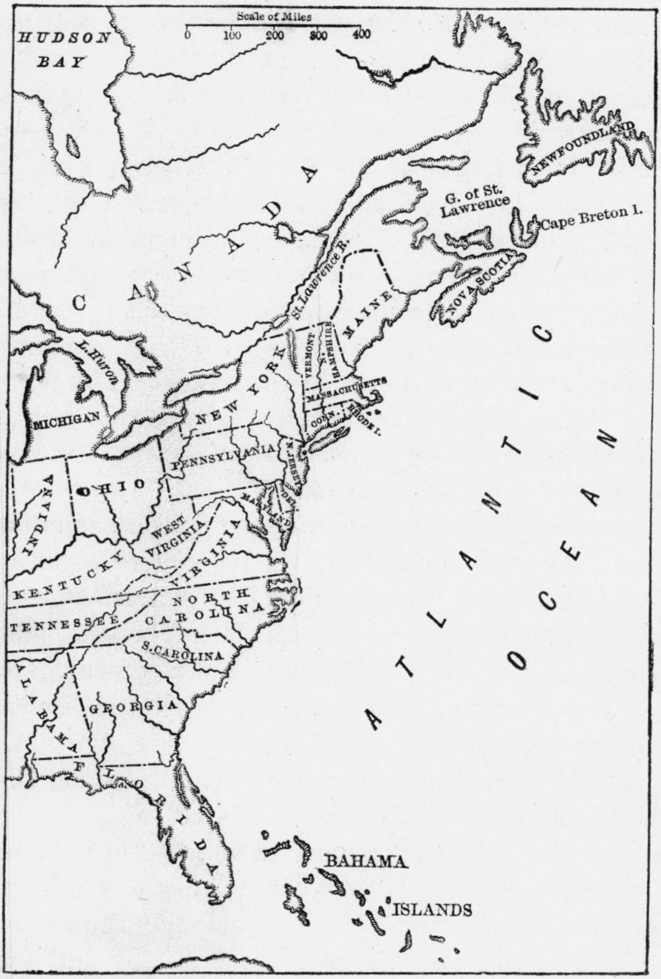

FIG. 168.—Coast of eastern North America, showing the broken coast line, with islands and peninsulas, each of which is, more or less, a center of consanguineous marriages. Such centers can be picked out by looking at the map.

"The inhabitants are farmers and fishermen of average intelligence and good character, not addicted to drunkenness. A lack of enterprise, associated doubtless with the

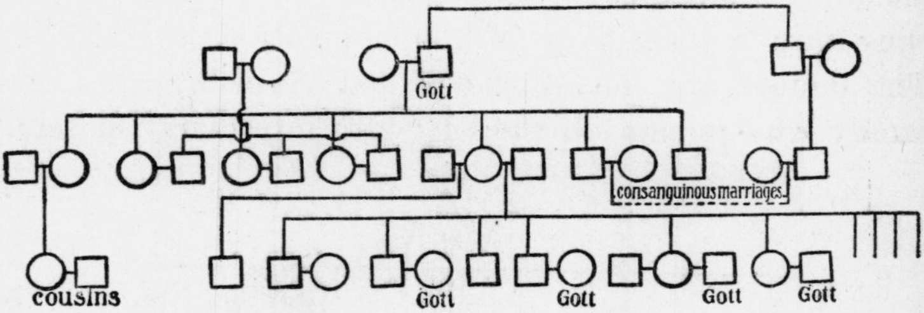

Fig. 169.—Pedigree of a portion of the Gott family of the Maine Islands, illustrating frequency of cousin marriages in an isolated community.

nature of their occupations, seems to be the cause of their intermarrying." In this locality deaf mutism is the striking trait. In 1880 there was a proportion of 1 to 25 of the whole

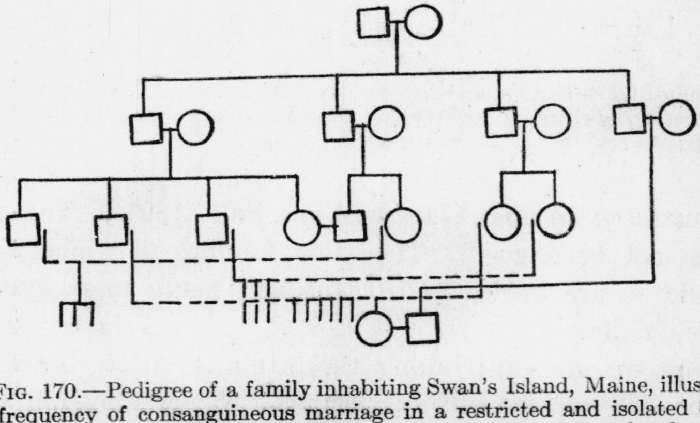

Fig. 170.—Pedigree of a family inhabiting Swan's Island, Maine, illustrating frequency of consanguineous marriage in a restricted and isolated community. The dotted lines connect cousins who have married each other.

population affected (Bell, 1889). Dr. Withington and Dr. Bell report cases of hermaphroditism also from this same locality.

Block Island, comprising about 10 square miles, lies about 40 miles both from Newport, Rhode Island, and from Montauk Point. There are some fine old family names including Ball, Cobb, Dodge, Hall and Littlefield, which constitute a large part of the population of 1,500 souls. The limited area has, however, led those branches of the family who remain on the island to intermarry closely, as

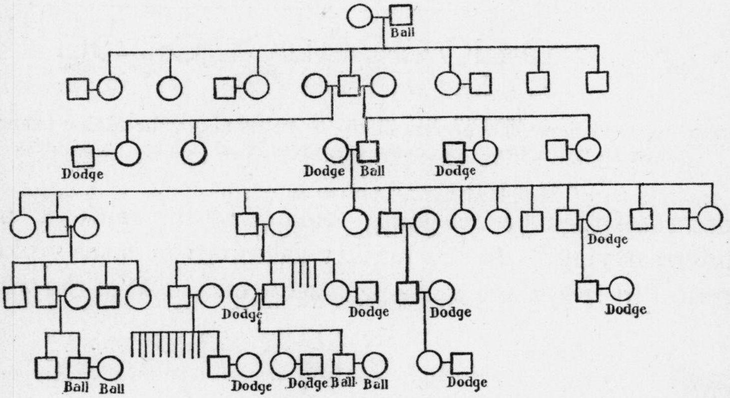

FIG. 171.—Portion of pedigree of the BALL family of Block Island showing frequency of marriage with DODGE and with BALL; a consequence of limited marriage selection in a small island.

illustrated in Fig. 171 based on Ball (1891). The result has not been good. There are families in which all the children are mentally deficient and many marriages that are childless.

As we go south along the Atlantic coast, beaches or "banks" replace offshore islands. When they are so far from the mainland, as at Pamlico Sound, as to make intercommunication difficult, consanguineous marriages occur in extraordinary frequency. A wide-spread trait that may be ascribed to such inbreeding is suspicion and mental dullness; and a relative high frequency of insanity. Even some of the islands of Chesapeake Bay show numerous marriages of kin. Thus Arner (1908, p. 16) states that in Smith's Island, separated from the peninsula of Maryland by twelve miles of water "consanguineous marriages have been very frequent until now nearly all are more or less interrelated. Out of a hundred or more families of which I obtained some record, at least five marriages were between cousins." Over 30 per cent of the inhabitants bear one surname (Evans) and they with Bradshaw, Marsh and Tyler comprise about 59 per cent of the population. The resident physician, here, had noted in 3 years in the community of 700 persons no case of idiocy, insanity, epilepsy or deaf mutism. At the tropics, islands appear again. In some parts of the Bahamas there is a record of consanguineous marriages. C. A. Penrose (1905, pp. 409–414) has described the condition at George Island near Eleuthera Island and at Hopetown, Abaco Island. In George Island close intermarriage occurs, and there is a large proportion of eye diseases, including cataract, and dwarfs with low mental acumen. At Hopetown there are about 1,000 whites. In 1785 a woman, Wyanne Malone, came from Charlestown, South Carolina, with her four children to Hopetown. Three of them married and settled there, a granddaughter marrying a Russell. "From this stock most of the present inhabitants of Hopetown have descended and the names of Malone and Russell are constantly met with throughout the settlement." At Hopetown consanguineous marriage is accompanied by deaf mutism, idiocy, insanity (melancholia) and abnormal appendages.

The island of Bermuda shows the usual consequence of island life. A correspondent writes: "In some of the Parishes (Somerset and Paget chiefly) there has been much intermarriage, not only with cousins but with double first cousins in several cases. Intermarriage has chiefly caused weakness of character leading to drink, not lack of brains or a certain amount of physical strength, but very inert and lazy disposition."

The foregoing studies will suffice to demonstrate, first, the importance of the barrier of water in tending to increase consanguineous marriage and second, the consequences of such consanguineous marriages.

In addition to islands, peninsulas also are more or less isolated and might be expected to yield the same results as islands. There is much evidence that this is so. Cape Cod is a good illustration of a peninsula. Thus Twining (1905, p. 12, note) after giving the pedigree of the descendants of Isabel Twining of Yarmouth who married Francis Baker says, "The frequency of intermarriage between Baker, Chase and Kelly in these records is distinctly observable; it is especially true of the first four generations, confined to the narrow limits of the Cape." Other data proving consanguinity in parentage of Cape families are not difficult to find. Thus Rich (1883, p. 525) tells of William and Mary Dyer, first cousins and Quaker immigrants from England and married. William Dyer (their son?), born 1653, came to Barnstable and married, in 1686, Mary Taylor. Their offspring all married and settled around him and soon became among the most influential people of the town—a position they maintain to this day. "At a recent visit to the Congregational Sunday School, I noticed," says the author, "all officers, many teachers, organist, ex-superintendent, and pastor's wife all Dyers. A lady at Truro united in herself 4 quarters Dyer; father, mother and both grandmothers Dyers." Whether consanguineous marriages at Cape Cod have led to an unusual frequency of any "defects" I cannot say.

Another peninsula of whose marriages there is a record is that of Point Judith. Withington (1885, pp. 14, 15) mentions five marriages of first cousins and two of second cousins. In these marriages insanity (manic-depressive?) and apoplexy were common.

Passing south the peninsulas projecting into Chesapeake Bay often offer extremely isolated situations. A physician of one of the extreme points of Dorchester County, seventeen miles from the railroad, writes me that most of the marriages of that locality—"in fact I may say all, were between relatives and usually of the same name, and with the usual result, dwarfed stature or born crippled, blunted intellect or born idiots." This statement seems to me probably exaggerated—what is meant doubtless is that an exceptional proportion were thus affected.

Finally at Carteret County, North Carolina, we have another example of peninsular conditions which have led to an extreme frequency of consanguineous marriages. Perhaps three-fourths of the inhabitants of the county bear one of four names, and mental deficiency is found in many of the children.

There are other points on our coast which I have not had time to inquire into. It is safe to assume that, in the absence of peculiar, disturbing conditions, all small, inhabited islands off the coast and most of the more isolated peninsulas will show numerous consanguineous marriages and a large proportion of some one of a variety of defects. You can pick out such localities by looking on the map.

b. Barrier of Topography.—A most important barrier is a height of land. How important it is is clear to anyone who has lived in a valley and noted the freedom with which movements of the population take place along the valley as contrasted with movements up the hills to an elevation of even 200 to 500 feet. The valley forms a social center and acquaintances are made and marriages arranged there. Hemmed in by the barriers of the hills and a human inertia that objects to raising the weight of the body, the valley becomes an endogamous center. Such a tendency is much exaggerated in the great valleys of the Appalachian chain. The cradle of the Jukes, however, was in a small valley hemmed in by steep hills only 300 feet high. The valleys of the Taconic Range, of the Catskills, of the Ramapo Mountains of New York are, or have been, regions of much inbreeding and not a little incest, and the product has been much feeble-mindedness, criminality and albinism (Fig. 172). As the mountains rise to the southwestward so do inbreeding, pauperism, and defect, reaching their fullest fruition in the mountain fastnesses of western Virginia and eastern Kentucky and Tennessee. But the story of the effect of this mountain range and its valleys upon consanguineous matings, defect, and crime in America has still to be written.

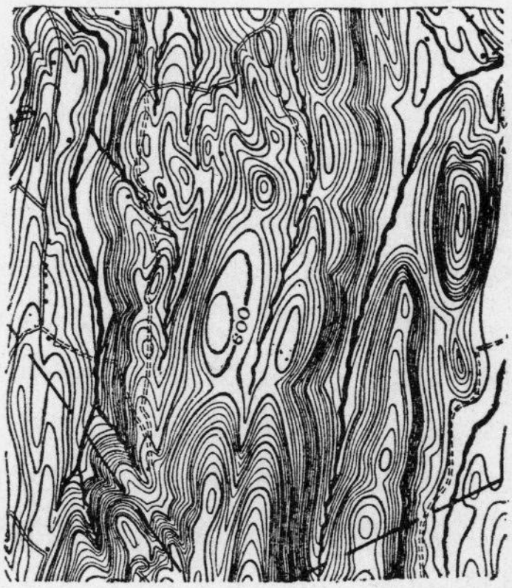

Fig. 172.—A portion of the U. S. Geological Survey topographic map of the region on the border of the center of the home of the Jukes, showing long, well watered valleys with relatively steep slopes; scale 1: 62,500. Contour interval, 20 feet.

In other countries, longer settled, the influence of mountain barriers is better appreciated. Very famous are the cretins and the imbeciles of the Alps. And from the Chin Hills of Burmah, the Rev. H. East writes about that place as follows (American Naturalist, 1909): "Rau Vau village has been isolated for about seven generations. It contains about sixty houses and possibly two hundred inhabitants. Of these, ten are idiots, many are dwarfs and some hydrocephalic. A number of cases of syndactylism and brachydactylism occur."

B. Social Barriers

The second set of barriers is *social*. These barriers are extremely numerous and complex. There is the barrier of

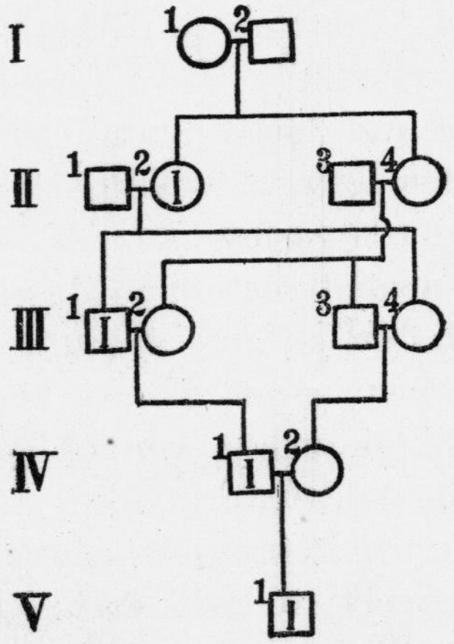

Fig. 173.—Inheritance of a neuropathic taint in a highly inbred family. I, 1, 2, Ferdinand and Isabella of Spain. II, 2, 4, two daughters, Joanna who was insane and Mary; II, 1, 3, their respective consorts, Philip, a weak man and Emanuel also weak; III, 1, is Charles V a great ruler but eccentric, cruel, and subject to melancholia; III, 2, is Isabel; III, 3, is John III of Portugal, a weak man; III, 4, Catherine; IV, 1, is Philip II, morose, sluggish, cruel; IV, 2, is Mary; V, 1, is Don Carlos, "one of the most despicable and unfortunate specimens of humanity in modern history." I (within the symbols) insane. Woods, 1906, pp. 145, 146.

the clan and pride of blood, the barrier of language, the barrier of race, and the barrier of religious sect.

a. The Barrier of the Clan with its pride of blood leads to self-satisfaction and not infrequently to a desire to concentrate wealth and power. This is the barrier that has led the royal families of Europe to inbreed with such disastrous effect, as illustrated by the house of Spain (Woods, 1902, p. 3), Fig. 173. The barrier of the clan is causing the downfall of more than one of America's grand families. The words of Mr. Francis N. Balch are apt here: "I tell you signs are not wanting that if the fine old New England blood despises the ignorant foreigner and stands aloof from him, there will soon be another interesting example of a fine old stock—and our Planters' stock *is* a fine old stock, and a *sturdy* stock,—making a pathetic and unedifying end" (Balch, 1905, p. 22).

b. The Barrier of the Social Status.—This is important where one social class forms a small portion of the community, represented by only a few families. I have in mind a group of persons in a small section of Massachusetts affected by albinism. Probably on this account, together with a mental inferiority, they seem to have been socially ostracized by their neighbors and so were obliged to marry each other. In another instance two families standing above the others in the community in progressiveness and wealth have intermarried extensively; almost exclusively. The effect on consanguineous marriage of an isolated position is well shown by the community of Fort Mardick concerning which a valuable monograph has been written by L. and G. Lancry. They say: "Four families constitute the origin (1670) of the population of Fort Mardick." "This small nucleus was implanted alongside of a population speaking another tongue, having other customs and other occupations than its own, being even more or less hostile to it." To-day, of 300 families 38 bear the name of Everard, of which 9 are Everard-Everard, 36 Hars, 27 Zoonekindt, 24 Benard, and so with the other surnames. To avoid inevitable confusion sobriquets are frequently applied, such as Gros-os, Gros-dos, Bosco, etc. In this community the striking character is sterility. Thus, consanguineous marriages are more than twice as apt to be sterile as non-consanguineous (7.5% : 16%); a single child is 2½ times as common with consanguineous as non-consanguineous marriages and the closer the relationship of the couple the greater the chance of sterile marriage.

In this category may be placed the barrier of life in an institution. A public institution brings together men and women so intimately that marriage frequently occurs after leaving the institution. Thus two persons with the same trait become parents. This is not, strictly, consanguineous marriage but it has much of the essential element of such marriage—viz., the marriage of persons with the same defects. Certainly almshouses in which segregation of the sexes is imperfect yield numerous depauperate and imbecile offspring and there is reason for suspecting that sanatoria and hospitals for the "curable" insane do likewise. That institutions for the deaf mutes lead to intermarriage of persons of this class is notorious. Thus Bell (1884, p. 4) says: "I desire to direct attention to the fact that in this country *deaf mutes marry deaf mutes*. An examination of the records of some of our institutions for the deaf and dumb reveals the fact that such marriages are not the exception but the rule," and later (p. 46) he cites as a cause for this preference "segregation for the purposes of education."

c. **The Barrier of Language** is extremely important in promoting consanguineous marriages or the matings of persons with the same defect. Thus with regard to deaf mutes Bell (1884,p. 44) says: "The practice of the sign language hinders the acquisition of the English language; it makes deaf mutes associate together in adult life, and avoid the society of hearing people; it thus causes the intermarriage of deaf mutes and the propagation of their physical defect." The importance of this barrier is seen among recent immigrants. These tend to herd together largely because of desire to be with people who speak the same language. Thus immigration instead of directly tending to promote matings of dissimilar and unrelated blood, under modern conditions at

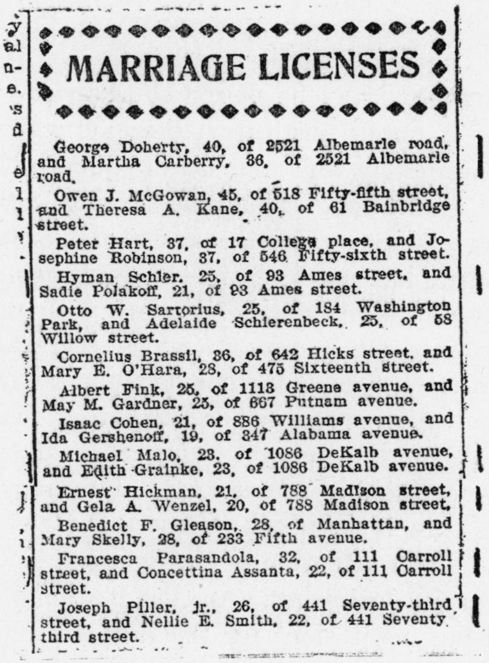

MARRIAGE LICENSES

George Doherty, 40, of 2521 Albemarle road, and Martha Carberry, 36, of 2521 Albemarle road.

Owen J. McGowan, 45, of 518 Fifty-fifth street, and Theresa A. Kane, 40, of 61 Bainbridge street.

Peter Hart, 37, of 17 College place, and Josephine Robinson, 37, of 546 Fifty-sixth street.

Hyman Schler, 25, of 93 Ames street, and Sadie Polakoff, 21, of 93 Ames street.

Otto W. Sartorius, 25, of 184 Washington Park, and Adelaide Schierenbeck, 25, of 58 Willow street.

Cornelius Brassil, 36, of 642 Hicks street, and Mary E. O'Hara, 28, of 475 Sixteenth street.

Albert Fink, 25, of 1118 Greene avenue, and May M. Gardner, 25, of 667 Putnam avenue.

Isaac Cohen, 21, of 886 Williams avenue, and Ida Gershenoff, 19, of 347 Alabama avenue.

Michael Malo, 23, of 1086 DeKalb avenue, and Edith Grainke, 23, of 1086 DeKalb avenue.

Ernest Hickman, 21, of 788 Madison street, and Gela A. Wenzel, 20, of 788 Madison street.

Benedict F. Gleason, 28, of Manhattan, and Mary Skelly, 28, of 233 Fifth avenue.

Francesca Parasandola, 32, of 111 Carroll street, and Concettina Assanta, 22, of 111 Carroll street.

Joseph Piller, Jr., 26, of 441 Seventy-third street, and Nellie E. Smith, 22, of 441 Seventy-third street.

Fig. 174.—Clipping from a Brooklyn (N. Y.) newspaper, spring of 1911, showing frequency of marriages between persons from the same address. In the case of recent immigrants this frequently implies that the pair have come from the same home village and are, very likely, somewhat closely related.

first has an exactly opposite effect. The marriage licenses of a large city frequently show bride and groom from the same house—this means frequently, if not usually, that they speak the same dialect, come, very likely, from the same town in the old country, and are probably cousins of some degree (Fig. 174). Even in the well-established populations a barrier of language may cause segregative marriage selection and, if the population is small, lead to consanguinity. Thus at Miscou Island part of the population speaks French and part English and this intensifies the liability to consanguineous marriage.

d. **The Barrier of Race** is of the very greatest importance in promoting marriage of kin—especially if one race be in a marked minority as the negroes are in New Hampshire and the whites are in the Mississippi River bottom around Vicksburg or in parts of the West Indies. As a striking instance of consanguinity in a colored population in the north may be cited the "Jackson-White" clan of the Ramapo mountain region.

e. Finally, the **barrier of religious sect** has been erected again and again to insure the intermarriage of the faithful only. This is illustrated by the teachings of the Society of Friends and smaller sects such as the Dunkers, Shakers and Amish. Of the Dunkers, Gillen (1906) states: "In their early history marriage out of the church was punishable by expulsion (Chronicon Ephraterise, pp. 96, 346f). It is still frowned upon, but the process of liberalization now in progress has modified the attitude of the Church. In some congregations families intermarry generation after generation. But the degree of kinship is not so close that any evil results appear in the offspring." Nevertheless one sees the danger that any small sect with such tenets runs. A critical study of the Amish of southeastern Pennsylvania with much marriage of kin shows a sufficient frequency of epilepsy and crippled children to serve as a warning that a defect is in the blood of some of the strain that in time will affect the entire sect who remain in that part of the country. It is difficult to see how any religious sect would have a tenet so opposed to the laws of Nature and God as practically to compel consanguineous marriage.

Many other sects are in a worse condition biologically than the Amish. Indeed, the smaller the sect the more apt are its adherents to be thrown closely together and so to become intimately acquainted with one another exclusively; and it is easy to see that in a few generations cousin marriage will be the rule in such sects. From this point of view the Special Report of the Census upon Religious Bodies (1906) becomes of great biological interest. In this report we read of the Duck River Baptists, one-third of whom (2,181) are in the Duck River Association; of the General Six Principle Baptists with 90 per cent of its membership in Rhode Island; of the Amana Society, all (about 1,700) located in Iowa County, Iowa; of the Braederhoef Mennonite Church of Bonhomme County, South Dakota, with 275 members, of the Reformed Presbyterian Church (covenanted) with 17 members, all at North Union, Pa.; and of the 725 Schwenkfelders of Eastern Pennsylvania. In some of these sects it is probable that the tenet of marriage inside the sect does not obtain, but without such a tenet the result tends to follow and we can but regard such small sects as eugenically unfortunate.

CHAPTER V

MIGRATIONS AND THEIR EUGENIC SIGNIFICANCE

1. Primitive Migrations

The human species has come to occupy the entire habitable globe. This fact is mute testimony of man's migratory capacity and tendencies. Just as the Norwegian lemming has been observed, in consequence of several years of favorable conditions for breeding in its mountain home, to spread over the surrounding territory in great bands seeking less crowded breeding-grounds; even as the army worm and the grasshopper swarm from their native territory; so man, also, under the pressure of crowded conditions, poverty and oppression or lured by brighter prospects elsewhere, may move in hordes to other lands that seem to offer better opportunities. Thus Asia seems to have debouched her surplus population upon Europe in the shape of the Huns during the fourth and fifth centuries of our era and the Turks during the fourteenth and fifteenth centuries. So the Anglo-Saxons and the Normans successively swarmed upon England. So, among savages, the Masai of Africa moved upon the neighboring tribes and established themselves over much of southeastern Africa. So in the last three centuries the Americas and Australia have witnessed the greatest migrations that the world has ever seen, hundreds of thousands annually coming from overcrowded Europe and Asia to the "New World."

2. Early Immigration to America

For us in America the phenomena of migration should have a special interest. Excepting for the few scores of thousands of Indians, there was a continent devoid of a population—a clean slate upon which history was to be written and where the effect of "blood" in determining that history might be traced. Fortunately, almost from the beginning, records were made and many have been preserved, despite fire, energetic housecleaners and rats, so that many materials for such a study are still available. It would be a grand contribution to scientific, biological history to show how *traits* of the individual immigrants, no less than conditions, political and other, determined the deeds of communities. For a community is the sum of its constituent individuals, and what each individual does depends on his innate sensitiveness and the vigor and kind of his reactions to the stimuli of conditions. With a given set of conditions the idiosyncrasies of response of the constituent individuals determine the details of history; and these idiosyncrasies depend quite as much on inheritable traits as on training and experience; for just what effect training and experience shall have on the individual depend upon the nature of his protoplasm. Into this grand but unworked historical field we cannot hope to enter here, but a hasty survey of the subject will be attempted.

It would be very difficult now to construct the wave of immigration to the territory of the present United States from 1607 to 1776. The census of 1790 gave a population of nearly 4,000,000; and making every allowance for the high net fecundity of the early immigrants, it is clear that at least a hundred thousand persons must have come in ships from Europe to North America during those 170 years. A concrete idea of the numbers may be gained by the statement (Fiske, 1905, pp. 77, 155, 197) that starting about 1615 Virginia had acquired in 4 years a population of 4,000 souls; between 1630 and 1640, 20,000 persons came to New England [1] but during the following century immigration practically ceased, having been discouraged; and from 1681 to 1684 Pennsylvania gained 8,000 inhabitants. The estimated arrivals from 1776 to 1820 number 250,000 and about 28,000,000 more to 1910.

Since the first few scores of thousands of immigrants had the greatest influence on the ideals of the colonies they established and since their blood has had the longer time to show its effects, and since their traits have had the greatest chance to disseminate widely, they deserve special consideration. The great interest taken in these "forefathers" by their descendants is justified even from the biologic-historic point of view, for their families were large, the pedigrees of their families were often carefully kept and are, for the most part, reliable, and we know much about the characteristics of many of the males who reached maturity. We observe, also, in the colonies the same tendency of persons similar in origin and tastes to segregate that is observed among modern immigrants.

On the James River the first settlers consisted chiefly of "discredited idlers and would-be adventurers," [2] more than half of them "gentlemen" of good family but untrained in labor, trusting for a change of fortune in the new land. Later, men, women and children were *sent* by the London Company to colonize the new land and that company was not particular as to quality. Even felons, murderers and women of the

[1] "It is positively known that early in the spring of 1630, eleven vessels left England for New England with 1700 passengers, arriving at the port of Salem, Mass. in June of that year. Fifty of these families settled in Lynn. In the same year the Massachusetts Bay Co. sent over 16 ships—all arrived safe in New England at the port of Salem." HARRIET R. COOKS, The Driver Family, N. Y. 1889, p. 26.

[2] WILSON, History of the American People, I., p. 45.

streets were at times sent over from London to relieve the city of them; and the governor, who was a pure euthenist, and seemed to think the better environment would cure their evil ways, welcomed all. However, in the middle of the seventeenth century, protests went out from the colony against being made a penal settlement, and in 1670 the House of Burgesses passed an act prohibiting the importation of convicts, but such importations did not wholly cease until declared illegal in Virginia in 1788. Perhaps 20,000 "convicts" altogether, by no means all immoral when judged by our present standards, were imported into the Virginia Colony (Butler, 1896).

But a better blood soon crowded into Virginia to redeem the colony. Upon the execution of Charles I (1649) a host of royalist refugees sought an asylum here, and the immigration of this class continued even after the Restoration. By this means was enriched a germ plasm which easily developed such traits as good manners, high culture, and the ability to lead in all social affairs,—traits combined in remarkable degree in the "first families of Virginia." From this complex and the similar complex of Maryland has come much of the bad blood that found the retreats of the mountain valleys toward Kentucky and Tennessee to its liking, and that spread later into Indiana and Illinois and gave rise, in all probability, to the Ishmaelites, a family of which hundreds have been supported in the almshouses and jails of Indiana. From this complex came also some of America's greatest statesmen and military leaders; the Randolphs, the Marshalls, the Madisons, the Curtises, the Lees, the Fitzhughs, the Washingtons and many others born with the instinct to command. Such are the descendants of the high-spirited cavaliers. It might have been predicted that the future state would be the Mother of Presidents and that in a civil war the hardest fought battles should be fought on her soil.

Further north, at Manhattan Island, a settlement was being made by another sort of people; a band of Dutch traders. The fur trade with the Indians waxed profitable. They maintained friendly relations with the Indians, as the main source of their wealth, and under their protection established trading posts up the North River even as far as the present site of Albany and along the valley of the Mohawk; while others went east as far as the Connecticut River. Little wonder that such blood, under the favorable environment of an admirable location, has created the commercial center of the western world.

On the bleak coasts of New England were being founded settlements of idealists, men who were willing to undergo exile for conscience' sake. They included many scholars like the pastor Robinson, Brewster who, while self-exiled at Leyden, instructed students at the University, John Winthrop "of gentle breeding and education," John Davenport whom the Indians named "So-big-study-man." [1] Little wonder that the germ plasm of these colonies of men of deep convictions and scholarship should show its traits in the great network of its descendants and establish New England's reputation for conscientiousness and love of learning and culture. As it was almost the first business of the founders of the colonies of Massachusetts Bay and New Haven to found a college, so their descendants—the families of Edwards, Whitney, Dwight, Eliot, Lowell, Woolsey and the rest have not only led in literature, philosophy and science but have carried the lamps of learning across the continent, lighting educational beacons from Boston to San Francisco. Nor is it an accident that on the soil tilled by these dissenters from the Established Church of England should be spilled the first blood of the American Revolution.

Later, to the shores of the Delaware, Penn led his band of

[1] COTTON MATHER, Magnolia III, 56.

followers, consisting of men and women whose natures were attracted to his principles of thrift, absence of show, and non-resistance. The germ plasm of his followers soon peopled Penn's woods and it is not due solely to chance that Pennsylvania has the largest number of homes owned and free from debt of any state and that the "powers that prey" prowl here so unmolested.

Thus the characteristics of each commonwealth were early determined by the traits of the persons who were attracted toward it. These traits still persist in their dwindling descendants who strive to secure the preservation in the state of the ideals inculcated by their forefathers.

One common characteristic these early immigrants had, which led them to leave family and friends, to undergo the trials of the long sea voyage in small ships and to settle in a rigorous climate among unreliable savages, and that was a willingness to break with tradition, to exchange the old for the new and better. This trait, that amounts in extreme cases to a "Wanderlust," is illustrated by the history of many a pioneer. For example, Simon Hoyt landed in Salem, Mass., in 1628, went in the first company of settlers to Charleston (1629); went to Dorchester (1630) with the first company of settlers there; joined the church at Scituate (1635) and built a house there; then, probably in the spring of 1636, migrated to Windsor, Connecticut colony, which he helped found. In 1649 he was granted land at Fairfield and in 1657 he died at Stamford. Thus in the space of thirty years Simon Hoyt lived in seven villages in America and was a founder of at least three of them—a truly restless spirit like many another settler, and the parent of a restless progeny.

Still another example is that of Hans Jorst Heydt of Strasburg. He fled to Holland when his native town was seized by Louis XIV, married there Anna Maria DuBois, a French Huguenot refugee from Wicres; came with her to

America and settled at New Paltz on the Hudson about 1710. Schismatic dissensions having broken out in the new colony, Heydt, with others, left and settled about 1717 in Philadelphia County not far from Germantown where he acquired several hundred acres of land, established a colony, built mills and entered upon various commercial enterprises. In 1731, having acquired a grant of 40,000 acres of land in the Shenandoah Valley, he migrated thither, became known as Baron Hite, and died there in 1760. One of his friends, Van Metre, who originally settled at New Paltz, had moved first to Somerset Co., New Jersey, then to Salem County in the same colony, later to Prince George's County, Maryland, and, finally, to Orange County, Virginia (Smyth, 1909). These are examples, merely, of the restlessness,—of the enterprising restlessness—of the early settlers.

This trait of restlessness and ambitious search for better conditions shows itself in the frequent migrations of the descendants of the early settlers. The abandoned farms of New England point to the trait in our blood that entices us to move on to reap a possible advantage elsewhere. "I don't know a farmer in Illinois," said a friend that has traveled over the state extensively, "who wouldn't sell his farm tomorrow and go to a distant state if he could be sure of bettering himself financially by doing so." This restlessness affects whole states. Thus from 1900 to 1910 the population of Iowa decreased because so many thousands of her people moved to the newly opened lands of Canada, Washington and Oklahoma. There was an ambitious tendency in the germ plasm out of which the forefathers developed that lured them from Europe and it is in the same germ plasm yet and shows itself in these later generations.

A shorter but not less pregnant migration is that to the metropolis from the surrounding rural districts. One after another, as they grow up, many or most of the young men and many of the young women also leave the farm for the office, shop and factory.

Now all of these migrations have a profound eugenic significance. The most active, ambitious and courageous blood migrates. It migrated to America and has made her what she has become; in America another selection took place in the western migrations and what this best blood—this crême de la crême—did in the west all the world knows. Great cities like Chicago, with its motto "I will," arose in a generation or two to the front rank of world metropolises, and New England, the early home of the sewing machine and the cotton gin, has yielded the palm to the central west, the home of the harvesting machine and the aëroplane.

And when the best and strongest migrated, the weaker minds were left behind to breed in the old homestead. A recent British Committee on Physical Deterioration[1] contains the testimony of Dr. C. R. Browne about conditions in the west of Ireland. He says: "The sound and the healthy—the young men and young women—from the rural districts emigrate to America in tremendous numbers, and it is only the more enterprising and the more active that go, as a rule." And Dr. Kelly, the Roman Catholic Bishop of Ross testified: "For a considerable number of years it has been only the strong and vigorous that go—the old people and the weaklings remain behind in Ireland." And even in New England we see signs of decadence of the old stock and men speak of racial deterioration. But the race as a whole has not deteriorated but only the New England representatives—the "left-behinds" of the grand old families, whose stronger members went west. Likewise in the rural and semi-rural population within a hundred miles of our great cities we find a disproportion of the indolent, the alcoholic, the feeble-

[1] Inter-departmental Committee on Physical Deterioration, Vol. I, p. 37, 1904.

minded, the ne'er-do-weel. I know intimately several such localities and have seen in one family after another, how the ambitious youth leave the parental roof-tree to try their fortunes in the city while the weakest young men stay behind, supported by their parents, or earning only enough to buy the liquor their defective natures crave, and are finally often forced to marry a weak girl and father her imbecile offspring. Such villages, depleted of the best, tend to become cradles of degeneracy and crime. Thus our great cities lure to themselves the best of the rural protoplasm, surround it with conditions that discourage reproduction, either by creating a disinclination to marriage or making it inconvenient and expensive to have children. So our great cities act anti-eugenically, sterilizing the best and leaving the worst to reproduce their like.

3. Recent Immigration to America

We have seen that the early immigrants to America were men of courage, independence, and love of liberty; and many of them were scholars or social leaders. Are these the characteristics of the immigrants at this later day? Let us examine the matter of immigration to America during the past hundred years. We shall find great differences from the immigration of the 17th and 18th centuries. Thus where the annual immigration was formerly a few thousand it is now hundreds of thousands. The wave of immigration is shown in Plate II. From 1820 to 1824, inclusive, the annual immigration was less than 10,000 but it has never fallen below that limit since. From 1825 to 1844 (with one exception) it has remained below 100,000, but in 1845 it passed that number and (excepting for 1862, in the depth of our Civil War) it has not since fallen below that limit. In 1905 it passed the 1,000,000 mark. The general population meanwhile rose from over 9,000,000 to 90,000,000, or only one-tenth as fast.

The wave of immigration shows great fluctuations in height. Referring to this the Commissioner General of Immigration (Keefe, 1910, p. 10) says: "This periodical rise and fall well represents the relative prosperity of the country, while the gradual increase from decade to decade may be taken as a fairly accurate index of the country's development and growth and its capacity to employ larger numbers of alien laborers."

It may be added that, on account of the departure of aliens, the net increase is less than the totals shown on the chart. Thus there were over 200,000 emigrants in the year ending June 30, 1910, leaving a net increase of something over 800,000. Even that is enormous, and no patriotic American can contemplate this vast annual addition to our kinds of germ plasm without inquiring as to the sort of potential traits they carry and the probable eugenic effect on our nation of this constant influx of new blood.

a. The Irish.—The consequences of the immigration of the earlier half of the period of 91 years are already seen. In 1846 there was a severe famine in Ireland and during the next five years over a million souls, or one-eighth of her population, emigrated thence to the United States, and Ireland has remained one of the most persistent sources of our foreign population. The traits that the great immigration from the south of Ireland brought were, on the one hand, alcoholism, considerable mental defectiveness and a tendency to tuberculosis; on the other, sympathy, chastity and leadership of men. The Irish tend to aggregate in cities and soon control their governments, frequently exercising favoritism and often graft. The young women were formerly much employed as household servants, but more recently have become shop girls and factory hands. Many of the Irish, most strikingly those of the northern part of that island, were among the nation's most intrepid frontiersmen and their descendants have served the nation in many important positions.

b. The Germans.—The year 1845 marked the rapid rise of the liberal spirit in Germany and a revolt against the attempt of the ruling class to weaken representative government. Then followed a great increase in immigration to America, advancing to over 140,000 a year for the three years 1852–54. The German immigrants of this period were lovers of freedom, full of courage and daring, and furnished the Union Army during the Civil War with many of its best officers. More recently the Protestant Germans have come to us as unskilled laborers and, after working for a time as farm hands, save enough to buy a place of their own. Great numbers, however, settle in the cities, make useful clerks and often rise to positions of trust. Germans are, as a rule, thrifty, intelligent and honest. They have a love of art and music, including that of song birds, and they have formed one of the most desirable classes of our immigrants.

c. The Scandinavian immigration first assumed considerable proportions in 1866 at the close of our Civil War, reached a maximum (105,000) in the prosperous year 1881, and has since declined somewhat, being now about 50,000 a year. Our Scandinavian population is found chiefly in the central west and northwest, above all in Minnesota, Wisconsin and Iowa. It tends to group itself into colonies; for example, 32 per cent of the entire population of Chisago Co., Minnesota, consisted, in 1900, of immigrants from Sweden; similarly, 26.5 per cent of the population of Traill Co. consists of persons who sailed to this country from Norway. In this tendency to form colonies the Scandinavian immigration of a decade ago shows much resemblance to that of the early English of the 17th century. Such colonization is bound to stamp the impress of the "national traits" upon the community. These national traits include a love of independence in thought and action, chastity, self-control of other sorts, and a love of agricultural pursuits. The latter is less marked in the Swedes than the Norwegians, for of the former only one-third, while of the later more than half, are engaged in farming.

d. **Austro-Hungary.**—The immigration from Austro-Hungary was the next to assume large proportions. It first became considerable with 17,000 in 1880; rose to 77,000 in 1892, and to 338,000 in 1907. It now consists of diverse races; Germans, Slavonians, Croatians and Dalmatians, Bohemians, Magyars, Slovaks, Ruthenians, Roumanians. The latter races are brunet in skin, hair and eye color and of average to short stature. The Bohemians that have migrated to the United States are engaged prevailingly in agriculture. Colonies are found in the prairie states of the upper Mississippi Valley, and in Nebraska and Texas. The Report of the Commissioner-General of Immigration gives Illinois as the intended home of 26 per cent of the immigrant Bohemians and Moravians, New York of 19 per cent, Ohio of 9 per cent and Texas and Pennsylvania each of 7 per cent. In both rural and urban conditions they show prevailing traits of self-respect and pertinacity. The Slovaks in America (to whom nearly 8,000 were added in 1910) are agricultural laborers, not farm owners, but they have founded a few colonies, like that at Slovaktown, near Stuttgard, Ark. Most of those in the East become miners, especially of bituminous coal, and have settled largely in Pennsylvania.

e. **Hebrews** have formed a marked proportion of the population of North America from an early period; even in prerevolutionary times they penetrated to the frontier as peddlers. But the great immigration began with that from Germany and has continued from that country, from Austro-Hungary and Russia in ever increasing numbers.

For the most part they have settled in our large cities, and their frequency is roughly proportional to the size of the city, yet with a preponderance in the East. Though it is superficial to attempt to name the traits of even so relatively homogeneous a company as the Hebrews, yet a sort of average or prevailing condition may be recognized. As the Abstract of the Report of the Immigration Commission on Recent Immigration in Agriculture says, p. 41, "The Hebrew on the land is peaceable and law abiding, but he does not tamely submit to what he believes to be oppression and he has a highly developed sense of personal rights, civil and economic." Probably with few changes this statement would stand for the Hebrews of the cities where the mass of recent Hebrew immigrants occupy a position intermediate between the slovenly Servians and Greeks and the tidy Swedes, Germans and Bohemians. In earning capacity both male and female Hebrew immigrants rank high and the literacy is above the mean of all immigrants. Statistics indicate that the crimes of Hebrews are chiefly "gainful offenses," especially thieving and receiving stolen goods, while they rarely commit offenses of personal violence. On the other hand, they show the greatest proportion of offenses against chastity and in connection with prostitution, the lowest of crimes. There is no question that, taken as a whole, the hordes of Jews that are now coming to us from Russia and the extreme southeast of Europe, with their intense individualism and ideals of gain at the cost of any interest, represent the opposite extreme from the early English and the more recent Scandinavian immigration with their ideals of community life in the open country, advancement by the sweat of the brow, and the uprearing of families in the fear of God and the love of country.

f. The Italian immigration first passed the 10,000 mark

in 1881. That from Southern Italy has always been five or six times as great as from Northern Italy. Immigrants from the former country are darker and doubtless have derived part of their blood from Greece and Northern Africa. It is these South Italians that we generally have in mind when we speak of Italians. Eighty per cent of those who come are males and a quarter of them return each year to their homes. In America they become, prevailingly, general laborers, relatively few specifically farm laborers; yet they are going into agriculture to a considerable extent and buying land as they save the money. Of the agricultural Italians many are truck farmers near large cities, and a few isolated settlements have been made like that at Hammonton or at Vineland, New Jersey. Others are found in central New York State, and a few colonies have been established in the South where they compete with negro labor. Apparently North Italians are to a certain extent influenced in locating in this country by topography like that of their homes. "While sentiment often has much to do with the choice of a location," says Cance (1911, p. 23) "it can not be said that the success of the settlement at Genoa, Wis., is due to the Alpine aspect of the topography rather than to the excellence of the soil and the favorable markets; nor that the fine North Italian settlers of Valdese, N. C., would not have made more progress every way had they settled nearer markets and on level land where there was more fertility and less Swiss scenery." The traits of the Southern Italians are thus expressed: "The Italian has not the self-reliance, initiative resourcefulness nor self-sufficing individualism that necessarily marks the pioneer farmer." "On the whole the Italian farmer compares well with other foreign farmers in his neighborhood in industry, thrift, careful attention to details, crop yields and surplus returns from his farm. His strength lies in his patience, unflagging industry and capacity for hard, monotonous labor." Aside from his tendency to crimes of personal violence the average Italian has many excellent characteristics, not one of the least of which is his interest in his work, even as a day laborer. He assimilates fairly rapidly, especially in rural districts; not a few Irish girls marry Italian husbands when both are Catholics; and this assimilation will add many desirable elements to the American complex.

g. The Poles are distributed under their political affiliations as German, Austrian, Russian and so on. The race constitutes one of the largest contributors to the American population. The cause of this emigration of a large proportion of the European Poles is doubtless the political disabilities under which they have labored. Poles first began to form colonies in the United States in 1885 (in Texas), from 1895 they came in numbers to Wisconsin and Michigan, and later to Indiana and Illinois. More than any other recent immigrants, except the Italians, they become general laborers, largely in rural districts, and as they save money they buy farms. The Poles are independent and self-reliant though clannish. They love the land and work hard to gain a piece of it. They are able to make pay the farms of New England which the sons of the early settlers have abandoned. We may welcome this freedom-loving people whose blood is bound largely to replace that of the old New England stock.

h. The Portuguese are among our more recent immigrants, since their numbers did not exceed 2,000 per year until 1889 and first reached 5,000 in 1902. They are classified either as white (largely from the Azores) or dark, from the Cape Verde Islands. The former become farm laborers, general laborers, mill hands, and farmers, and are steady, reliable, and efficient. In Rhode Island they form a notable colony of potato planters; in Massachusetts their headquarters are at New Bedford and from this city they have spread through the "Old Colony" region and into Cape Cod. The Black Portuguese are the principal cranberry pickers employed on the Massachusetts bogs. "They are largely recruited from the ranks of dock laborers near New Bedford and neighboring cities. Five-sixths of them are men or boys, many of them single or without families in the United States." The cranberry pickers of Massachusetts are illiterate and neither resourceful nor intelligent; but this has the less eugenic significance since few settle permanently in this country.

Summarizing this review of recent conditions of immigration it appears certain that, unless conditions change of themselves or are radically changed, the population of the United States will, on account of the great influx of blood from South-eastern Europe, rapidly become darker in pigmentation, smaller in stature, more mercurial, more attached to music and art, more given to crimes of larceny, kidnapping, assault, murder, rape and sex-immorality and less given to burglary, drunkenness and vagrancy than were the original English settlers. Since of the insane in hospitals there are relatively more foreign-born than native it seems probable that, under present conditions, the ratio of insanity in the population will rapidly increase.

As to the question of increasing dependence and credulity among recent immigrants it appears that "the immigrant to the United States in a large measure assists as well as advises his friends in the Old World to emigrate." Next to this "the propaganda conducted by steamship agents is undoubtedly the most important immediate cause of emigration from Europe to the United States," especially in Austria, Hungary, Greece and Russia. While America will be slow to relinquish her position as the home of the oppressed of all nations, she may well oppose any practice that tends to lure persons here by raising false hopes of an easy acquisition of riches.

4. Control of Immigration

It has long been recognized in this country that it is a national duty to regulate immigration. Our present immigration laws recognize this right and duty. Section 2 of the Immigration Act has the following eugenic provisions:

"That the following classes of aliens shall be excluded from admission into the United States: All idiots, imbeciles, feeble-minded persons, epileptics, insane persons, and persons who have been insane within five years previous; persons who have had two or more attacks of insanity at any time previously; paupers; persons likely to become a public charge; professional beggars; persons afflicted with tuberculosis or with a loathsome or dangerous contagious disease; persons not comprehended within any of the foregoing excluded classes who are found to be and are certified by the examining surgeon as being mentally or physically defective, such mental or physical defect being of a nature which may affect the ability of such alien to earn a living; persons who have been convicted of or admit having committed a felony or other crime or misdemeanor involving moral turpitude; polygamists, or persons who admit their belief in the practice of polygamy, anarchists, or persons who believe in or advocate the overthrow by force or violence of the Government of the United States, or of all government, or of all forms of law, or the assassination of public officials; prostitutes, or women or girls coming into the United States for the purpose of prostitution or for any other immoral purpose; persons who procure or attempt to bring in prostitutes or women or girls for the purpose of prostitution or for any other immoral purpose."

Now while few dispute the right and the duty of this country to control immigration there is a difference of opinion as to the degree and nature of that control. There are those who think that the present restrictions are sufficient and beyond them immigration should be encouraged; there are others who believe that immigration should be much further restricted by requiring educational, property and other qualifications. This difference of opinion is based partly on differences of needs and ideals. Those who would keep the door open are largely employees of labor who need most of it to "develop" or exploit the resources of the country. Those who wish to restrict belong partly to the class of laborers and low-grade artisans who desire to keep wages high and partly to the old families who fear the consequences of this copious infusion of South-eastern European blood. This difference of opinion must, as is generally the case, be ascribed to ignorance. If we knew the probable consequences upon our national life we would probably be agreed what to do.

To a biologist it seems that the economic aspects of the immigration problem will take care of themselves, just because immigration is, from this side, self-regulatory. When wages fall immigration diminishes to a third or a quarter of the volume that it has in times of prosperity and high wages. Moreover, it is (isn't it?) a rather selfish policy to keep out those who are qualified to become good citizens that we may fatten the faster on their destitution. But on its biologic side the problem is real and urgent. How can we keep out defective germ plasm while we admit that which is strong? The attempt to do this by examination of the immigrant is as unscientific as it is inadequate. A person who by all physical and mental examinations is normal may lack in half of his germ cells the determiner for complete mental development. In some respects such a person is more undesirable in the community than the idiot (who will probably not reproduce) or the low-grade imbecile, who will be recognized as such and be selected against in marriage, or be sent by his neighbors to an institution where he may be kept from reproducing. Nor can the immigration problem be solved by excluding on the ground of race or native country. No one has suggested excluding the natives of Switzerland, yet a normal woman from the neighborhood of

Tenna, Canton Graubunden, may become a focus of hemophilia in this country. On the other hand, the exclusion of one Hungarian family of my acquaintance would have deprived American Universities of three of their best scientific professors. The fact is that no race *per se*, whether Slovak, Ruthenian, Turk or Chinese, is dangerous and none undesirable; but only those individuals whose somatic traits or germinal determiners are, from the standpoint of our social life, bad. While all somatically defective may well be excluded at once, it is, within limits, hazardous to admit any person permanently to this country because he has no undesirable somatic trait—for no one transmits to his progeny his somatic traits but rather the determiners in his germ plasm. The proper way to classify immigrants for admission or rejection is on the basis of the probable performance of their germ plasm. In other words, immigrants are desirable who are of "good blood"; undesirable who are of "bad blood."

Since "blood" cannot be judged by inspection of the individual what practicable method remains for separating the sheep from the goats? Experience indicates the one best way. Before any one person is admitted to citizenship let something be learned concerning his family history and his personal history on the other side of the ocean. How can this be done? By means of field workers performing a service similar to that which they are doing in this country, visiting the relatives of the person in question and learning his personal and family history. Is this feasible? Governments might interpose an objection, but it seems probable that the matter could be put before them so that they would not. Experience indicates that few families approached in the proper spirit would decline to give information. It is then only a matter of money to pay for the required studies. How much money? It appears that about 200,000 declarations of intention to become naturalized are filed annually in the United States. It seems probable that field workers by properly sorting their families geographically could each report on the average on ten persons a week or, say, 500 a year. This average is the more reasonable since brothers sometimes make declaration simultaneously so that the history of two persons can be got in one visit. At this rate 400 field workers would be required. At the low price of living abroad the cost of each field worker's salary and traveling expenses would not exceed $1,200, or $480,000 for all. With 10 district inspectors at $2,000, including traveling expenses, and a central office at $10,000, the total cost would be $510,000 a year, and this amount should furnish our government with a report on practically every applicant for naturalization, which would serve as a proper basis for judging of his desirability. Compared with the annual expenditure of over $100,000,000 in this country to take care of our defectives this amount seems small and would be well invested, for, within a decade, the annual saving to our institutions would pay for the work. Moreover, an increase of 50 cents in the head-tax of immigrants would supply funds enough for the entire undertaking.

With a control such as is outlined above we may, it seems to me, face the addition annually of 200,000 Europeans to our citizenship with equanimity. Despite the tendency of encouraged immigration to bring in a less independent and self-reliant class, a significant selection is still exercised. This is clearly expressed in the Report on Emigration Conditions in Europe, published by the Immigration Commission, p. 11.

> The present-day emigration from Europe to the United States is for the most part drawn from country districts and smaller cities or villages and is composed largely of the peasantry and unskilled laboring classes. This is particularly true of the races or peoples from countries furnishing the newer immigration, with the conspicuous exception of Russian Hebrews, who are city dwellers by compulsion. Emigration being mainly a result of economic conditions, it is natural that the emigrating spirit should be

strongest among those most seriously affected, but notwithstanding this the present movement is not recruited in the main from the lowest economic and social strata of the population. In European countries, as in the United States, the poorest and least desirable element in the population, from an economic as well as a social standpoint, is found in the larger cities, and as a rule such cities furnish comparatively few emigrants. Neither do the average or typical emigrants of to-day represent the lowest in the economic and social scale even among the classes from which they come, a circumstance attributable to both natural and artificial causes. In the first place, emigrating to a strange and distant country, although less of an undertaking than formerly, is still a serious and relatively difficult matter, requiring a degree of courage and resourcefulness not possessed by weaklings of any class. This natural law in the main regulated the earlier European emigration to the United States, and under its influence the present emigration represents the stronger and better element of the particular class from which it is drawn.

A most potent adjunct to the natural law of selection, however, is the United States immigration act, the effect of which in preventing the emigration, or even attempted emigration, of at least physical and mental defectives is probably not generally realized. The provisions of the United States immigration law are well known among the emigrating classes of Europe, and the large number rejected at European ports, or refused admission after reaching the United States, has a decided influence in retarding emigration, and naturally that influence is most potent among those who doubt their ability to meet the law's requirements.

If increasing attention is paid to the selective elimination at our ports of entry of the actually undesirable (those with a germ plasm that has imbecile, epileptic, insane, criminalistic, alcoholic, and sexually immoral tendencies); if agents in Europe learn the family history of all applicants for naturalization; if the luring of the credulous and suggestible by steamship agents abroad and especially in the south-east of Europe be reduced to its lowest limits, then we may expect to see our population not harmed but improved by this mixture with a more mercurial people.

CHAPTER VI

THE INFLUENCE OF THE INDIVIDUAL ON THE RACE

As one stands at Ellis Island and sees pass the stream of persons, sometimes 5,000 in a day, who go through that portal to enter the United States and, for the most part, to become incorporated into it, one is apt to lose sight of the potential importance to this nation of the individual, or, more strictly, the germ plasm that he or she carries. Yet the study of extensive pedigrees warns us of the fact. Every one of those peasants, each item of that "riff-raff" of Europe, as it is sometimes carelessly called, will, if fecund, play a rôle for better or worse in the future history of this nation. Formerly, when we believed that factors blend, a characteristic in the germ plasm of a single individual among thousands seemed not worth considering: it would soon be lost in the melting pot. But now we know that unit characters do not blend; that after a score of generations the given characteristic may still appear unaffected by the repeated unions with foreign germ plasm. So the individual, as the bearer of a potentially immortal germ plasm with innumerable traits becomes of the greatest interest. A few examples will illustrate this law and its practical importance.

1. Elizabeth Tuttle

From two English parents, sire at least remotely descended from royalty, was born in Massachusetts Elizabeth Tuttle. She developed into a woman of great beauty, of tall and commanding appearance, striking carriage, "of strong will, extreme intellectual vigor, of mental grasp akin to rapacity, attracting not by a few magnetic traits but repelling" when she evinced an extraordinary deficiency of moral sense.

"On November 19, 1667, she married Richard Edwards of Hartford, Connecticut, a lawyer of high repute and great erudition. Like his wife he was very tall and as they both walked the Hartford streets their appearance invited the eyes and the admiration of all." In 1691, Mr. Edwards was divorced from his wife on the ground of her adultery and other immoralities. The evil trait was in the blood, for one of her sisters murdered her own son and a brother murdered his own sister. After his divorce Mr. Edwards remarried and had five sons and a daughter by Mary Talcott, a mediocre woman, average in talent and character and ordinary in appearance. "None of Mary Talcott's progeny rose above mediocrity and their descendants gained no abiding reputation."

Of Elizabeth Tuttle and Richard Edwards the only son was Timothy Edwards, who graduated from Harvard College in 1691, gaining simultaneously the two degrees of bachelor of arts and master of arts—a very exceptional feat. He was pastor of the church in East Windsor, Connecticut, for fifty-nine years. Of eleven children the only son was Jonathan Edwards, one of the world's great intellects, preeminent as a divine and theologian, president of Princeton College. Of the descendants of Jonathan Edwards much has been written; a brief catalogue must suffice: Jonathan Edwards, Jr., president of Union College; Timothy Dwight, president of Yale; Sereno Edwards Dwight, president of Hamilton College; Theodore Dwight Woolsey, for twenty-five years president of Yale College; Sarah, wife of Tapping Reeve, founder of Litchfield Law School, herself no mean lawyer; Daniel Tyler, a general of the Civil War and founder of the iron industries of north Alabama; Timothy Dwight, the second, president of Yale University from 1886 to 1898; Theodore William Dwight, founder and for thirty-three years warden of Columbia Law School; "Henrietta Frances, wife of Eli Whitney, inventor of the cotton gin, who, burning the midnight oil by the side of her ingenious husband, helped him to his enduring fame; Merrill Edwards Gates, president of Amherst College; Catherine Maria Sedgwick of graceful pen; Charles Sedgwick Minot, authority on biology and embryology in the Harvard Medical School, and Winston Churchill, the author of *Coniston*."[1] These constitute a glorious galaxy of America's great educators, students and moral leaders of the Republic.

Two other of the descendants of Elizabeth Tuttle through her son Timothy, have been purposely omitted from the foregoing catalogue since they belong in a class by themselves, because they inherited also the defects of Elizabeth's character. These two were Pierrepont Edwards, who is said to have been a tall, brilliant, acute jurist, eccentric and licentious; and Aaron Burr, Vice-President of the United States, in whom flowered the good and the evil of Elizabeth Tuttle's blood. Here the lack of control of the sex-impulse in the germ plasm of this wonderful woman has reappeared with imagination and other talents in certain of her descendants.

The remarkable qualities of Elizabeth Tuttle were in the germ plasm of her four daughters also: Abigail Stoughton, Elizabeth Deming, Ann Richardson and Mabel Bigelow. All of these have had distinguished descendants of whom only a few can be mentioned here. Robert Treat Paine, signer of the Declaration of Independence, descended from Abigail, the Fairbanks Brothers, manufacturers of scales and hardware at St. Johnsbury, Vt., and the Marchioness of

[1] From a manuscript furnished by a reliable genealogist. The statements have not all been checked.

Donegal were descended from Elizabeth Deming; from Mabel Bigelow came Morrison R. Waite, Chief Justice of the United States, and the law author, Melville M. Bigelow; from Ann Richardson proceeded Marvin Richardson Vincent, professor of Sacred Literature at Columbia University, the Marchioness of Apesteguia of Cuba, and Ulysses S. Grant and Grover Cleveland, presidents of the United States.[1] Thus two presidents, the wife of a third and a vice-president trace back their origin to the germ plasm from which (in part) Elizabeth Tuttle was also derived, but of which, it must never be forgotten, she was not the author. Nevertheless, had Elizabeth Tuttle not been this nation would not occupy the position in culture and learning that it now does.

2. The First Families of Virginia

This remarkable galaxy arose by the intermarriage of representatives of various English aristocratic families. The story of these early matings is briefly as follows: Richard Lee, of a Shropshire family that held much land and many of whose members had been knighted, went, during the reign of Charles I, to the Colony of Virginia as Secretary and one of the King's Privy Council. "He was a man of good stature, comely visage, enterprising genius, sound head, vigorous spirit and generous nature." He gained large grants of land in Virginia. His son Richard married, in 1674, Laetitia, daughter of Henry Corbin and Alice Eltonhead. The Corbins were wealthy and extensive landowners in England for 14 generations, and the Eltonheads were also an aristocratic family and extensive landowners of Virginia, holding high offices in the colony. Richard and Laetitia had six sons and one daughter (Fig. 175). Their daughter Ann married Colonel William Fitzhugh, a descendant of the English barons of that name who took prominent parts in

[1] From the genealogist's manuscript, deposited at the Eugenics Record Office.

political and military movements of the day and occupied seats in parliament generation after generation. Their eldest son, Henry Fitzhugh, married Lucy Carter. One of their granddaughters married a Randolph; one of their sons, William Fitzhugh, a near neighbor and trusted friend of Washington, married Anne Randolph. *Their* daughter Anne married Judge William Craik; their daughter Mary married George Washington Parke Custis and became the mother of Mary Anne Randolph Custis and the grandmother of Robert E. Lee; and their son William Henry Fitzhugh married Anna Goldsborough.

Richard Lee, son of Richard and Laetitia (Corbin) Lee, married an English heiress, Martha Silk, and had several children of whom one married a Fairfax, another a Colonel Corbin and a third Major George Tuberville of an ancient English family, himself Justice, Sheriff and Clerk.

Philip Lee, another son of Richard, married a daughter of Hon. Thomas Brooke and Barbara Addison and their children married well. Thomas, brother of Philip, was a member of the House of Burgesses, member, and later president of the Council and later Acting Governor of the Colony. He married Hannah, daughter of Colonel Philip Ludwell, a descendant of a brother of Lord Cattington, a prominent statesman and diplomat of the reign of Charles II. One of the sons of Thomas and Hannah was Richard Henry Lee, a representative to the Continental Congress, who prepared the resolutions for independence; and another son was Francis Lightfoot Lee, a member of Congress; still another, Thomas, was a judge of the General Court.

Finally there was Henry Lee, son of Richard and Laetitia, who lived quietly at the ancestral Lee Hall. He married Mary, daughter of Colonel Richard Bland, descendant of Sir Thomas Bland, of ancient and honorable family, created baronet by Charles I. Mary Bland's grandfather, Theod-

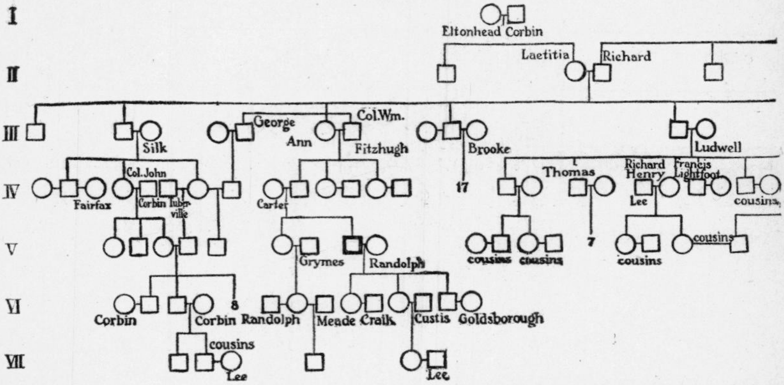

FIG. 175.—Portion of the LEE family

rick Bland, was speaker of the House of Burgesses, a member of the Council, inferior to none in his time. Of the three sons of Henry Lee and Mary Bland, John was a clerk of courts and a member of the House of Burgesses; Richard, was in the house of Burgesses and the House of Delegates; Henry, in the House of Burgesses, Conventions, and the State Senate. Such is a sample, merely, of the intermarriages of the first families of Virginia and their product—statesmen and military men, the necessary consequence of the determiners in their germ plasm.

3. THE KENTUCKY ARISTOCRACY

Nearly two centuries ago John Preston of Londonderry, Irish born though English bred, married the Irish girl Elizabeth Patton, of Donegal, and to the wilderness of Virginia took his wife and built their home, Spring Hill. "Of this union there were five children, Letitia, who married Colonel Robert Breckinridge; Margaret, who married the Rev. John Brown; William, whose wife was Susannah Smith; Anne, who married Colonel John Smith; and Mary, who married Benjamin Howard." From them have come the most conspicuous of those who bear the name of Preston, Brown,

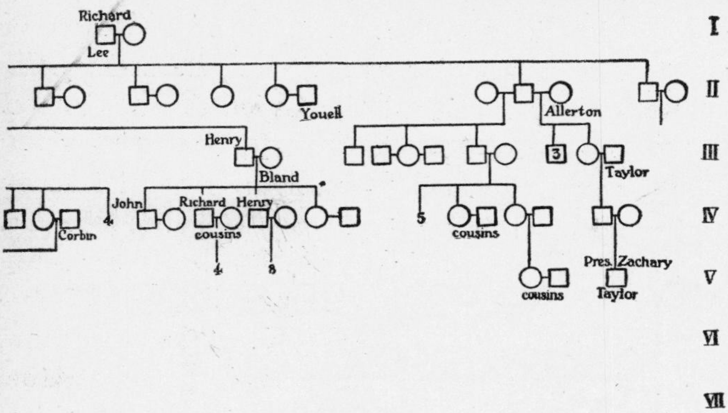

of Virginia, showing intermarriages.

Smith, Carrington, Venable, Payne, Wickcliffe, Wooley, Breckinridge, Benton, Porter and many other names written high in history.

"They were generally persons of great talent and thoroughly educated; of large brain and magnificent physique. The men were brave and gallant, the women accomplished and fascinating and incomparably beautiful. There was no aristocracy in America that did not eagerly open its veins for the infusion of this Irish blood; and the families of Washington and Randolph and Patrick Henry and Henry Clay and the Hamptons, Wickliffes, Marshalls, Peytons, Cabells, Crittendens, and Ingersolls felt proud of their alliances with this noble Irish family.

"They were governors and senators and members of Congress, and presidents of colleges and eminent divines, and brave generals from Virginia, Kentucky, Louisiana, Missouri, California, Ohio, New York, Indiana, and South Carolina. There were four governors of old Virginia. They were members of the cabinets of Jefferson and Taylor and Buchanan and Lincoln. They had major-generals and brigadier-generals by the dozen; members of the Senate and House of Representatives by the score; and gallant officers in the army and navy by the hundred. They furnished three of the recent Democratic candidates for Vice-president of the United States. They furnished the Union Army General B. Gratz Brown, General Francis P. Blair, General Andrew J. Alexander, General Edwin C. Carrington, General Thomas C. Crittenden, Colonel Peter A. Porter, Colonel John M. Brown, and other gallant officers. To the southern army they gave Major-General John C. Breckinridge, Major-General William Preston, General Randall Lee Gibson, General John B. Floyd, General John B. Grayson, Colonel Robert J. Breckinridge, Colonel W. C. P. Breckinridge, Colonel William Watts, Colonel Cary Breckinridge, Colonel William Preston Johnson, aide to Jefferson Davis, with other colonels, majors, chaplains, surgeons, fifty of them at least the bravest of the brave, sixteen of them dying on the field of battle, and all of them, and more than I can enumerate, children of this one Irish emigrant from the county of Derry, whose relatives are still prominent in that part of Ireland, one of whom was recently mayor of Belfast."

Overlooking the pardonable rhetoric and family pride in the last sentence, that neglects the hundreds of other ancestors of these famous men, the quotation has a scientific value in comparison with the product of Elizabeth Tuttle. The New England family glows with scholars and inventors, the Virginia and Kentucky families with statesmen and military men. The result is not due to the differences in the characteristics of Elizabeth Tuttle and Richard Edwards, Richard and Laetitia Lee, John and Elizabeth Preston, respectively, but to the different traits of the New England settlers as a whole and Virginia cavalier-colonists as a body. The initial person becomes a great progenitor largely because of some fortunate circumstance of personal gift or excellent reputation that enables his offspring to marry into the "best blood."

4. The "Jukes"

On the other hand, we have the striking cases of families of defectives and criminals that can be traced back to a single ancestor. The case of the "Jukes" is well known. We are first introduced to a man known in literature as Max, living as a backwoodsman in New York State and a descendant of the early Dutch settlers; a good-natured, lazy sot, without doubt of defective mentality. He has two sons who marry two of six sisters whose ancestry is uncertain but of such a nature as to lead to the suspicion that they are not full sisters. One of these sisters is known as "Ada Juke," also as "Margaret, the mother of criminals." She was indolent and a harlot before marriage. Besides an illegitimate son she had four legitimate children. The first, a son, was indolent, licentious and syphilitic; he married a cousin and had eight children all syphilitic from birth. Of the 7 daughters 5 were harlots and of the others one was an idiot and one of good reputation. Their descendants show a preponderance of harlotry in the females and much consanguineous marriage. The second son was a farm laborer, was industrious and saved enough to buy 14 acres of land. He married a cousin and the product was 3 stillborn children, a harlot, an insane daughter who committed suicide, an industrious son, who, however, was licentious, and a pauper son. The first daughter of "Ada" was an indolent harlot who later married a lazy mulatto and produced 9 children, harlots and paupers, who produced in turn a licentious progeny.

Ada had an illegitimate son who was an industrious and honest laborer and married a cousin. Two of the three sons were licentious and criminalistic in tendency and the third, while capable, drank and received out-door relief. All of the three daughters were harlots or prostitutes and two married criminals. The third generation shows the eruption of criminality. Excepting the children of the third son, none of whom were criminalistic, we find among the males 12 criminals, 1 licentious, 5 paupers, 1 alcoholic and 1 unknown; none were normal citizens. Among the females 3 were harlots, 1 pauper, 1 a vagrant and 2 unknown; none were known to be reputable. Thus it appears that criminality lies in the illegitimate line from Ada and not at all in the legitimate—doubtless because of a difference in germ plasm of the fathers.

The progeny of the harlot Bell Juke is a dreary monotony of harlotry and licentiousness to the fifth generation. Two in the fourth generation there are and two in the fifth against whom there is nothing and their progeny mostly moved to another neighborhood and are lost sight of. Very likely they have married into stronger strains and are founders of reputable families.

The progeny of Effie Juke and the son of Max (a thief) show to the fifth generation a different aspect. Some larceny and assault there is and not a little sexual immorality, but pauperism is the prevailing trait.

Thus, in the same environment, the descendants of the illegitimate son of Ada are prevailingly *criminal;* the progeny of Bell are *sexually immoral;* and the offspring of Effie are *paupers.* The difference in the germ plasm determines the difference in the prevailing trait. But however varied the forms of non-social behavior of the progeny of the mother of the Juke girls the result was calculated to cost the State of New York over a million and a quarter of dollars in 75 years—up to 1877, and their protoplasm has been multiplied and dispersed during the subsequent 34 years and is still marching on.

5. The Ishmaelites

Another example of a great family tracing back to a single man may be taken from "the Tribe of Ishmael" of Central

Indiana, as worked out under the direction of the Rev. Oscar C. McCulloch of the Charity Organization Society, Indianapolis. The progenitor of this tribe, Ben Ishmael, was in Kentucky as far back as 1790, having come from Maryland through Kentucky. One of his sons, John, married a half-breed woman and came into Marion County, Indiana, about 1840. His three sons who figure in this history married three sisters from a pauper family named Smith. They had altogether 14 children that survived, 60 grandchildren and 30 great-grandchildren living in 1888. "Since 1840 this family has had a pauper record. They have been in the almshouse, the House of Refuge, the Woman's Reformatory, the penitentiaries and have received continuous aid from the townships. They are intermarried with the other members of this group,—and with over two hundred other families. In this family history are murderers, a large number of illegitimacies and of prostitutes. They are generally diseased. The children die young. They live by petty stealing, begging and ash-gathering. In summer they "Gipsy" or travel in wagons, east or west. We hear of them in Illinois about Decatur and in Ohio about Columbus. In the fall they return. They have been known to live in hollow trees on the river bottoms or in empty houses. Strangely enough, they are not intemperate to excess."

"A second typical case is that of the Owens family, also from Kentucky. There were originally four children, of whom two have been traced, William and Brook. William had three children, who raised pauper families. One son of the third generation died in the penitentiary; his two sons in the fourth generation have been in the penitentiary; a daughter in the fourth generation was a prostitute with two illegitimate children. Another son in the third generation had a penitentiary record and died of delirium tremens." An illegitimate half-breed Canadian woman enters this family. There have been several murders and a continuous pauper and criminal record. There is much prostitution, but little intemperance.

"Brook had a son John, who was a Presbyterian minister. He raised a family of 14 illegitimate children. Ten of these came to Indiana, and their pauper record begins about 1850. Of the ten, three raised illegitimate children in the fifth generation."

The families with which the Ishmaelites intermarried (30 in number) came mostly from Kentucky, Tennessee, and North Carolina. "Of the first generation—of 62 individuals—we know certainly of only three. In the second generation we have the history of 94. In the third generation, we have the history of 283. In the fourth generation (1840–1860) we have the history of 644. In the fifth generation (1860–1880) we have the history of 57. Here is a total of 1,750 individuals. Before the fourth generation (from 1840–1860), we have but scant records. Our more complete data begin with the fourth generation, and the following are valuable. We know of 121 prostitutes. The criminal record is very large,—petty thieving, larcenies, chiefly. There has been a number of murders. The first murder committed in the city was in this family. A long and celebrated murder case known as the 'Clem' murder, costing the State immense sums of money, is located here, nearly every crime of any note belongs here." What a vivid picture has McCulloch drawn of the influence on a community of its "bad blood," forming an intergenerating, self-perpetuating, anti-social class—anti-social because possessed of such traits as feeble-mindedness, wandering mania, eroticism, and "moral imbecility." How slow the community is to protect itself by adopting some method of preventing their reproduction!

6. The Banker Family

The examples given above are extreme, to be sure; they were selected just because they are extreme. But it is just as true that every family whose early ancestors showed some striking trait reveals that trait now and again in the offspring. One can find evidence of this in almost any intelligently compiled genealogical history. Take, for example, the Banker family. There were two Dutchmen who were early settlers in New York State: Gerrit, who settled about 1654 in Albany, and Laurens, who settled some years later in Tarrytown. They were, apparently, not related and their descendants have not intermarried. The two lines present some striking contrasts.

"Gerrit appears to have been well educated for that time and was a very successful merchant and Indian trader, accumulating a considerable property. His descendants were largely merchants, although many become farmers." In general they maintained a high degree of culture and social rank. Several of them attained to positions of prominence in the affairs of the Colony before and during the Revolution. For example, the first Treasurer of the State and the first Speaker of the Assembly were both from this family, while several held commissions in the Revolutionary Army. Since that period they have been less prominent in public affairs, although maintaining a position of high social standing and respectability."

Laurens, on the other hand, had no education, could not write his name, at least when a young man, and was a laborer and farmer. His descendants "may be said in some ways to have started at the bottom. The family prior to the Revolution was obscure, its members were chiefly laborers, farmers, and artisans with only limited opportunities for education and acquiring but little of this world's goods. In the Revolution they actually furnished more soldiers than the Gerrit Banker family, but none of them held rank above a corporal. They were, in fact, as often described in legal documents, yeomen, and yeomen under a semi-feudal system. With the organization of the new nation a larger opportunity opened. To-day many of this family have reached places of high social standing while a few have been brought into a considerable degree of public prominence."[1] In this instructive example we see the persistence of an initial difference with a final tendency to approach a common level. Because in the absence of caste, and the desire to marry as well as possible, new and strong characters are introduced into the germ plasm.

[1] Compare Banker, 1909.

CHAPTER VII

THE STUDY OF AMERICAN FAMILIES

Nowhere else is a genealogical interest keener than in America. The possibility of tracing one's pedigree back to the first ancestor of the name in the country has inspired thousands of genealogical researches, and the demand for assistance in working out pedigrees has created the professional genealogist. Still the amateur's work, like most labors of love, is usually to be preferred because of the personal element involved.

1. The Study of Genealogy

The study of genealogy, under the stimulus of our modern insight into heredity, is destined to become the most important handmaid of eugenics. The conscientious and scientific genealogist records a brief biography of each person of the pedigree and such a biography should be an analysis of the person's traits; an inventory of his physical and mental characteristics; his special tastes and gifts as shown by his occupation and especially his avocations. It would be well, so far as possible, to go further than that, if not for publication at least for record.[1] It will be desirable to get a statement of physical weaknesses, diseases to which there was liability and causes of death. There are none of these classes of data that are not included in some genealogies; it

[1] The Eugenics Record Office has an isolated fire proof vault at Cold Spring Harbor, N. Y., in which it will receive and keep safe and confidential any records that genealogists will deposit there. All genealogical data is indexed on cards so as to be made accessible to properly qualified persons who wish to use it for justifiable purposes.

would be well if all were included in all genealogies. Another desideratum is abundant photographs of the persons whose biographies are given; especially, strictly full-face and profile, to facilitate comparisons; and two or three photographs at successive ages would be still better than one.

Attention should be paid to the form of the pedigree. The commonest form is that which begins with the first known male ancestor bearing the surname. His children are given, but in the later generations only the offspring of males are named. Few genealogies attempt either to trace the lines going through females or to give the ancestry of the consorts. A second form of pedigree begins with the author or some other one person and gives an account of all of his direct ancestors in ever expanding number toward the earlier generations. This method is scarcely more valuable than the other from a scientific point of view, based as it is upon the exploded idea that inheritance is from parents, grandparents, etc.

The ideal genealogy, it seems to me, starts with a (preferably large) fraternity. It describes fully each member of it. It then describes each member of the fraternity to which the father belongs and gives some account of their consorts (if married) and their children. It does the same for the maternal fraternity. Next, it considers the fraternity to which the father's father belongs, considers their consorts, their children and their grandchildren and it does the same for the fraternities to which the father's mother belongs. If possible, earlier generations are to be similarly treated. It were more significant thus to study in detail the behavior of all the available product of the germ plasms involved in the makeup of the first fraternity than to weld a chain or two of links through six or seven generations. A genealogy constructed on such a plan would give a clear picture of heredity, would be useful for the prediction of the characteristics of the generations yet unborn, and would, indeed, aid in bringing about better matings. It is to be hoped that the time will come when each person will regard it as a patriotic duty to coöperate in the compilation of such genealogical records even to the statement of facts which are, according to the (often false) conventions of the day, not considered "creditable."

2. Family Traits

The results of such genealogical studies will be striking. Each "family" will be seen to be stamped with a peculiar set of traits depending upon the nature of its germ plasm. One family will be characterized by political activity, another by scholarship, another by financial success, another by professional success, another by insanity in some members with or without brilliancy in others, another by imbecility and epilepsy, another by larceny and sexual immorality, another by suicide, another by mechanical ability, or vocal talent, or ability in literary expression. In some families the members are prevailingly slender, in others stout; in some tall, others short; some blue-eyed, others dark-eyed; some with flaxen hair, others with black hair; some have diseases of the ear, others of the eye, or throat or circulation. In some nearly all die of consumption; in others there is no weakness of the mucous membranes but a tendency to apoplexy; others die prevailingly of Bright's disease or valvular disease of the heart, or of pneumonia. In some families nearly all die at over 80, in others all die under 40 years of age. Stammering, hirsuteness, extra dentition, aquiline nose, lobeless-ears, crooked digits, extra digits, short digits, broad thumbs, ridged nails,—there is hardly an organ or the smallest part of an organ that has not its peculiar condition that stamps a family.

Said a lady to me, "I was traveling in Egypt and met a

man who was introduced to me as Mr. Osborn. I said to him 'My mother was an Osborn. I wonder if we are related.' He replied, 'Let me see if you have the Osborn thumb,'" and she was able to show the family trade-mark. How often a peculiar laugh, a trick of speech or gesture will serve to identify the family of a stranger. Once in a city where my family was well known but where I was a stranger I needed to get a check cashed and went to an office where my father and brother had done business. On explaining my need to the head of the firm he supplied it without hesitation, saying: "Though I have never seen you before I would know anywhere that you were a Davenport." So wonderfully are details of facial muscles, form of skull bones and nose cartilage stamped in the family blood. Such features as these deserve full treatment in the philosophical family history.

Many works on genealogy, as I have said, give a little account of family traits. A few of those have been excerpted from the published works and are reproduced here chiefly to illustrate the specificity of human families. Of course, except where there is much consanguineous marriage, not all traits will appear in all or even most individuals of the family, and new traits are being introduced by marriage. But certain characteristics because of their special nature or the frequency with which they occur in certain branches of the family will come to be known as "family traits."

Allerton (Allerton, 1888). The great majority of the family to-day, as always, are farmers; have never showed a tendency to city life. Next to farming, machinist is the most favored occupation. Mostly large framed, few blondes, slender and lithe in youth; fleshy in old age. A quick-tempered race; decided, uncommunicative, reserved.

Balch (MSS.). "Balch spelling" said to be a recognizable trait.

Bascom (Harris, 1870). Stout, compact form, head well set back upon the shoulders, dark skin, dark gray eye, massive head and round, high, full forehead.

Banning (Banning, 1908). Determination and will-power almost to point of stubbornness; faithful to friends and families, fairness to enemies; clannishness, ability for hard, reliable work, firmness of mouth.

Breed (Breed, 1892). As a rule, positive, determined, industrious and persevering in business and careful of their income.

Brinckerhoff (Brinckerhoff, 1887). Blue eyes, Roman features, magnetic and generous; ofttimes impulsive, sometimes absolutely wrong in actions and convictions but true and steadfast in the wrong. Usually can whistle a tune or sing a song without any apparent effort.

Buck (Buck, 1893). Quickness and activity in movement; fast walkers. One could seize with his right hand the toe of his left boot and whilst so holding it and standing erect jump with his right foot backwards and forwards over his left leg. Fluency in conversation and aptness for acquiring languages.

Cole (Cole, 1887). Asa Cole was a man of immense physical strength and endurance; he suffered a paralytic stroke. His son, John Cole, was a man of fine physique, and died from a stroke of apoplexy; a second cousin, Salmon Cole, was almost a giant in strength.

Colegrove (Colegrove, 1894). Strong individuality of character, often called peculiar or secretive, very self-reliant.

Doolittle (Doolittle, 1901). Large, robust physique, florid complexion, high spirit, jovial disposition.

Dwight (Dwight, 1874). Moderate sized families; longevity not high, commonly well-to-do and inclined to liberal culture; much military talent.

Humphreys (Humphreys, 1883). Self-reliance, readiness

of acquisition; professional men, few tradesmen and mechanics; artistic temperament, good talkers and eloquent speakers; benignity and quietness.

Johnsons of Harpswell, Maine (Sinnett, 1907). Hospitality, story-telling.

Kimball (Morrison, 1897). Powerful memory; few politicians.

Lemen (Lemen, 1898). Strongly accentuated mental and moral traits; a "family habit" of slight despondency; some gift for poetry.

Lindsay (Lindsay, 1889). Cheerfulness, hospitality.

Mell (Mell, 1897). Social, genial, fun-loving temperaments.

Mickley (Mickley, 1893). No lawyers, but other professions; nearly all in comfortable circumstances.

Neighbor or Nachbar (Neighbor, 1906). Not restive; neighborly, temperate.

Reed of Massachusetts (Reed, 1861). Few die of pulmonary complaints. Generally live to old age, 85 or 90 or even 100 years being nothing unusual. Capable of great endurance. Taller than average. One custom has prevailed among them to some extent; that of marrying relatives. "Consequences have been injurious; many of the offspring of such marriages dying in infancy, early youth or middle age, few living to advanced years, to say nothing of cases where effect has been still more melancholy."

Riggs (Wallace, 1901). A large proportion are governed by strong religious convictions and are active in religious thought and work. Many daughters of the family have married Presbyterian ministers and in due time became mothers of Presbyterian ministers themselves.

Root (Root, 1870). Eight sons of Samuel were tall (with two exceptions), quick, subject to frequent attacks of headache; general family trait a prominent (frequently aquiline) nose, light complexion, blue eyes, somewhat commanding presence and vivacity of manner.

Sinclair (Morrison, 1896). Fond of athletic sports and feats of strength and skill, much mechanical knowledge, practical, loving activities and experiences of frontiersman better than books or studies of scholars and of professional life. Love of military life.

Slayton (Slayton, 1898). Musical, especially vocally. Large families, twenty pairs of twins and one set of triplets recorded.

Tapley (Tapley, 1900). Quick and nervous movements, fondness for music, short stature, genial disposition. Men of affairs rather than of professions.

Tiffany (Tiffany, 1903). Complexion dark, eye bright with expression changing rapidly with mood indicating health, sympathy, grief, determination or anger with quickness and unerring certainty; "a Tiffany mark."

Twining (Twining, 1905). Broad-shouldered, dark hair, prominent nose, nervous temperament, temper usually quick, not revengeful. Heavy eyebrows, humorous vein and sense of ludicrous; lovers of music and horses.

Varick (Wheeler, 1906). A colored family, very light in complexion, some members pass for white.

Zahniser (Zahniser, 1906). Tall, many 6 feet or over, heavy black hair, rarely falling out, face broad, cheek-bones prominent, eyebrows protruding. Type becoming rarer in recent generations.

The traits named in the foregoing list have a very dissimilar value and significance as inheritable characters. But some, at least, have the same value as the famous "Hapsburg lip." Were our population so closely inbred as European royalty it would show hundreds of characteristics with the same family value. But our families are constantly outmarrying and a definite trait becomes disseminated into scores of family names so that its family signification becomes lost.

The facts that we have been considering above lead to a conclusion quite in line with modern experimental work in heredity and with the interpretation of varieties. The white race as seen in America to-day is made up of thousands, yes, hundreds of thousands of kinds of protoplasm which differ by the possession of at least one determiner for a peculiar, differentiating trait. The potential strains that are constituted by these different kinds are not, however, real strains because they are constantly crossed into other strains. Only when there is a high degree of consanguineous marriage, as in small islands, or mountain valleys, is this potentiality realized. Otherwise the traits soon become dissociated from the family names of those who brought them to this country and they become disseminated into many related families. But the potentiality for the production of a strain or race remains.

Now the fact of the existence of such strains in this country has an important bearing upon studies made on man. For example, our text-books on anatomy give an account of structure that is based on the finding of numerous autopsies. The original author of such a work records for each organ and part the condition in which he has found it in the material that he has dissected. If he goes into enough detail he has to state in connection with each description that it does not hold universally but that, on the contrary, in one cadaver or another this and that modification has been found. The name of the family to which the cadaver belongs, its ancestral history, is usually not given (and indeed it frequently cannot be obtained), but it is important that it should be ascertained, if possible, for the same reason that it is important to know if the cadaver were of a Caucasian or a Chinaman. Indeed, as a textbook of Human Anatomy must be rewritten for the Chinese, for the Ethiopians, and for the Eskimos, so must it be rewritten for the Rumanian, for the North Italian, for the Norwegian and for the Spaniard. Nor will the same description of structure of the human body serve, in all details, for the Lees of Virginia, the Ishmaelites of Indiana and the Edwards family of New England. Similarly the text-books of pathology are not universally applicable. There are hundreds of diseases listed that you and I could no more have than we could have extra fingers or a retina without pigment. Even the symptoms of a disease will differ in different strains; for the symptoms of a disease like typhoid fever are not due only to the typhoid germ but to the reaction of the particular living body to those germs. In not a few cases the prognosis, or prospect of the course of the disease, should read: The prognosis can be got by asking the head of the family "What is the usual course of the disease in this family?" Indeed, the classification and diagnosis of a disease is often got better by a comparison of the brother and sister of the patient than by reference to a book of symptoms. "I knew a family of four sisters," said Dr. E. E. Southard to me, "three of whom had manic-depressive insanity; the fourth had a mental disorder that had been classified quite otherwise by another physician. But a comparison of the sisters showed that the mental disorder was of the same type in all." Bleeders in different families differ in the ease with which hemorrhage is induced and the difficulty in stopping it; and in the Sullivan County bleeders the disorder runs a peculiar course so that they are called "nine-day bleeders." Of imbecility there are, as we have seen, all grades and all usually incurable; but the great "moron" or simpleton family of New Jersey is peculiar in that mental development is not permanently arrested but only much retarded.

So albinism varies much in degree and certain families are recognized as containing partial albinos; others, nearly complete albinos; still others, complete albinos.

Pathologies describe some diseases as common, others as rare; yet, within limits, this must depend on the geographical location of the author. At the east end of Long Island Huntington's chorea is not a rare disease as it seems to be in Eastern Massachusetts. Deaf mutism was found in 4 per cent of the population of Chilmark, in 1880, and the practitioner of that place would gain an impression of its frequency which would differ from that of a hospital surgeon in New York City. Hospital surgeons in great cities believe they get a better *average* view because they get random samples out of a great mixture; but in just so far they lose sight of the essential feature of the specificity of the different strains of human germ plasm and too often gain the impression that the sporadic examples of a disease that come to their hands prove the purely accidental nature of its incidence. The metropolitan hospital with its random sampling is the last place to get a proper idea of the relation of disease to germ plasm. It is the venerable country doctor in a long settled and stable community who can tell tales of hereditary tendencies.

It was stated above that coöperation in putting on record one's family history should be regarded as a patriotic duty. I might go further and say that, just as the traits of criminals and defectives go on public or semi-public records, with even more reason a record should be kept of our best families and of their traits. Enlightened communities preserve records of births, marriages and deaths and of various business transactions, especially in land. It is not less important to keep a record of innate capacities and valuable traits. For it is not too much to say that the future of our nation depends on the perpetuation by reproduction of our best protoplasm in proper matings and we cannot have proper matings unless our best protoplasm is located and known. The day may come when in intelligent circles a woman will accept a man without knowing his biologico-genealogical history with as much hesitation as a stock-breeder will accept as a sire for his colts or calves an animal without a pedigree. Since restriction of the number of children seems, for better or worse, to be the fashion with our older families, let every effort be put forth to secure that each child shall be of the best quality in respect to inborn capacities.[1]

3. The Integrity of Family Traits

We often hear persons who are impressed by the multiplicity of one's ancestors make light of family pride in some preëminent forbear. They ask of what significance can such an ancestor be whose blood is diluted to one part in a thousand? This way of looking at heredity is a relic of a former view that a trait when mated to its absence produced a half trait in the progeny as skin color was considered to do, and which gave rise to the conception of quadroons, octaroons, etc., with successive lightening of the skin to ¼, ⅛ and so on. Now that we know that even skin color may segregate out in the ancestral full grades we are ready to accept as practically universal the rule that unit characters do not blend; that apparent blends in a trait are a consequence of its composition out of many units. Since this is so, a unit character (especially a negative character) which a remote ancestor possessed may reappear, after many generations have passed, in its pristine purity. A germ plasm that produced a mathematical genius only

[1] The need for a full Family Record is, we may hope, about to be filled by Dr. J. Madison Taylor of Philadelphia. Meanwhile those who wish a copy of the Family Records of the Eugenics Record Office may obtain it on application.

once, a century ago, may produce another not less noteworthy again.

A feature of positive unit characters, which from their very nature tend to reappear in each generation is that of *anticipation.* This means that the trait appears at an earlier age in each generation. Nettleship (1910, pp. 23–25) has referred to some striking cases of this. Thus he gives three pedigrees of hereditary glaucoma and diabetes illustrating this law. In one case the average known age in successive generations for the incidence of glaucoma is 66 and 48 years; in another family 71, 45, and 23 years; in still another, 47 and 20. In the case of diabetes deaths occurred, on the average, at 69, 35 and 26 years. Nettleship explains this result "by assuming that certain defects, taints or vices of the system, say of the blood, are not only hereditary in the true or germinal sense, but able to produce toxic agents in the embryo which have an evil influence upon all its cells, and thus so lower their power of resistance that the innate hereditary factor has freer play and is likely to manifest itself earlier."

The law of segregation of traits, the disproof of the blending hypothesis, is of the utmost importance since it shows how a strain may get completely rid of an undesirable trait. If the undesirable character is a positive one, like polydactylism, it will disappear if the normal children alone have offspring. If it is a negative character its complete and certain elimination is not so easy to be assured of, but offspring without the undesirable trait are easily secured if marriage be always with germ plasm that is without the defect. Thus a simpleton married into a mentally strong strain will probably have mentally well endowed offspring. Here is where the beneficence of heredity clearly appears.

But do traits never arise *de novo* is often asked. If you deny it, how do you account for the presence of great men from obscure origin? For example, Mohammed, Napoleon, Lincoln. First of all, in seeking for an explanation of the origin of such "sports" of which history is full, we must inquire if the putative paternity is the real one. Not infrequently a weak woman has had illegitimate children by the wayward scion of a great family. The oft repeated story that Abraham Lincoln was descended on his mother's side from Chief Justice John Marshall of Virginia, whether it has any basis or not, illustrates the possibility of the origin of great traits through two obscure parents. In the second place we have seen that many elements of genius are negative characters and, as such, they may be transmitted without influencing the soma of the transmitter.

Thus two parents without mathematical genius might bring together germ cells whose union would favor a mathematical prodigy; and the same is true of many other traits. Indeed, as many of our pedigrees show, genius frequently, if not usually, appears in families with mental defects, insanity, or at least neurotic tendencies. It is just these sturdy, stolid communities of which not a few are found in Eastern Pennsylvania that, I am informed, produce few insane persons as well as few geniuses. The connection between genius and mental defect or aberration has been often referred to, especially by Lombroso and his followers, and as often scoffed at. But, apart from the significant association of the two conditions in pedigrees, there is no *a priori* objection to the view that the flights of the imagination, one of the most constant features of genius, should be associated with that flightiness that is a symptom of insanity, or that the absence of complete mental development should be associated with the absence of one or more of these inhibitors that marks the man or woman of great talent.

CHAPTER VIII

EUGENICS AND EUTHENICS

1. Heredity and Environment

Admitting, as we must, the importance of hereditary tendencies in determining man's physical traits, his behavior and his diseases, we cannot overlook the question that must occur to all—What relation have the facts of heredity to those of environmental influence, to the known facts of infection and bad conditions of life? Indeed, were we to accept the teachings of some, environment alone is important, good training, exercise, food, and sunlight can put anybody in a "normal" condition.

So long as we regard heredity and environment as opposed so long will we experience endless contradictions in interpreting any trait, behavior or disease. The truth seems to be that for human phenomena there is not only the external or environmental cause but also an internal or personal cause. The result is, in most cases, the reaction of a specific sort of protoplasm to a specific stimulus. For example, the controversy as to the inheritableness versus the communicableness of "the itch" receives a simple solution if we recognize that there is an external agent, probably a parasite, that can, however, develop only in persons who are non-immune. Since such persons are rather uncommon and the absence of immunity is inheritable, the disease tends to run in families and can rarely be caught even through inoculation, by persons outside such families. Even in cases where the hereditary factor is universally admitted as in manic-depressive insanity, the onset of the symptoms may be delayed by very favorable conditions of life. But though such symptoms may be diminished and the patient be discharged from the hospital as "cured," yet the weakness in his germ plasm is not removed and it will, unless he be fitly mated, show itself in his children when they, in turn, experience an unusual stress. Even the fugue tendency of the child of three years (page 89) might not have expressed itself so acutely had he lived in the country with freedom to wander widely at will instead of being restrained within the confines of city houses and narrow streets, In extreme cases, however, of which complete albinism is an example, the trait seems to be due to the entire absence in both of the united germ cells of any determiner for the character. Under these circumstances not even the best of environmental conditions can bring about pigmentation. Albinism is a protoplasmic "accident" as independent of environment as drowning by the overturning of an ocean steamship is independent of heredity.

With few exceptions, the principle that the biological and pathological history of a child is determined both by the nature of the environment and the nature of the protoplasm may be applied generally. It is an incomplete statement that the tubercle bacillus is the cause of tuberculosis or alcohol the cause of delirium tremens or syphilis the cause of paresis. Experience proves it, for not all that harbor the tubercle bacillus show the dread symptoms of tuberculosis (else there were little hope of escape for any of us); nor do all drunkards have delirium tremens, nor are all who are infected by syphilis paretic, else our hospitals for the insane would be fuller than they are. Rather, each of these diseases is the specific reaction of the organism to the specific poison. In general, the causes of disease as given in the pathologies are not the real causes. They are due to inciting conditions acting on a susceptible protoplasm. The real cause of death of any person is his inability to cope with the disease germ or other untoward conditions.

How prone we are to neglect the personal side of the result! We explain that Mr. A. has gone insane from business losses or overwork. Yet hundreds suffer great losses and work hard and show no signs of nervous breakdown. It would be more accurate to say A. went insane because his nervous mechanism was not strong enough to stand the stresses to which it was put. As a matter of fact insanity rarely occurs except where the protoplasm is defective. Also epilepsy, which is so often ascribed to external conditions, is, like imbecility, determined chiefly by the conditions of the germ plasm; and the trivial circumstance that first reveals the defect is as little the true cause as the touching the electric button that opens an exposition is the motive power of its vast engines. "Father," says the young hopeful, "may I go skating?" "So far as I am concerned; but you had better ask your mother," replies the father. "No, indeed," puts in the mother, "for I read in the paper the other day of a boy who fell on the ice and had an epileptic fit." Thus does the untrained mind confuse contributing and essential causes.

2. Eugenics and Uplift

The relation of eugenics to the vast efforts put forth to ameliorate the condition of our people, especially in crowded cities, should not be forgotten.

Education is a fine thing and the hundreds of millions annually spent upon it in our country are an excellent investment. But every teacher knows that the part he plays in education is after all a small one. In the same class will be two boys who have had the same school training. One catches ideas almost before they are expressed, makes knowledge his own as soon as it is acquired, and passes with swiftness and thoroughness to the limit of the teacher's capacity to impart. Another comprehends slowly, advances only by constant drill and hammering, and seems as little plastic as a piece of wood. Another may be slow in most work but rapid in mathematics, and still another may be first in English composition and incapable of acquiring algebra. The expert teacher can do much with good material; but his work is closely limited by the protoplasmic makeup—the inherent traits—of his pupils.

Religious teachers do a grand work and the value to the state of properly developed and controlled emotions is incalculable. Yet how dependent, after all, are religious or moral teachings upon the nature of those who receive them. I have heard ministers express regret that they preached only to those who least needed their ministrations, but they forgot that to others their ministrations would be of little avail. Religion would be a more effective thing if everybody had a healthy emotional nature: and it can do nothing at all with natures that have not the elements of love, loyalty and devotion.

Of the importance of fresh air, good food, and rest in curing tuberculosis I have no doubt, yet how often have I seen persons brought up in the best of hygienic conditions, with every need supplied, forced to live in a camp in the Adirondacks or in Southern Arizona and, despite the best of trained nursing, gradually fade away. That cleaner milk, more air and sunlight will still further reduce the death rate of infants in New York city cannot be denied; yet there are infants who do not succumb to infantile diarrhea even in the slums. The personal side must not be overlooked in properly estimating the value of prophylaxis.

3. The Elimination of Undesirable Traits

The practical question in eugenics is this: What can be done to reduce the frequency of the undesirable mental and bodily traits which are so large a burden to our population? This question has often been asked. It has been answered in diverse ways, and, indeed, there are several methods of stopping the reproduction of undesirable traits.

There is, first, the method of surgical operation. This prevents reproduction by either destroying or locking up germ cells. There are two principal methods of surgical interference. One is castration, which removes the reproductive gland and destroys sexual desire. The other is vasectomy which prevents the escape of the germ cells to the exterior but does not lessen desire. Neither of these operations is necessarily painful or liable to cause death or much inconvenience to the males. Corresponding operations can be performed on the female but they are more serious in this sex since they involve opening the abdominal cavity.

Concerning the power of the state to operate on selected persons there can be little doubt, not only since the right to the greater deprivation—that of life—includes the right to the lesser deprivation—that of reproduction—but also since these operations are actually made to-day and that of sterilization is legalized, under certain precautions, in six states of the union. There is no question that if every feeble-minded, epileptic, insane, or criminalistic person now in the United States were operated on this year there would be an enormous reduction of the population of our institutions 25 or 30 years hence; but is it certain that such asexualization or sterilization is, on the whole, the best treatment? Is there any other method which will interfere less with natural conditions and bring about the same or perhaps better results? One is struck by the contrast between the haste shown in legislating on so serious a matter compared with the hesitation in appropriating even a small sum of money to study the subject.

First, it may be pointed out that such legislation as is enacted does not square with what we know about heredity. It is based on the old notions that parents transmit their traits to their children. Now we know that traits are transmitted by means of the germ cells and by them alone, and the resemblance of children to parents is due to the fact that both arise from the same material—the father is half-brother to his child. While a feeble-minded person lacks, *ipso facto*, the determiner for normal development in his germ cells, still we do not know that his children will be defective. Such evidence as we have goes rather to show that if, for example, a man whose germ cells have the determiner for normal mentality marry a feeble-minded woman all of the children will be mentally normal or practically so. I can well imagine the marrying of a well-to-do, mentally strong man and a high-grade feeble-minded woman with beauty and social graces which should not only be productive of perfect domestic happiness but also of a large family of normal happy children. Half of the germ cells of such children would, indeed, be defective, but as long as the children married into normal strains the offspring, through an indefinite number of generations, would continue to be normal. Yet in many states of the Union such a marriage cannot be legalized; and, in others, the potential mother might be sterilized.

Secondly, the laws against the marriage of the feeble-minded are unscientific because they attempt no definition of the class. If feeble-mindedness were always as clearly distinct from normality as polydactylism then there would be no objection to the law on this score. But this is by no means the case. If we measure the mentality of 10,000 individuals by a quantitative test, such as that of Binet and Simon, then we shall find that the retardation in mental development for 1 year, 2 years, 3 years, etc., shows nowhere a sharp change indicating where the normal ceases and the abnormal begins. Shall we sterilize or forbid marriage to all children whose mental development is retarded as much as one year? That would include 38 per cent of all children, and one of yours, O legislator! Shall the limit be two years of retardation? That would include 18 per cent of the children. Shall the limit be three years? That will still be over 8 per cent—full one-twelfth of the population to be sterile. Is it not reckless to pass such serious legislation in such loose terms?

Third, have we good ground for denying marriage, generally and under all circumstances, to persons who as school children were even four years behind their fellows? Is it certain that the progeny of such a person will be four years older than their classmates at school, or three years, or two years or even one year? Is it desirable to encourage non-legal and irregular unions to sustain a law passed without inquiry and based on no certain knowledge? Oh, fie, on legislators who spend thousands of dollars on drastic action and refuse a dollar for an inquiry as to the desirability of such action!

Fourth, even if it were desirable to prevent procreation of feeble-minded males of a certain grade, is it certain that vasectomy is to be preferred to castration? It is urged as one of the advantages of vasectomy that it does not interfere with desire nor its gratification but only with paternity. But is it a good thing to relieve the sexual act of that responsibility that it ought to carry and of which it has hitherto not been entirely free? Is not many a man restrained from licentiousness by recognizing the responsibility of possible parentage? Is not the shame of illicit parentage the fortress of female chastity? Is there any danger that the persons operated upon shall become a peculiar menace to the community through unrestrained dissemination of venereal disease? Will the frequency of the crime of rape be diminished by vasectomy? To many it would seem that to secure to a rapist his eroticism and uninhibited lust while he is released from any responsibility for offspring is not the way to safeguard female honor. Castration for rapists would seem preferable to vasectomy. Perhaps Indiana's experiment will give an answer to these questions.

Fifth. Is there any alternative besides sterilization or asexualization? There doubtless is, though it may at first be more expensive. This method is the segregation throughout the reproductive period of the feeble-minded below a certain grade. If, under the good environment of institutional life, they show that their retarded development is a result merely of bad conditions they may be released and permitted to marry. But such as show a protoplasmic defect should be kept in the institution, the sexes separated, until the reproductive period is passed. If this segregation were carried out thoroughly there is reason to anticipate such a reduction in defectiveness in 15 or 20 years as to relieve the state of the burden of further increasing its institutions, and in 30 years most of its properties, especially acquired to accommodate all the seriously defective, could be sold. We have the testimony of Dr. D. S. Jordan (1910) that the cretins who formerly abounded at Aosta in Northern Italy were segregated in 1890 and by 1910 only a single cretin of 60 years and 3 demi-cretins remained in the community. "Soeur Lucie, at the head of the work of the Little Sisters of the Poor, summed up the position in these words 'Il n'y en a plus'"—there are no more. Such then, would seem to be the proper program for the elimination of the unfit—segregation of the feeble-minded, epileptic, insane, hereditary criminals and prostitutes throughout the reproductive period and the education of the more normal people as to fit and unfit matings.

4. The Salvation of the Race through Heredity

Heredity is often regarded as a terrible fact; that we suffer limitations because of the composition of our germ plasm is a blow to pride and ambition. But, on the other hand, with limitation in capacity goes limitation in responsibility. Those who held the hazy doctrine of freedom of the will must have postulated uniformity of capacity for discriminating between right and wrong and uniformity in responsiveness to similar stimuli. Of course such an assumption is false. How we respond to any stimulus depends on the nature of our protoplasm. The nature of the response may be modified by training, by the formation of habits; but the result of training is, within limits, determined by the impressibility of the protoplasm. So I do not condemn my neighbor however regrettable or dangerous he may be.

And while heredity limits capacity in one point it extends it in others. If I have mental limitations, I have also gifts of natural health, of physical vigor, of persistence, and so on. Thus, as there is hardly a strain of human germ plasm that is without some defect or limitation so there is hardly a strain without the determiner of some admirable characteristic. While education and moral and religious instruction may do much to develop one's native traits, heredity can introduce the desirable determiner that will make such training more useful or less necessary. Indeed, while by good conditions we help the individual to make the most of himself, by good breeding we establish a permanent strain that is strong in its very constitution. The experience of animal and plant breeders who have been able by appropriate crosses to increase the vigor and productivity of their stock and crops should lead us to see that proper matings are the greatest means of permanently improving the human race—of saving it from imbecility, poverty, disease and immorality.

5. The Sociological Aspect of Eugenics

Human society, as its exists in these United States in this twentieth century, is complex. How complex it is, is indicated in some degree by the vast number of laws that have been passed and represent the rules of that society. These rules apply generally to all people alike. They tacitly assume that all people are alike; while admitting that there are some who are different and who constitute special classes that must be specially provided for. These special classes are of eugenic interest. Although well defined at one extreme, at the other they merge with the great mass of the population. The individuals composing these special classes are not in all respects distinct, but rather they are more or less peculiar in one or more respects. In fact the special classes which are the concern of the boards and associations of charities and correction consist of individuals with one or more traits that are more or less disturbing to the social organization. These individuals, or rather their traits—cause a disturbance and an expense of time and money quite out of proportion to their numbers in the community—they seem to be the main hindrance to our social progress. Moreover, their numbers seem to be increasing, hence it is a pressing need of the day to find out what is the cause and cure of defectiveness and delinquency.

The diversity of answers to such inquiry shows the depth of our helplessness. Mental defectiveness is ascribed to malnutrition of the fetus, to asphyxiation of the child during the labor of birth, to adenoids, to infection with venereal disease—despite the fact that (excepting mongolism) it usually occurs only in families with the defect on both sides of the house. Likewise criminality is ascribed to poverty, to bad example, to bad or inadequate education, despite the fact of incorrigibility. Even when there is some relation between the alleged cause and the result one feels that all these explanations are based on the logical error: *post hoc ergo propter hoc:* and that the cart is often put before the mule. The very multiplicity of explanations shows their inadequacy. There is a more fundamental explanation for these non-social traits than any of those that are usually ascribed.

First of all we can see clearly that the traits that cause so much trouble are "unfortunate" or "bad" only in relation to our society, i. e., relatively, not absolutely. Lack of speech, inability to care for the person or to respond in the conventional fashion to the calls of nature, failure to learn the art of dressing and undressing, inability to count, entire lack of ambition beyond getting a meal, abject slothfulness, love of sitting by the hour picking at a piece of cloth—these are unfortunate traits for a twentieth-century citizen but they constitute a first-rate mental equipment for our remote ape-like ancestors, nor do we pity infants, who invariably have them. So likewise with crimes:—the acts of taking and keeping loose articles, of tearing away obstructions to get at something desired, of picking valuables out of holes and pockets, of assaulting a neighbor who has something desirable or who has caused pain or who is in the way, of deserting family and other relatives, of promiscuous sexual relations—these are crimes for a twentieth-century citizen but they are the normal acts of our remote, ape-like ancestors and (excepting the last) they are so common with infants that we laugh when they do such things. In a word the traits of the feeble-minded and the criminalistic are normal traits for infants and for an earlier stage in man's evolution. There is an aphorism that biologists use which is apt here—ontogeny recapitulates phylogeny. This means that the individual (ontos) in its development passes through stages like those the race (phylum) has traversed in its evolution. The infant represents the ape-like stage.

Just as certain adult persons show ancestral organs that most of us have lost—such as a heavy coat of hair, an elongated coccyx (tail), an unusually large appendix, a third set of teeth,—so some adult persons retain certain ancestral mental traits that the rest of us have got rid of. And just as the heavy coat of body hair can be traced back generation after generation until we cannot avoid the conclusion that these hairy people represent a human strain that has never gained the naked skin of most people, so imbecility and "criminalistic" tendency can be traced back to the darkness of remote generations in a way that forces us to conclude that these traits have come to us directly from our animal ancestry and have never been got rid of.

The question how these traits ever came to be so rare in mankind is one with the question of human evolution and on this subject there is no historical evidence. It is clear, however, that after the new traits became established and constituted the basis for the new society, those persons who had the old traits stood a good chance of being killed off and many a defective line was ended by their death. We are horrified by the 223 capital offenses in England less than a century ago, but though capital punishment is a crude method of grappling with the difficulty it is infinitely superior to that of training the feeble-minded and criminalistic and then letting them loose upon society and permitting them to perpetuate in their offspring these animal traits. Our present practices are said to be dictated by emotion untempered by reason; if this is so, then emotion untempered by reason is social suicide. If we are to build up in America a society worthy of the species *man* then we must take such steps as will prevent the increase or even the perpetuation of animalistic strains.

6. Freedom of the Will and Responsibility

The consideration of the facts of heredity inevitably raises the ancient question of the freedom of the will, and throws a new light upon it. What is this free will? As I sit here in my study I will that to-morrow I shoot my dog. But when, to-morrow, I approach the dog to carry out my resolution his signs of fondness for me, the *abandon* with which he throws himself in the most helpless position at my feet, make the act impossible for me. I go to a neighbor and say, "My dog is decrepit and enjoys life no longer. I cannot kill him, will you do me the favor of shooting him?" He says, "I will" and does. We both had the will, why the difference in execution? Was he more resolute, more indomitable than I? It does not follow; simply his reaction to the sight of the dog did not overcome his resolution; mine did. There are various ways in which I might bring myself to do such an act. I might shut out the stimulus of the sight of the dog by covering him, or I might train myself to view him with indifference by associating him with some wrong, or I might picture more vividly my duty so that it would be a stronger motive than my affection or sympathy. By these means I might strengthen my "will." But except in some such indirect way my conduct is unmodifiable. Given such and such conditions I am bound to react in such and such ways.

A man of indomitable will is one who pictures so vividly the work he plans to do that other, minor, stimuli are relatively ineffective in opposition to the major stimulus. The man of weak will has usually a less vivid and powerful imagination and hence his actions are more determined by numerous incidental stimuli. "Free will" is predicated in matters of small consequence or concern to the person so that his action is determined by habit or slight stimuli whose source is unperceived. Though a man pride himself on the freedom of his will his every action is determined by his protoplasmic makeup, plus the modification it has received through experience, plus the relative vigor and quality of the stimulus he receives.

Is a man on this view less of a responsible agent? It depends on what is meant by responsible. I am responsible in the sense of answerable to society if I kill a man. If I kill him without intention or knowledge—if, for instance, my foot sets a stone rolling that starts an avalanche—then society decides that there is no evidence that my freedom imperils it and nothing is done. If I kill in self-defense society decides that my reaction is, on the whole, not prejudicial or disadvantageous to it and I am set free. If I kill on sudden anger society decides, whether rightly or wrongly, that my action does not prove that I may not, by training, gain inhibitions such that I shall thereafter react more slowly, giving time for other stimuli to play their part. But if I kill after prolonged premeditation, so that there is no question of merely temporary absence of inhibitions or of chance for numerous other stimuli to act, then society decides that my makeup is fundamentally bad and that the acquisition of a new method of reacting is not to be expected and so, properly enough, cuts me off. My name may indeed become a by-word, since society, rather unreasonably, takes that method of designating the combinations of characteristics that are antisocial. But I am not responsible in the sense of "deserving" pain because of the inadequacy of the determiners in my protoplasm. I am what the determiners in my two fused germplasms have developed into under the culture which they have experienced during their development. I am not responsible for my early culture nor for the reactions determined by it; but that culture is partly determined by my makeup, as when I find pleasure in the society of bad companions, and partly is imposed by the formal "good influences" that society has organized. Now, what I do depends on what I am, on the one hand, and the nature of the stimuli I receive, on the other, and neither what I am nor the nature of the stimuli I receive can be an excuse for adding more than is necessary to society's welfare to the sum of the world's pain. But organized society, on the contrary, has a responsibility towards its members in the sense of a duty to perform under penalty of dire consequences that will follow automatically. That responsibility involves, first, preventing the mating that brings together the antisocial traits of the criminal; second, after this damage is done, in securing the highest development of the good traits and the inhibition of the bad, surrounding the weak protoplasm with the best stimuli and protecting it from harmful stimuli. Here is where society must act to cut off the evil suggestions of immoral theaters, yellow journals and other bad literature. These stimulate those who react violently to this kind of suggestion. "The prisoner was a paranoiac and had a delusion of persecution; but had the play at the theater not been what it was he would not have murdered *that* night."

CHAPTER IX

THE ORGANIZATION OF APPLIED EUGENICS

1. State Eugenic Surveys

The commonwealth is greater than any individual in it. Hence the rights of society over the life, the reproduction, the behavior and the traits of the individuals that compose it are, in all matters that concern the life and proper progress of society, limitless, and society may take life, may sterilize, may segregate so as to prevent marriage, may restrict liberty in a hundred ways.

Society has not only the right, but upon it devolves the profound duty, to know the nature of the germ plasm upon which, in last analysis, the life and progress of the state depend. It has not only the right, but the duty, to make a thorough study of all of the families in the state and to know their good and bad traits. It may and should locate traits of especial value such as clear-headedness, grasp of details, insight into intricate matters, organizing ability, manual dexterity, inventiveness, mechanical ability and artistic ability. It may and should locate antisocial traits such as feeble-mindedness, epilepsy, delusions, melancholia, mental deterioration, craving for narcotics, lack of moral sense and self-control, tendency to wander, to steal, to assault and to commit wanton cruelties upon children and animals. It may and should locate strains with an inherent tendency to certain diseases such as tuberculosis, rickets, cancer, chronic rheumatism, gout, diabetes insipidus, goitre, leuchemia, chlorosis, hemophilia, eye and ear defects and the scores of other diseases that have an hereditary factor. It should know where the traits are, how they are being reproduced, and how to eliminate them. It should locate in each country the centers of feeble-mindedness and crime and know what each hovel is bringing forth. In fact it should let the bright light of knowledge into all matters of the reproduction of human traits, as the most dangerous of its enemies or the most valuable of its natural resources.

We take our census decennially or at more frequent intervals. We learn how many persons there are of military age, their race, birthplace and occupation, and we learn how many are blind and deaf, and it is well. But by a very little additional labor we could gain many not less significant facts, such as how each of our blind and deaf and feeble-minded came to be, so that the laws of their origin can be studied and the defective germ plasm located. It would seem worth while to use the census as a means of securing data on human blood lines and tracing the descent of defects.

A state eugenic survey should be taken in at least the older states. The organization of the survey could be relatively simple; the 630,000 teachers of state and city schools might be used to secure the census of the 24,000,000 children of "school age" and their parents. Through a series of visits on Saturday afternoons or during vacations the parents could be interested to furnish the desired data. The teachers could be instructed how to fill out the schedules by superintendents or at teachers' institutes. They should, of course, receive special compensation, but it would be difficult to think of any other method of making a census so cheaply and effectively; the more so since the teacher through her pupil has ready access to most homes. The schedules of questions should be prepared so as to avoid giving any offense, to secure the required data as to physical and mental family traits, and to get such names and places of birth and residence as would serve to tie families together. After study the data might be used to give particular families advice as to how their children should marry to avoid the recurrence of undesirable traits in the children's children.

Objection will probably be offered to any such survey on the ground that inheritable traits are private and personal matters; but this is surely a narrow and false view. The collective traits of any person constitute a mosaic whose elements have been derived from thousands of germ plasms and parts of which may be passed on to thousands of the persons who will constitute the social fabric of a few generations hereafter. What justification have I, whose elements are derived from the society of the past and will pass into the society of the future, to maintain that the society of to-day has no right to question me—who is merely a sample of this universal germ plasm. No one who looks broadly at the relation his family bears to the commonwealth will hesitate to put on record an account of his family traits.

The objection that such a survey is impracticable can be met by the assertion that in the State of New Jersey such a survey is already well advanced, largely through private initiative. The work has been done by means of field workers attached to various institutions for defectives. Massachusetts, also, has made a good beginning in this direction. The suggestion as to a state survey is merely an extension of such work as is being carried on in a more limited fashion to-day.

2. A Clearing House for Heredity Data

While states should undertake eugenic surveys, it is clear that, in a country like ours where extensive intermigration takes place between States, "blood lines" are not limited by state boundaries. There is need, consequently, of a central clearing house for data concerning family traits in America. This will serve not only as a headquarters for investigation but also for education.

It will be interesting to trace the history of institutions of this sort in America. One was planned in 1881 or 1882 by Mr. Loring Moody of Boston. In his booklet entitled "Heredity: its relations to human development. Correspondence between Elizabeth Thompson and Loring Moody," he tells how he had hoped for aid from a philanthropist. He adds "in the earnest hope and expectation that such persons will soon appear ready for their work, as a colaborer therein and as preliminary steps toward the formation of an

INSTITUTE OF HEREDITY

which shall found a library, establish lectureships with schools of instruction and take in hand the diffusion of knowledge on the subject of improving our race by the laws of physiology, I propose, with the aid of such as may volunteer their patronage and support, to open a school and lecture room in Boston with the nucleus of a library for such conversations, consultations and illustrated lectures as may awaken interest and lead toward a realization of these great and beneficent ends." This plan failed because of the early death of its projector.

About 1887 or 1888 Dr. Alexander Graham Bell founded at Washington, D. C., the Volta Fund which has grown to over $100,000. Out of this was established the Volta Bureau, which collects all valuable information that can be obtained with reference not only to deaf mutes as a class but to deaf mutes individually. In this bureau can be found the names of over twenty thousand deaf and the particulars respecting their history. They are so systematically arranged that without a moment's delay the facts with reference to any of them can be turned to. These valuable manuscripts and indices are placed in a perfectly fire-proof section of the building of the Bureau. The library is rich in New England town histories and genealogies, in addition to works on the deaf.

About 1905 the late Sir Francis Galton contributed to the support of a Eugenics Laboratory at University College, London, under the direction of Professor Karl Pearson, and at his death in 1911 Galton made it his residuary legatee. This laboratory is publishing an important "Treasury of Human Inheritance."

In October, 1910, The Eugenics Record Office was started at Cold Spring Harbor, Long Island, N. Y., in connection with the Eugenics Section of the American Breeders' Association in a tract of 80 acres, with a good house to which has been added a fire-proof vault for the preservation of records. Mr. H. H. Laughlin is its superintendent. At this place the collecting and cataloguing of records goes on apace. It is hoped to establish here a very completely indexed collection of published genealogical and town histories for the United States as well as the manuscript reports of the field investigators. The main work of the office is investigation into the laws of inheritance of traits in human beings and their application to eugenics. Two series of publications are contemplated, an octavo series of Bulletins and a quarto series of Memoirs. Several numbers of the Bulletin are issued or in press. The Eugenics Record Office wishes to coöperate with Institutions and State Boards of Control in organizing the study of defectives and criminalistic strains in each State. It will offer suggestions as to the organization of local societies devoted to the study of Eugenics. It proffers its services free of charge to persons seeking advice as to the consequences of proposed marriage matings. In a word it is devoted to the advancement of the science and practice of Eugenics.

BIBLIOGRAPHY

The following method of citation is adopted. 1. Name of author, in capital letters. 2. Date of publication, used, with the author's name, for reference (in the body of the work) to the publication. 3. Title of the publication. 4. If published in a periodical, name of periodical, in italics, followed by volume number and page. If published as a separate book, the place of publication is given, and sometimes the name of the publisher. *p.* stands for page; *pl* for plate; *v* for volume.

ALLERTON, WALTER S., 1888. A History of the Allerton Family in the United States, 1585 to 1885, and a genealogy of the descendants of Isaac Allerton. N. Y., 166 pp.

ANDERSON, T. MCCALL, 1863. Hereditary Deaf-mutism. *Med. Times and Gazette,* London, II, 247.

APERT, E., 1907. Traité des maladies familiales et des maladies congénitales. Paris, Libraire J. B. Baillière et fils.

ARNER, G. B. L., 1909. Consanguineous Marriage in the American Population. *Studies in Hist., Economics and Public Law.* Columbia Univ., XXXI, No. 3.

ATKINSON, J. E., 1875. Observations upon Two Cases of Fibroma Molluscum. *New York Medical Journal,* XXII, 601–610.

BABINGTON, B. G., 1865. Hereditary Epistaxis. *Lancet,* London, Sept., 1865, II, 362–363.

BAER, TH., 1907. Zuer Kasuistik der Hypotrichosis Congenita Familiaris. *Arch. f. Dermatologie und Syphilis,* LXXXIV, 1 Th., pp. 15–18.

BALCH, W. L. (Secretary), [1905]. First Reunion and organization of the Balch Family Association by the descendants of John Balch one of the "Old Planters" of Naumkeag, now Salem, Beverly and North Beverly, Massachusetts, 52 pp.

BALL, NICHOLAS, 1891. Edward Ball and some of his Descendants. Newport, R. I., *Mercury Print,* pp. 1–15.

BANKER, H. J., 1909. A partial history and genealogical record of the Bancker or Banker families of America and in particular the descendants of Laurens Mattipe Bancker. Rutland, Vt., The Tuttle Co., 458 pp.

Banning, Pierson W., 1908. The First Banning Genealogy. Chicago.

Barr, Martin W., 1897. Some Studies in Heredity. *Jour. Nerv. and Mental Diseases*, N. Y., XXIV, 155–162.

—, 1904. Mental Defectives: their History, Treatment and Training. Phila., P. Blakiston's Son, 368 pp.

Bateson, W., 1906. Address on Mendelian Heredity and its Application to Man. *Brain*, V. 29, p. 157.

—, 1906. Progress of Genetics since the Rediscovery of Mendel's Papers. *Progr. Rei Bot.*, I, p. 368.

—, 1908. Methods and scope of genetics. Cambridge, Eng., Univ. Press.

—, 1909. Mendel's Principles of Heredity. Cambridge, Univ. Press.

Bell, Alexander Graham, 1884. Memoir upon the Formation of a Deaf Variety of the Human Race. *Mem. of National Acad. of Sciences*, 86 pp.

—, 1889. Royal Commission on the Blind, the Deaf and Dumb, etc.: Minutes of Evidence taken by the Royal Commission. London, Eyre & Spottiswoode.

—, 1906. The Blind and the Deaf, 1900. Special Report to Bureau of the Census. Washington, Gov't Printing Office, ix+264 pp.

Bemiss, S. M., 1858. Report on Influence of Marriages of Consanguinity upon Offspring. *Trans. Am. Med. Ass'n*, Phila., XI, 321–425.

Bentley, Madison, 1909. Mental Inheritance. *Pop. Sci. Mo.*, v. 75, p. 458.

Bernhardt, M., 1885. Beitrag zur Pathologie der sogenannten "Thomsen'schen Krankheit." *Centralb. f. Nervenh.*, Leipzig, VIII, 122–126.

Berze, J., 1910. Die hereditären Beziehungen der Dementia Praecox. Beitrag zur Hereditätslehre. Leipzig a. Main.

Bonajuti, F., 1890. Contributo allo studio della epidermolysis bullosa hereditaria di Köbner. *Il Morgagni*, Milano, I, 770–780.

Bond, C. J., 1905. The Correlation of Sex and Disease. *British Med. Jour.*, Lond., II, Oct., 1094–1095.

Bordley, J., Jr., 1908. A Family of Hemeralopes. *Johns Hopkins Hosp. Bull.*, XIX, 278–280, 1 pl.

Bovaird, D., 1900. Primary Splenomegaly; Endothelial Hyperplasia of the Spleen; 2 cases in children, autopsy and morphological examination in one. *Am. Jour. Med. Science*, Phila., CXX 377–402.

Bramwell, Byrom, 1876. Progressive Pernicious Anemia. *Rep. Proc. Northumb. & Durham M. Soc.*, Newcastle-upon-Tyne, 1876–7, pp. 151–167.

—, 1901. Wednesday Cliniques. Case VIII. Case of Hereditary Ichthyosis of the Palms and Soles. *Clinical Studies*, Edinburgh, I, 1903, pp. 77–80.

—, 1903. Wednesday Cliniques. Case IV. Hereditary Optic Atrophy. *Clinical Studies*, Edinburgh, II, 1904, pp. 44–55.

—, 1906. Wednesday Cliniques. Case XLV. Haemophilia. *Clinical Studies*, Edinburgh, V, 1907, 368–370.

—, 1907. Wednesday Cliniques. Hereditary Webbing of Second and Third Toes of the Left Foot. *Clinical Studies*, Edinburgh, v, 1907, pp. 373.

—, 1907. Wednesday Cliniques. Case XXXVIII. Diabetes Mellitus: strong hereditary history; differential diagnosis of glycosuria and diabetes mellitus. *Clinical Studies*, Edinburgh, VI, 1908, pp. 263–266.

Breed, J. Howard, 1892. A Record of the Descendants of Allen Breed. Phila., Hathaway & Bros.

Brill, N. E., 1901. Primary splenomegaly. *Am. Jour. Med. Sci.*, Phila. and N. Y., April, 1901, CXXI, 377–392.

Brinckerhoff, R., 1887. The Family of Joris Dircksen Brinckerhoff. New York, pp. 1–188.

Broca, Paul, 1866–9. Traité de Tumeurs, Vols. I and II. Paris, P. Asselin.

Bronardel, P., 1900. Le Mariage, Nullité, Divorce, Grossesse, Accouchement. Paris, Libraire J. B. Baillière et fils, pp. 1–452.

Buck, Wm. J., 1893. Account of the Bucks Family of Bucks Co., Pa. Philadelphia, pp. 1–142.

Bulloch, W. and P. Fildes, 1911. Haemophilia. *Treasury of Human Inheritance*, Parts V and VI. London.

Bureau of the Census (Department of Commerce and Labor), Special Reports, 1910. Religious Bodies: 1906, Part I, 576 pp. Summary and General Tables, Part II, 670 pp. Separate Denominations: History, Description, and Statistics. Washington, Gov't Printing Office.

Burger, Eugen, 1900. Ueber Haemophilie mit Geschichte einer Bluterfamilie. Inaugural Diss., Freiburg, pp. 1–30.

Buschan, G., 1894. Die Basedow'sche Krankheit. Eine Monographie. Leipzig u. Wien.

Butler, James D., 1896. British Convicts Shipped to American Colonies. *Am. Hist. Review*, II, 1, Oct., pp. 12–33.

Cance, Alex. E., 1911. Abstract of the Report on Recent Immigrants in Agriculture. Reports of the Immigration Commission. Washington, Gov't Printing Office, 75 pp.

Cannon, G. and A. J. Rosanoff, 1911. Preliminary Report of a Study of Heredity in Insanity in the Light of the Mendelian Laws. *Bull. Eugenics Record Office*, No. 3, 11 pp.

Carpenter, G., 1899. A case of absence of the clavicles, with an account of various deformities of the clavicles in 5 other members of the same family. *Lancet*, London, Jan., 1899, I, 13–17.

Carson, W., 1890. Congenital Abnormalities of the Extremities. In Neilson, H. R.: Keating's *Encyclopedia of the Diseases of Children*, III, p. 935. Philadelphia, 1890.

Castle, W. E., 1903. Heredity of Sex. *Bull. Mus. Comp. Zool. Harvard*, v. 40, No. 4.

—, 1903. Laws of Heredity of Galton and Mendel and Some Laws Governing Race-improvement by Selection. *Proc. Amer. Acad. Arts and Sci.*, v. 39, p. 223.

—, 1903. Mendel's Law of Heredity. *Science*, N. S., 24, p. 396.

— and others, 1906. Effects of Inbreeding, Cross-breeding and Selection upon the Fertility and Variability of Drosophila. *Amer. Acad. Arts and Sci. Proceed.*, v. 41, No. 33.

— and Forbes, Alexander, 1906. Heredity of Hair-length in Guinea-pigs and its Bearing on the Theory of Pure Gametes. Wash., Carnegie Inst., Wash., Pub. No. 49.

—, 1906. Origin of a Polydactylous Race of Guinea-pigs. Wash., Carnegie Inst. Wash., Pub. No. 49.

—, 1909. Studies of Inheritance in Rabbits. Wash., Carnegie Inst. Wash., Pub. No. 114.

—, 1911. Heredity, N. Y.

Cheadle, W. B., 1900, Occasional Lectures on the Practice of Medicine, London, 324 pp.

Church, Sir William S., and others, 1909. Influence of Heredity on Disease, with Special Reference to Tuberculosis, Cancer and Diseases of the Nervous System: a discussion by Sir W. S. Church, Sir W. R. Gowers and others. London: Longmans, 1909.

Clarke, Ernest, 1903. Hereditary Nystagmus. *Ophthalmoscope*, London, I, 86–87.

Cluble, W. H., 1872. Hereditariness of Stone. *Lancet*, London, Feb. 1872, 204.

Cole, Frank T., 1887. Early Genealogies of the Cole Families in America. Columbus, Ohio, Hann & Adair, pp. 1–308.

Colegrove, William, 1894. History and Genealogy of the Colegrove Family in America with Biographical Sketches, Portraits, etc. Chicago, Ill., pp. 1–792.

Cooke, Harriet R., 1889. The Driver Family. A Genealogical Memoir of the Descendants of Robert and Phebe Driver, of Lynn, Mass. New York. John Wilson & Son, pp. 1–531.

COUCH, J. KYNASTON, 1895. A Family History of Hernia. *Lancet*, London, October 1895, II, pp. 1043.

CUNIER, 1838. Annales Soc. Méd. de Gand.

CUTLER, C. W., 1895. Ueber angeborene Nachtblindheit und Pigment-Degeneration. *Arch. f. Augenheilk*, XXX, p. 92.

DARWIN, C., 1894. The Variation of Animals and Plants under Domestication, 2d Ed. N. Y., D. Appleton.

DAVENPORT, C. B., 1906. Inheritance in Poultry. Carnegie Inst. Wash., Pub., No. 52.

—, 1908. Degeneration, Albinism and Inbreeding. *Sci.*, N. S. 28, p. 454.

—, 1908. Heredity of Some Human Physical Characteristics. *Proc. Soc. Exper. Biol. and Med.*, V, pp. 101–2.

—, 1909. Influence of Heredity on Human Society. *Annals Amer. Acad. Polit. and Soc. Sci.*, v. 34, p. 16 (Race improvement in the United States).

—, 1909. Heredity in Man. Mar. 6. *Harvey Lectures, 1908–09*, pp. 280–90.

—, 1910. The Imperfection of Dominance and Some of its Consequences. *Amer. Nat.*, v. 44, Mar.

—, G. C. and C. B., 1907. Heredity of Eye Color in Man. *Science*, N. S., pp. 589–592, Nov.

—, 1908. Heredity of Hair Form in Man. *Amer. Nat.*, v. 42, p. 341.

—, 1909. Heredity of Hair Color in Man. *Amer. Nat.*, v. 43, No. 508, Apr.

—, 1910. Heredity of Skin-Pigment in Man. *American Naturalist*, XLIV, Nov. and Dec., pp. 642–672, 705–731.

DAVIS, C. H. S., 1870. History of Wallingford, Conn., Meriden, 956 pp.

DE BECK, D., 1886. A Rare Family History of Congenital Coloboma of the Iris. *Arch. of Ophthal.*, XV, p. 8, and ibid., 1894, XXIII, p. 264.

DEBORE, M. and RENAULT, JULES, 1891. Du tremblement hereditaire. *Bull. et Mém. Soc. Méd. des Hôpitaux de Paris*, Paris, VIII, 3d series, July, 1891, pp. 355–361.

DENIKER, J., 1906. The Races of Man. London and N. Y., pp. xxiii + 611.

DEPARTMENT OF COMMERCE AND LABOR, 1911. Immigration, Laws and Regulations of July 1, 1907. Washington, Gov't Printing Office, 97 pp.

DERCUM, F. X., 1897. Three Cases of the Family Type of Cerebral Diplegia. *Jour. Nerv. and Ment. Dis.*, New York, 24, 396–399.

DEVRIES, HUGO, 1906. Species and Varieties, their Origin by Mutation, ed. by D. T. MacDougal. Chicago, Open Court Pub. Co.

DOBELL, HORACE, 1863. A Contribution to the Natural History of Hereditary Transmission. *Med.-Chir. Trans.*, London, XLVI, pp. 25–28.

DOOLITTLE, WM. F., 1901. The Doolittle Family in America. Parts I–VII. Cleveland, Acme Printing Co., pp. 1–730, 1901–8.

DREW, DOUGLAS, 1905. Acquired Club Foot with Marked Hereditary History. *Reports of the Soc. for the Study of Dis. in Children*, London, V, 1904–05, 172–3.

DRINKWATER, H., 1908. An account of a Brachydactylous Family, *Proc. Roy. Soc.*, Edinburgh, 28, p. 35.

DUGDALE, R. L., 1902. The Jukes; a study in crime, pauperism, disease and heredity. 7th edition. N. Y., G. P. Putnam's, viii + 120 pp.

DWIGHT, BENJ. W., 1874. History and Descendants of John Dwight of Dedham, Mass. Vol. I and II. New York, John F. Trow & Son.

ELLIS, H., 1904. A Study of British Genius. London, Hurst, 300 pp.

EUGENICS REVIEW. Vol.—date. Apr. 1909—date.

FARRABEE, W. C., 1905. Inheritance of Digital Malformations in Man. *Papers of Peabody Mus. of Am. Arch. and Ethn.*, Harvard Univ., III, 3, p. 69.

FAY, EDWARD ALLEN, 1898. Marriages of the Deaf in America. Wash. D. C., vii + 527 pp., Volta Bureau.

FEER, E., 1907. Der Einfluss der Blutesverwandschaft der Eltern auf die Kinder. *Jahrb. f. Kinderh.* Berlin, LXVI, 188–219.

X FERNALD, WALTER E., 1909. The Imbecile with Criminal Instincts. *Am. Jour. of Insanity*, LXV, pp. 731–749, April.

FISKE, JOHN, 1905. The Discovery and Colonization of North America. Boston, xiv + 224 pp.

FOOT, A. J. A., 1869. Des difformités congénitale et acquise des doigts. Paris.

FREUD, SIGM., 1893. Ueber familiare Formen von cerebralen Diplegien. *Neurol. Centralblatt.*, Leipzig, XII, 512–515; 542.

GALTON, FRANCIS, 1869. Hereditary Genius: an Inquiry into its Laws and Consequences. London. Macmillan.

—, 1889. Natural Inheritance. N. Y., Macmillan, ix + 259 pp.

—, 1892. Finger Prints. London. Macmillan.

—, 1895. English Men of Science; their Nature and Nurture. N. Y., Appleton & Co.

—, and SCHUSTER, EDGAR, 1906. Noteworthy Families (Modern Science); an index to kinships in near degrees between persons whose achievements are honorable, and have been publicly recorded. London, J. Murray.

GARROD, ARCHIBALD E., 1902. The Incidence of Alkaptonuria; a Study in Chemical Individuality. *Lancet*, London, Dec. 13, 1902, 1616–1620.

—, 1908. Inborn Errors of Metabolism (Croonian lectures). *Lancet*, 1908, II, pp. 1, 73, 142, 214.

GILLIN, J. L., 1906. The Dunkers, N. Y. (pp. 221, 222).

GODDARD, H. H., 1911. Heredity of Feeblemindedness. *Bull. No. 1*, Eugenics Record Office. Cold Spring Harbor, N. Y., pp. 1–14.

—, and HELEN F. HILL. 1911. Feeblemindedness and Criminality. *The Training School*, VIII, pp. 3–6, March.

GOSSAGE, A. M., 1907. The Inheritance of Certain Human Abnormalities. *Quarterly Jour. Med.*, Oxford, I, 331–347.

VON GRAEFE, 1869. Beiträge zur Pathologie und Therapie des Glaucoms. *Arch. f. Ophth.*, Bd. XV, p. 228.

GRAY, 1907. Memoir on the Pigmentation Survey of Scotland. *Jour. Roy. Anthropological Inst.*, XXXVII, pp. 375, 401, pl. XXVII–XLVII.

GREAT BRITAIN, 1904. Inter-departmental committee on physical deterioration. Report on physical deterioration. v. 1, Report and appendix.

GUILFORD, S. H., 1883. A dental anomaly (a man 48 years of age, edentulous from birth, totally lacking the sense of smell and almost devoid of the sense of taste, surface of body destitute of fine hairs, and he has never perspired). *Dental Cosmos*, Phila., 1883, XXV, 113–118.

GUNZBERG, F. 1889. Kasuistik der Angeborenen Muskelanomalien. *Klin. Monatsbl. f. Augenheilk*, S. 263.

GUTBIER, 1834. Inaug. Diss., Wurzburg. Quoted by Loeb.

HAMMERSCHLAG, VICTOR, 1905. Zur Frage der Vererbbarkeit der Otosklerose. *Wien. Klin. Rundschau*, Wien., XIX, 5–7.

—, 1906. Beitrag zur Frage der Vererbbarkeit der "Otosklerose." *Monats. f. Ohrenh.*, Berlin, XL, 443–464.

—, 1908. Zur Atiologie der Otosklerose. *Wien. Med. Wochensch.*, Wien., LVIII, 566–567.

—, 1909. Zur Kenntnis der hereditär-degenerativen Taubstummheit. *Zeits. f. Ohrenh.*, B. 59, 315–329.

HARRINGTON, HARRIET L., 1885. A family record showing the heredity of disease. *Physician and Surg.*, Ann Arbor, Mich., VII, 49–51.

HARRIS, EDWARD DOUBLEDAY, 1870. A Genealogical Record of Thomas Bascom and his Descendants. Boston, Wm. P. Lunt, pp. 1–79.

HARTMANN, ARTHUR, 1881. Deaf-mutism, and the Education of Deaf-mutes by Lip-reading and Articulation. London, Bailliere, Tindall & Cox, XIV, 1–224.

HERRINGHAM, 1889. Muscular Atrophy of the Peroneal Type Affecting Many Members of a Family. *Brain*, Vol. XI, 230.

HERTEL, E., 1903. Uber Myopie, klinische-statistische Mitteilungen. V. Graefe's, *Archiv. f. Opthal.*, Leipzig, LVI, 326–386.

VON HIPPEL, E., 1909. Die Missbildungen des Auges; in E. Schwalbe. Missbildungen des Menschen. III, Theil., 1 Lief., 2 Abth.

HOLMES, S. J., and H. M. LOOMIS, 1909. The Heredity of Eye Color and Hair Color in Man. *Biol. Bull.*, XVIII, 50–65, Dec.

HOWE, L., 1887. A Family History of Blindness from Glaucoma. *Arch. of Ophthalmology*, N. Y., XVI, 72–76.

—, S. G., 1858. On the Causes of Idiocy; being the supplement to a report by Dr. S. G. Howe . . . . appointed by the governor of Massachusetts to inquire into the condition of the idiots of the commonwealth. Feb. 1848, Edinburg, 1858.

HUMPHREY, FREDERICK, 1883. The Humphreys Family in America. New York, Humphreys Print, pp. 1–1115.

HUNTINGTON, GEORGE, 1872. On chorea. *Med. and Surg. Reporter*, Phila., 1872, XXVI, 317.

HURST, C. C., 1906. Mendelian Characters in Plants and Animals *Report Conf. on Genetics, R. Hortic. Soc.* London, p. 114.

—, 1908. Mendel's Law of Heredity and its Application to Man. *Leicester Lit. Phil. Soc. Trans.*, 12, p. 35.

—, 1908. On the Inheritance of Eye Color in Man. *Proc. Royal Soc.*, B. vol. 80, pp. 85–96.

HUTCHINSON, JONATHAN, 1886. Congenital Absence of Hair and Mammary Glands. *Med.-Chir. Trans.*, London, LXIX, May, 473–477.

HUTCHINSON, JOSHUA, 1876. Brief Narrative of the Hutchinson Family. Boston, Lee & Shepard, 73 pp.

HUTH, A. H., 1887. The Marriage of Near Kin, 2d edition. London and N. Y., x+475 pp.

IMMIGRATION COMMISSION, 1911. Abstract of the Report on Emigration Conditions in Europe. Washington, Gov't Printing Office.

IWAI, T., 1904. La Polymastie au Japon. *Arch. de Medecine Experimentale*, XVI, 489–518.

JACKSON, V. H., 1904. Orthodontia. Phila., 517 pp.

JACOBS, P. J., 1911. A Tuberculosis Directory, containing a list of institutions, associations and other agencies dealing with tuberculosis in the United States and Canada. New York; Nat. Ass'n for Study and Prevention of Tuberculosis, 331 pp.

JENNINGS, H. S., 1909. Heredity and Variation in the Simplest Organisms. *Amer. Nat.*, v. 43, No. 510, June.

JOHANNSEN, W., 1903. Uber Erblichkeit in Populationen und in reinen Linien. Jena, Fischer.

—, 1909. Elemente der Exakten Erblichkeitslehre. Jena, G. Fischer.

Johnston, A., 1887. Connecticut, A Study of a Commonwealth-Democracy. Boston.

Jolly, F., 1891. Uber Chorea Hereditaria. *Neurol. Centrabl.*, Leipzig, 1891, X, 321.

Jordan, D. S., 1907. The Human Harvest. Boston, Amer. Unitarian Assoc.

—, 1910. Cretinism in Aosta. *The Eugenics Review*, II, 3, Nov. 247–248.

Jörger, J., 1905. Die Familie Zero. *Archiv. für Rassen und Gesellschafts Biologie*, Berlin, 1905, II, 494–559.

Keefe, D. J., 1910. Annual Report of the Commissioner-General of Immigration to the Secretary of Commerce and Labor, for the fiscal year ended June 30, 1910. Washington, Gov't Printing Office, 248 pp., 2 charts.

Kellicott, William E., 1911. The Social Direction of Human Evolution. N. Y., 249 pp.

Kellogg, Vernon L., 1907. Darwinism To-day. N. Y., Henry Holt.

Kelly, A. B., 1906. Multiple Telangiectases of the Skin. *Glasgow Med. Jour.*, Glasgow, LXV, June, 411–422.

Lancry, Louis and Gustav, 1890. La Commune de Fort-Mardick près Dunkerque (étude historique, démographique et médicale). Paris, 72 pp.

Launois and Apert, 1905. Achondroplasie hereditaire. *Soc. méd. des hôpitaux*, 30 juin, 1905.

Leber, Th., 1871. Ueber anomale Formen der Retinitis pigmentosa, *Arch. f. Ophth.*, XVII, 1, S. 314.

Lee, Edmund J., 1895. Lee of Virginia, 1642–1892, Biographical and Genealogical Sketches of the Descendants of Colonel Richard. Philadelphia, Franklin Printing Co., pp. 1–586.

Leichtenstern, 1878. Ueber das Vorkommen und die Bedeutung Supernumerärer (accessorischer) Brüste und Brustwarzen. Virchow's Archiv., Berlin, LXXIII, 222–256.

Lemen, Frank B., 1898. History of the Lemen Family of Illinois, Virginia and elsewhere. Two Parts. Collinsville, Ill., pp. 1–643.

Lewis, G. G., 1904. Hereditary Ectopia Lentis with Report of Cases, *Archives of Ophth.*, XXXIII, No. 3, p. 275.

Lewis, T. and Embleton, D., 1908. Split-hand and Split-foot Deformities, their Types, Origin, and Transmission. *Biometrika*, 6, p. 26.

Lindsay, Margaret T., 1889. The Lindsays of America: A Genealogical Narrative and Family Record. Albany, Joel Munsell's Sons, pp. 1–275.

LINGARD, A., 1884. The Hereditary Transmission of Hypospadias and its Transmission by Indirect Atavism. *Lancet*, London, 1884, i, 703.

LOCY, WILLIAM A., 1908. Biology and its Makers. N. Y., Henry Holt.

LOEB, CLARENCE, 1909. Hereditary Blindness and its Prevention. St. Louis, 1909. *Annals of Ophthalmology*, Jan.-Oct.

LONDON COUNTY COUNCIL, 1909. Report of the Medical Officer (Education) for the 12 Months ended December 31, 1909, pp. 96.

LORENZ, OTTOKAR, 1898. Lehrbuch der gesammten wissenschaftlichen Genealogie. Berlin, W. Hertz.

LOSSEN, 1905. Die Bluterfamilie Mampel in Kirchheim bei Heidelberg. Deutsche Zeitschr. f. Cherurgie, LXXVI, 1.

LUCÆ, A., 1907. Die chronische progressive Schwerhörigkeit, ihre Erkenntnis und Behandlung. Berlin, 403 pp., 2 pl.

LUCAS, R. CLEMENT, 1880. On a Remarkable Instance of Hereditary Tendency to the Production of Supernumerary Digits. *Guy Hosp. Repts.*, London, XXV, 417–419.

LYDSTON, G. FRANK, 1904. The Diseases of Society. Philadelphia, 1904, pp. 1–626. J. B. Lippincott Co.

MCCULLOCH, REV. OSCAR C., 1888. The Tribe of Ishmael: a study in social degradation. *Proc. of 15th National Conf. Char. and Correction*, Buffalo, July.

X MACDONALD, A., 1908. Juvenile Crime and Reformation. Washington, Gov't Printing Office, 339 pp.

MCQUILLEN, J. H., 1870. Hereditary Transmission of Dental Irregularities. *Dental Cosmos*, Phila., XII, Feb., pp. 73–75.

MARSHALL, L. 1903. Deformity of the Hands and Feet Transmitted through Five Generations. *Reports Soc. Stud. Disease in Children*, III, 222--225.

MARTIN, F. 1888. Ueber Microphthalmus. Inaug. Diss. Erlangen.

MASON, L. D., 1910. The Etiology of Alcoholic Inebriety, with special reference to its true status and treatment from a medical point of view. *Monthly Cyclopedia and Med. Bull.*, Phila., III, Sept., 521–532.

MELL, DR. and MRS. P. H., 1897. Genealogy of the Mell Family in the Southern States. Auburn, Ala., 61 pp.

MENDEL, GREGOR. Versuche über Pflanzen-Hybriden. Brünn, G. Gastl, 1866.

MERZBACHER, L., 1909. Gesetzmässigkeiten in der Vererbung und Verbreitung Verschiedener Hereditär-familiärer Erkrankungen. *Archiv. f. Rassen u Ges. Biologie*, VI, 172–198, May.

MICKLEY, MINNIE F., 1893. Genealogy of the Mickley Family of America. Newark, N. J., Advertiser Printing House, pp. 1–182.

MITCHELL, A., 1866. Blood-Relationship in Marriage, Considered in its

Influence on the Offspring. *Anthropolog. Soc. of London*, II, pp. 402–456.

Molenes, Paul, 1890. Sur un cas d'alopecie congenitale. *Ann. de Derm. et Syph.*, Paris, 3d series, I, 548–557.

Moore, Anne, 1911. The Feeble-Minded in New York. A report prepared for the Public Education Association of New York. Published by the State Charities Aid Association. Special Committee on provision for the feeble-minded. N. Y. United Charities Bldg., 111 pp., June.

Morgan, T. H., 1910. Chromosomes and Heredity. *Amer. Nat.*, v. 44. p. 449, Aug.

Morrison, Leonard A., 1896. History of the Sinclair Family in Europe and America. Boston, Mass., Damrell & Upham, pp. 7–453.

—, 1897. History of the Kimball Family in America from 1634 to 1897 and of its Ancestors. The Kemballs or Kemboldes of England. Boston, Damrell & Upham, Vol. I and II.

Mott, F. W., 1905. A Discussion on the Relationship of Heredity to Disease. *Brit. Med. Jour.*, London, Oct., 1086–1091.

Nareth, 1903. Beiträge zur Luxatio coxæ Congenitalis. Wien u. Leipzig.

Neighbor, Lambert B., 1906. Descendants of Leonard Neighbor, Immigrant to America, 1738. Dixon, Ill., 48 pp.

Nelson, E. W., 1899. The Eskimo about Bering Strait. *18th Ann. Rept. Bureau of American Ethnology*, pp. 289–291.

Nettleship, E., 1905. On Heredity in the Various Forms of Cataract. Additional cases of hereditary cataract. *Report Roy. Lond. Ophth. Hosp.*, v. 16, p. 1.

—, 1905. Cases of Color-Blindness in Women. *Ophth. Soc. Trans.*, v. 26.

—, 1906. On Retinitis pigmentosa and Allied Diseases. *Report Roy. Lond. Ophth. Hosp.*, v. 17, pts. I, II, and III.

—, 1907. History of Congenital Stationary Night-blindness in Nine Consecutive Generations. *Ophth. Soc. Trans.*, v. 27, 269–293.

—, 1908. Three New Pedigrees of Eye Disease. *Ophth. Soc. Trans.*, v. 28, p. 220.

—, 1910. Some Points in Relation to the Heredity of Disease. *St. Thomas's Hospital Gazette*, March, 1910, pp. 37–65.

—, and Ogilvie, F. M., 1906. Peculiar Form of Hereditary Congenital Cataract. *Ophth. Soc. Trans.*, v. 26.

New York Institution for the Instruction of the Deaf and Dumb, 1853. *35th Annual Report and Documents.* Albany, 1854, pp. 95–120.

Nicollé, C., and Haliprè, A., 1895. Maladie Familiale Caracterisée par des Alterations des Cheveux et des Ongles. *Ann. de Derm. et Syph.*, Paris, 3d series, VI, 1895, 804–811.

Osler, Wm., 1901. On a Family Form of Recurring Epistaxis Associated with Multiple Telangiectases of the Skin and Mucous Membranes. *Johns Hopk. Hosp. Bull.*, XII, 333.

Oswald, Agnes B., 1911. Hereditary Tendency to Defective Sight in Males only of a Family. *Brit. Med. Jour.*, London, Jan., 1911, p. 18.

Pardoe, George Molyneux, 1894. Genealogy of Wm. Molyneux and Descendants. Sioux City, Iowa, 1894, 1–24.

Parker, R. W., and Robinson, H. B., 1887. A Case of Inherited Congenital Malformation of the Hands and Feet: . . . . with a Family Tree. *Clin. Soc. Trans.*, Vol. XX, London, April, pp. 181–189.

Pearson, Karl, 1909. Note on the Skin Color of the Crosses between Negro and White. *Biometrika*, V. 6, pt. 4, p. 348.

Pelizaeus, Fr., 1885. Ueber eine Eigenthümliche Forms pastischer Lähmung mit Cerebralerscheinungen auf hereditärer Grundlage (Multiple Sklerose). *Archiv. f. Psych.*, XVI, 698–710.

Penrose, C. A., 1905. Sanitary Conditions on the Bahama Islands, pp. 387–416; in G. B. Shattuck: The Bahama Islands. N. Y.

Ploss, H., and M. Bartels, 1905. Das Weib in der Natur und Volkerkunde. 8 Aufl. Leipzig, Th. Grieben's Verlag, Bd. I u. II.

Politzer, Adam, 1907. Geschichte der Ohrenheilkunde. Stuttgart, F. Enke, Bd. I and II.

Potain, C., 1870. Anemie. *Dict. Encycl. des Sci. Méd.*, Paris, IV, 1st series, 327–406.

Poucet, M. A., and Leriche, M. R., 1903. Nains d'aujourd'hui et nains d'autrefois. Nanisme ancestral. Achondroplasie ethnique. *Bull. de l'Acad. de Med.*, Paris, L, 3d series, Oct., 174–188.

Poulton, E. B., and others, 1909. Fifty Years of Darwinism: Modern Aspects of Evolution. N. Y., Henry Holt.

Punnett, R. C., 1905. Mendelism. Cambridge, Macmillan.

—, 1908. Mendelism in Relation to Disease. *Proc. Roy. Soc. Med.*

Radcliffe-Crocker, H., 1903. Diseases of the Skin, their Description, Pathology, Diagnosis and Treatment. Philadelphia, Blakiston's Son & Co., pp. 1–1439.

Reber, W., 1895. Six Instances of Color Blind Women Occurring in Two Generations of One Family. *Medical News*, Phila., 1895, LXVI, 95–97.

Reed, Jacob W., 1861. History of Reed Family in Europe and America. Boston, John Wilson & Son, pp. 1–588.

Rezek, 1877. Hereditäre Herzfehler. Allg. Wien-med. Zeitschr. Wien, XXXVII, Sept., 338–339.

RICH, SHEBNAH, 1883. Truro, Cape Cod or Land Marks and Sea Marks. Boston, D. Lothrop & Co., pp. 1–580.

RIPLEY, WM. Z., 1899. The Races of Europe, a sociological study. New York, D. Appleton & Co., XXXII, 624.

—, 1908. The European population of the United States. *Jour. Royal Anthrop. Inst. of Great Britain and Ireland*, XXXVIII, 221–240, also *Ann. Rept. Board of Regents of The Smithsonian Inst.*, for 1909, pp. 585–606.

RISCHBETH, H., 1909. Hare Lip and Cleft Palate. *Treasury of Human Inheritance*, Part IV. *Eugenics Laboratory Memoirs*, XI. London, pp. i–vii, 79–126, 8 plates.

ROBERTS, CHARLES, 1878. A Manual of Anthropology or a Guide to the Physical Examination and Measurement of the Human Body. London, J. & A. Churchill, 115 pp.

ROOT, JAMES P., 1870. Root Genealogical Records, 1600–1870, comprising the General History of the Root and Roots Families in America. N. Y., R. C. Root, Anthony & Co., pp. 1–533.

ROSE, FELIX, 1907. Obesité familiale. *L'encephale*, II, 299–303.

ST. HILAIRE, E., 1900. La surdi-mutité. Paris, 1–300. Maloine, Editeur.

SALEEBY, CALEB WILLIAMS, 1909. Parenthood and Race Culture; an Outline of Eugenics. London, Cassell & Co.

SCHAMBERG, JAY FRANK, 1908. Diseases of the Skin and Eruptive Fevers. Phila. and London, W. B. Saunders Co., 1–534.

SENATOR, H. and S. KAMINER, 1904. Health and Disease in Relation to Marriage and the Married State. N. Y., 1257 pp.

SILCOX, A. G., 1892. Hereditary Sarcoma of eyeball in 3 generations. *Brit. Med. Jour.*, I, p. 1079.

SIMON, CHAS. E., 1903. Heredity in Ménière's Disease. *Johns Hopkins Hosp. Bull.*, Baltimore, IV, pp. 72–84.

SINNETT, REV. CHAS. N., 1907. Jacob Johnson of Harpswell, Maine, and his Descendants, East and West. Concord, N. H., pp. 1–132.

SLAYTON, ASA W., 1898. History of the Slayton Family, Biographical and Genealogical. Grand Rapids, Mich., pp. 1–330.

SMALL, H. W., 1898. History of Swan's Island, Me. Ellsworth, Me., pp. 1–244.

SMYTH, S. GORDON. 1909, Hans Joest Heydt, The Story of a Perkiomen Pioneer. *The Pennsylvanian-German*, July, pp. 11.

SPOKES, SIDNEY, 1890. Report at Monthly Meeting of Odontological Society. *Trans. Odont. Soc.*, London, XXII, 229–232.

STELWAGON, HENRY W., 1907. Treatise on Diseases of the Skin. Philadelphia, W. B. Saunders Co., 1150 pp.

STOCKS, A. W., 1861. Sterility in Twin Sisters. *Lancet*, Lond., July, 1861, II, 78.

STREATFIELD, J. F., 1858. Coloboma Iridis. Heredity and rare cases. *Roy. London Ophthal. Hospital Reports*, I, p. 153.

SWIFT, C. F., 1888. Genealogical Notes of Barnstable Families, being a reprint of the Amos Otis Papers originally published in the Barnstable Patriot, Vols. I and II. Barnstable, Mass.

TAPLEY, HARRIET S., 1900. Genealogy of the Tapley Family. Danvers, Mass., pp. xix, 1–256.

THOMSEN, A. 1885. Zur Thomsen'schen Krankheit. *Centralbl. f. Nervenheilk, Psychiatrie, u. ger. Psych.*, VIII, 193–196, May.

THOMSON, J. ARTHUR, 1908. Heredity. London, J. Murray.

TIFFANY, NELSON O., 1903. The Tiffanys of America: History and Genealogy. Buffalo, N. Y., 254 pp.

TOMES, JOHN, 1906. A System of Dental Surgery Revised and Enlarged by Chas. S. Tomes and Walter S. Nowell. London, J. & A. Churchill, 1906, 770 pp.

TREASURY OF HUMAN INHERITANCE, Pt. 1–2—Diabetes insipidus, Split-foot, Polydactylism, Brachydactylism, Tuberculosis, Deaf-mutism, Legal Ability. Pt. 3—Angioneurotic Oedema, Hermaphroditism, Deaf-mutism, Insanity, Commercial Ability. Pt. 4—Cleft palate, Hare-lip, Deaf-mutism, Congenital Cataract.

TREDGOLD, A. F., 1908. Mental deficiency (Amentia). London, Bailliere, Tindall & Cox.

TURNER, J. G., 1906. Hereditary Hypoplasia of Enamel. *Trans. Odont. Soc.*, XXXIX, new series, March, 137–151.

TWINING, T. J., 1905. The Twining Family, Descendants of Wm. Twining. Fort Wayne, Ind., 251 pp.

UNNA, P. G., 1883. Ueber des Keratoma Palmare et Plantare Hereditarium. *Viertelj. f. Derm. u. Syph.*, Wien., X, 231–270.

VICE COMMISSION OF CHICAGO, 1911. The Social Evil in Chicago. Chicago, 399 pp.

VIERORDT, KARL HERMANN, 1901. Die angeborenen Herzkrankheiten. In Nothnagel. *Specielle Pathologie and Therapie*, XV, Wien, 1901, Th. 1, Abth. 2.

VIGNES, 1889. Epicanthus hereditaire. *Rec. d'Ophth.*, Paris, pp. 422–425, 3d series, XI.

VIRCHOW, R., 1881. Ueber die Weddas von Ceylon. *Abh. d. königl. Akad. der Wiss. zu Berlin*, 1881.

VOISIN, A., 1865. Contribution à l'histoire des Mariages entre consanguins. *Mém. de la Soc. d'Anthropol. de Paris* (3), II, pp. 433–459, Paris.

WAKLEY, THOMAS 1895. The Influence of Inheritance on the Tendency to have Twins. *Lancet*, London, Nov., 1895, II, pp. 1289–1290.

WALLACE, JOHN H., 1901. Genealogy of the Riggs fámily, with a number of Cognate Branches descended from the Original Edward through Female Lines and many Biographical Outlines. New York, Vols. I and II.

WEBER, F. PARKES, 1907. Multiple Hereditary Developmental Angiomata (Telangiectases) of the Skin and Mucous Membranes Associated with Recurring Hemorrhages. *Lancet*, 1907, II, 160–162.

WEIL, A. 1884. Ueber die hereditäre Form des Diabetes insipidus. Virchow's *Arch. f. Path. Anat*., etc., Berl., XCV, 70–95.

WHEELER, B. F., 1906. The Varick Family. Mobile, Alabama, 58 pp.

WHITE, CHARLES J., 1896. Dystrophia Unguium et Pilorum Hereditaria. *Jour. Cut. and Gen. Urin. Dis.* N. Y., XIV, 1896, pp. 220–227.

WILSON, E. B., 1900. The Cell in Development and Inheritance. N. Y., xxi + 483 pp.

—, 1902. Mendel's Principles of Heredity and the Maturation of the Germ-cells. *Science*, Dec., p. 991.

—, 1911. Studies on Chromosomes, VII. A Review of the Chromosomes of Nezara; with some more General Considerations. *Journal of Morphology*, XXII, 71–110, Mar., 1911.

—, ERASMUS, 1869. Lecture on Ekzema. *Jour. Cutan. Med.*, London, B. III, 1869, pp. 106–117.

—, WOODROW, 1902. History of the American People. Vols. I–V, New York.

WITHINGTON, C. F., 1885. Consanguineous Marriages; their effect upon offspring. *Mass. Med. Soc.*, Boston, XIII, 453–484.

WOOD, T. B., 1906. Note on the Inheritance of Horns and Face Color in Sheep. *Journ. Agri. Sci.*, v. I, p. 364.

WOODS, FREDERICK ADAMS, 1903. The Correlation between Mental and Moral Qualities. *Pop. Sci. Mo.*, Oct.

—, 1903. Mental and Moral Heredity in Royalty. *Pop. Sci. Mo.*, Aug., 1902, Apr.

—, 1906. Mental and Moral Heredity in Royalty. N. Y., Holt & Co., 312 pp.

—, 1906. Non-inheritance of Sex in Man. *Biometrika*, V, p. 73.

—, 1908. Recent Studies in Human Heredity. *Amer. Nat.*, V. 42, p. 685.

WORTH, CLAUD, 1905. Hereditary Influence in Myopia. *Trans. Ophth. Soc.*, London, XXVI, 141–143.

YULE, G. UDNY, 1902. Mendel's Laws and their Probable Relations to Inter-racial Heredity. *New Phytologist*, I, Nos. 9, 10.

ZAHNISER, KATE M., and CHAS. R., 1906. The Zahnisers: A History of the Family in America. Mercer, Pa., pp. 1–218.

APPENDIX

LIST OF PLACES REFERRED TO, GEOGRAPHICALLY ARRANGED

INDEX

NAMES PRINTED IN SMALL CAPS ARE CONSIDERED AS SUBJECTS, THOSE IN ITALICS AS AUTHORS. THE NUMBERS REFER TO PAGES